Physical Science

cpo science

Author

Thomas C. Hsu, Ph.D., Massachusetts Institute of Technology

Writers and Content Reviewers

Patsy Eldridge, M.Ed., Tufts University

Stacy Kissel, M.Ed., Physics Education, Boston College

Sylvia Gutman, M.S., Curriculum and Instruction, University of San Diego

Jodye Selco, Ph.D., Professor, California State Polytechnic University

Kelly McAllister, M.Ed., Science Education

Michael Vela, Ph.D., Inorganic Chemistry, Brandeis University

Melissa Vela, Ph.D., Inorganic Chemistry, Brandeis University

Editorial Team

Lynda Pennell – Senior Editor
Jennifer Locke – Editor
Polly Crisman – Graphics Manager/Illustrator
Bruce Holloway – Senior Designer/Illustrator
Jesse Van Valkenburgh – Designer/Illustrator
James Travers – Illustrator
Susan Gioia – Administrator
Tracy Morrow – Technical Consultant

Contributing Writers and Editors

Laine Ives, Kristen Dolcimascolo, Jill Elenbaas, Pamela J. W. Gore, Daniel P. Murray, Christine Golden

Equipment Design and Materials

Thomas Narro – Senior Vice President
Tom Hsu, Ph.D, Massachusetts Institute of Technology
Danielle Dzurik – Mechanical Engineer
Kathryn Gavin – Purchasing and Quality Control Manager
Lisa LaChance – Senior Materials Specialist

Ancillary Materials

Catherine Reed – Connections
Sharon O. Faulkner – Connections
John K. Manos – Connections
Laura J. Tierney – Connections
Lainie Ives – Connections
Mary Ann Erickson – Assessment
Kelly A. Story – Assessment
David Bliss – Assessment
Erik Benton – Assessment

Reviewers

Pamella Ferris – Evans, GA
Brian E. Goodrow – Apple Valley, CA
Sylvia Gutman – Wildomar, CA
Tony Heinzman – Apple Valley, CA
Philip L. Hunter – Westminster, CA
Nancy Joplin – Ontario, CA
Brad Joplin – Ontario, CA
Margaret J. Kilroy – Cartersville, GA
Dakhine Lee – Hinesville, GA

Jason C. Lee – Ludowici, GA
Mark Matthews – McDonough, GA
Kelly McAllister – Riverside, CA
Bianca N. McRae – Menifee, CA
Jodye Selco, Ph.D. – Pomona, CA
Tia L. Shields – Fullerton, CA
Sharon Strefling – Kingsland, GA
Robert M. Strong – McDonough, GA

Special Thanks

Dr. Geerat Vermeij
Mary Doval Graziose
Curtis Ebbesmeyer
Jim White
Dr. Adam Dziewonski
Sarah Herve
Joan Buhrman
John M. Watson

David A. Abel
Peter C. Neil, Jr.
Stock Photography provided by Shutterstock, Inc.

CPO Science *Physical Science*

ISBN: 978-1-62571-843-3
Part Number: 1576054

Printing 2—May 2017
Printed by LSC Communications, US, LLC
Kendallville, IN

CPO Science
80 Northwest Boulevard
Nashua, New Hampshire 03063
(800) 932-5227
www.cposcience.com

Science Safety Practices and Procedures

PART ONE: Read and follow the Science Safety Guidelines for each investigation, activity, or field experiment.

1. Listen to all teacher instructions before, during, and after investigations.

2. Prepare for each investigation or activity.
   a. Sign the Science Safety Student Responsibility Agreement.
   b. Read each activity or investigation carefully.
   c. Identify the investigation purpose.
   d. Work ONLY on activities approved by your teacher.
   e. Follow all oral and written safety instructions.
   f. Know the location of Emergency Safety Equipment such as fire extinguisher, eye and face wash station, safety shower, and first aid kit.

3. Dress for laboratory work.
   a. Wear protective equipment such as chemical splash goggles, laboratory aprons, and protective gloves as needed.
   b. Roll long sleeves above the wrist.
   c. Tie back long hair.
   d. Remove dangling jewelry and any loose or bulky outer layers of clothing.
   e. Wear shoes that enclose the feet (no flip flops, sandals, or open-toe shoes).

4. Prevent unsafe situations.
   a. Be aware of classmates and their safety.
   b. Do not touch, taste, or smell any substance without teacher instructions.
   c. Never work alone in the laboratory.
   d. Don't enter science or chemical storage or preparatory areas without a teacher.
   e. Keep your work area clean and uncluttered.

PART TWO: Know what to do when...

1. working with glassware.
   a. Don't use glassware that is chipped or cracked.
   b. Use special care to prevent breakage and cuts or scratches.

2. working with heat.
   a. Wear eye protection at all times. Use safety goggles if heating chemicals.
   b. Do not touch hot items with bare hands. Use heat-resistant gloves, pads, or tongs.
   c. Heat water only in open containers of heat-resistant glass.
   d. Watch all burners, hot plates, or open flames.
   e. Warn others if they come close to your hot items or liquids.

3. working with electricity.
   a. Keep electric cords away from water.
   b. Don't use frayed cords or plugs in outlets.

4. finished experimenting.
   a. Return clean materials to their proper locations.
   b. Dispose of all used solids and liquids according to teacher instructions. Do not put items in trash or wash down sink without permission.
   c. Wash your hands with soap and water for 20 seconds.

5. you have safety concerns. Tell your teacher, or get help immediately if:
   a. You have trouble using your equipment.
   b. You do not understand the instructions for the investigation.
   c. You injure yourself, or see someone injured.
   d. You see or smell something burning.
   e. You smell chemical or gas fumes.

Lab Safety

For more information or questions about legislation and details regarding teacher responsibilities, student behavior, hazardous materials, and classroom safety, call your school administration.

Observing safety precautions is an extremely important practice while completing science investigations.

Using science equipment and carrying out laboratory procedures always requires attention to safety. The purpose of learning and discussing safety in the lab is to help you learn how to protect yourself and others at all times.

The investigations in this program are designed to reduce safety concerns in the laboratory. The physics investigations use stable equipment that is easy to operate. The chemistry investigations use both household and laboratory chemicals. Although these chemicals might be familiar to you, they still must be used safely.

You will be introduced to safety by completing a skill sheet to help you observe the safety aids and important information in your science laboratory. In addition to this skill sheet, you may be asked to check your safety understanding and complete a safety contract. Your teacher will decide what is appropriate for your class.

Safety icons and words and phrases like *caution* and *safety tip* are used to highlight important safety information. Read the description for each icon carefully and look out for them when reading your book and doing investigations.

	Wear safety goggles: Requires you to wear protective eyewear such as chemical splash goggles or safety glasses to prevent eye injuries.
	Wear a lab apron or coat: Requires you to wear a lab apron or coat to prevent damage to clothing and to protect from possible spills.
	Wear gloves: Requires you to protect your hands from injury due to heat or chemicals.
	Hazardous chemicals: Requires you to use extreme caution when working with chemicals in the laboratory and to follow all safety and disposal instructions from your teacher.
	Skin irritant: Requires you to use extreme caution when handling chemicals in the laboratory due to possible skin irritation and to follow all safety and disposal instructions from your teacher.
	Respiratory irritant: Requires you to perform the experiment under a laboratory hood and to avoid inhaling fumes while handling the chemicals.
	Laser: Requires you to use extreme caution while using a laser during investigations and to follow all safety instructions.
	Sharps: Requires you to use extreme caution when handling sharp objects such as scalpels or glass.

UNIT 4 — ELECTRICITY, SOUND, AND LIGHT

UNIT 5 — MATTER

Throughout your text book you will see this icon, which stands for STEM (Science, Technology, Engineering, and Math). STEM is an integrated way to approach learning that connects academic disciplines to real-world situations.

In today's changing world, new and improved products and processes are developed every day. For example, improvement in technology allows your cell phone to perform multiple tasks, such as texting, surfing the internet, and listening to music at the same time. Powerful computer chips have become smaller and smaller, allowing you to work on portable devices at any location.

The field of engineering is focused on creating and improving products and processes that people need or want. Engineers and designers use some or all of the STEM disciplines in their work. They also use a process called the engineering cycle to design and improve products and processes.

The engineering cycle has the following steps:

Identify a need or problem – What is the problem or process that needs to be solved or improved?

Design – Identify why this product or process is needed by making a list of everything your solution needs to accomplish. Identify the constraints or limitations that need to be taken into account such as the cost, time, materials, and size.

Create a prototype – Many ideas and a variety of solutions may be a result of brainstorming and research. Building prototypes or trying out new processes is necessary to work toward a solution.

Test the prototype – Test all the prototypes to see if they work or have flaws.

Evaluate the design – Complete an analysis by collecting data and testing the design against what needs to be accomplished. Analyze the results of the tests and make improvements to the design, or, if necessary, start all over again with a new design.

Read the following scenario and try to identify the steps of the engineering cycle and the STEM disciplines used.

Your school has a recycling committee that ensures that all plastic bottles are recycled, but the school does not recycle paper and still produces too much waste.

Your teacher breaks the class into groups and asks each group to identify the reasons why the school does not recycle paper. The groups must research the recycling system and decide the constraints they need to take into account when recycling paper.

Each group develops a solution or prototype design to address the paper-recycling problem. The groups present their plans to the class.

Each team analyzes the various solutions and decides on one that will work or decides that all the plans are flawed.

The class makes a decision on one solution and checks it against the initial problem and constraints.

UNIT 1

THE PHYSICAL SCIENCES

CHAPTER 1
What Physics and
Chemistry Are About

CHAPTER 2
Science and
Measurement

Exploring on Your Own

Ergonomists create safe and well-organized workspaces. Your classroom is like a workspace. In what ways can you improve the design of your classroom? How could the new layout make it easier to move around the classroom, work in groups, or share resources? Make a sketch of your ideas and present it to your teacher.

What Physics and Chemistry Are About

Can you imagine a life without cars and electricity? How did the things we use every day, such as cars, electric lights, and CDs, come to be? The answer has a lot to do with physics and chemistry. Physical science, the subject of this book, includes the study of physics and chemistry. Physics tells us how and why things move. Chemistry tells us how to make things such as batteries, plastic, and even medicine. In short, virtually everything around you, from cars and airplanes to the workings of your own body, depends on chemistry and physics.

Physical science teaches us the rules by which *everything* in the physical world works, down to the smallest detail. The whole world around you unfolds according to the laws of physical science. This entire book is about physical science, and we will take a look at what physical science actually *is* in the first chapter.

Key Questions:

1. What is physical science and why is it important to learn?

2. What is "everything" in terms of science?

1.1 Physical Science in Your Life

 **VOCABULARY**

force - a push or a pull.

mass - the amount of "stuff" (matter) an object contains.

This chapter looks at the "big picture" of physical science. After reading it you will be able to answer the following questions: (1) What is physical science?; (2) Where do the rules of physical science apply?; and (3) What can we learn by studying physical science?

The physics of a car

Cars changed the way people live

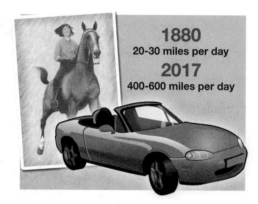

1880
20-30 miles per day
2017
400-600 miles per day

Let's take a look at the physics involved in a car. Few inventions have changed the world as much as the car. In 1880, it took about two weeks to go 400 miles from Boston to Washington, D.C., on horseback. Today, you can drive the trip in a day because cars are much faster than horses. Speed and motion are both part of physics.

A heavy garbage truck has more mass than a light-weight sports car.

More mass
Garbage truck

Less mass
Sports car

Forces are described by physics

When you push on the gas pedal at a stoplight, a stopped car starts moving. The car starts moving because the engine causes a **force** that pushes the car forward. If there were no force, the car would not move. Forces are described by physics. Physics tells us how much force it takes to get moving, to turn, or to stop. You'll learn more about force in Section 1.3.

Mass is also described by physics

Suppose you try to push a sports car and a garbage truck. Which is easier to push? If you guessed the car you are right; but *why* is a sports car easier to push than a garbage truck? The answer is **mass**. Mass is the amount of matter contained in an object. A big, heavy garbage truck has more mass than a small sports car (Figure 1.1). Physics tells us what mass is and how it affects what we do. You'll learn more about mass in the next section.

Figure 1.1: *A heavy garbage truck has more mass than a small sports car. That is why a sports car is easier to push.*

The chemistry of a car

Chemistry describes the different forms of matter

Think about a car and describe what it's made of. To a scientist, a car is made of **matter**. Matter is everything that has *mass* and takes up space. This book is matter. You are matter. Even the air is matter. At the next level of detail, a car contains many different kinds of matter, such as steel, aluminum, plastic, and rubber. Chemistry tells us about the different kinds of matter and how they are created. Chemistry also tells us how matter can be changed from one form to another.

Some of the many kinds of matter in a car

Glass
Steel
Oil (in engine)
Plastic (grill)

Gasoline (in fuel tank)
Air (in tires)
Aluminum
Rubber

Matter appears as solid, liquid, and gas

The matter in a car comes in three forms we call *solid*, *liquid*, and *gas* (Figure 1.2). Solid matter (like ice) is stiff, holds its shape, and may be strong. The frame of a car is made of solid steel. Liquid matter (like water) flows and does not hold its shape. Gasoline, oil, and windshield washer fluid are all liquids that are used in a car. Gas (like air) can expand and contract. The air in the tires is a gas.

Is air matter?

Does air takes up space? Imagine pushing a cylinder into an "empty" glass. If the air inside can't escape, you won't be able to push the cylinder all the way to the bottom. Why? Because air is matter—it takes up space (Figure 1.3). You don't always notice the mass of air because the mass is spread thinly. However, the total mass of air in a classroom is about equal to the mass of a student!

Burning gasoline is a chemical reaction

Many of today's cars and trucks run on gasoline. You put gasoline in the tank and it is burned in the engine. The burning gasoline releases energy that makes the engine run, which makes the car work. Burning is a *chemical reaction* that converts gasoline into other kinds of matter. Chemistry describes what gasoline is, and how gasoline burns in a chemical reaction that releases energy.

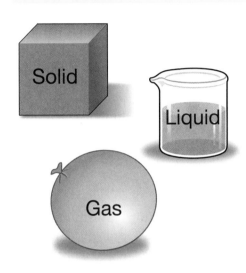

Figure 1.2: *Matter appears in three different forms that we call solid, liquid, and gas.*

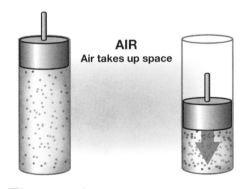

AIR
Air takes up space

Figure 1.3: *Air is matter because it has mass and takes up space.*

Physical science and living things

Physical science applies to everything

Physical science applies to *everything*, not just to machines like cars. Even living organisms are governed by the rules of physics and chemistry. These rules apply to actions like walking and swimming. They also apply to everything that goes on within your body such as digestion and the flow of blood.

A cheetah is the fastest land animal

The cheetah is the fastest land animal. Reaching speeds up to 70 miles per hour (mph) (or 112 km/h) a cheetah can go from 0 to 60 mph in about 3 seconds! That's faster than an expensive sports car! How does the cheetah move so quickly? The answer is in the physics of its muscles and bones. A cheetah's skeleton is built for speed, with long legs and a flexible spine (Figure 1.4). A running cheetah covers more than 20 feet (8 meters) in each stride. The forces created by the cheetah's muscles are directed by its long bones. The result is a very high-speed cat!

Animals eat to get chemical energy

Running takes a lot of energy. Where does the cheetah gets its energy? From chemistry! When a cheetah eats, chemicals in its stomach break food down into other chemicals. One of these chemicals is a sugar called glucose. Glucose is a chemical fuel for living muscles. The same chemistry happens when humans run or do any other form of physical exercise (Figure 1.5).

Why living organisms need food to survive

Your body uses chemistry to extract energy from food

It takes energy to run, to keep your body from freezing in winter, and even to think. All living organisms use energy to live. They cannot make energy themselves, but get their energy from food (animals) or sunlight (plants). To exchange, store, and release energy, living things have evolved special chemicals called fats and carbohydrates. *Biochemistry* is a branch of chemistry that explores exactly how plants and animals use chemicals and energy for living.

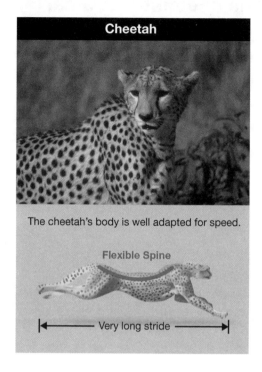

Cheetah

The cheetah's body is well adapted for speed.

Flexible Spine

Very long stride

Figure 1.4: *The cheetah has a body that is highly evolved for speed.*

All forms of human activity rely on chemistry and physics

Figure 1.5: *Physics and chemistry allow us to do everything we do as living organisms.*

Science and technology

Inventions solve problems
You are surrounded by inventions, from the toothbrush you use to clean your teeth to the computer you use to do your school projects (and play games). Where did these inventions come from? Most of them came from a practical application of science knowledge.

What is technology?
Science helps us understand the natural world. **Technology** is the application of science to meet human needs and solve problems. All technology—from the windmill to the supersonic jet—arises from the perception that "There must be a better way to do this!" Although technology is widely different in the details, there are some general principles that apply to all forms of technological design or innovation. People who design technology to solve problems are called engineers. Scientists study the natural world to learn the basic principles behind how things work. Engineers use scientific knowledge to create or improve inventions that solve problems.

 VOCABULARY

technology - the application of science to solve problems or accomplish useful tasks.

GPS

GPS stands for *Global Positioning System*. A GPS receiver can determine its position to within a few meters anywhere on Earth's surface. How does this work? How does the GPS receiver "know" its position?

There are 24 satellites in orbit around Earth that transmit radio signals as part of a global navigation system. At any one time, you can receive signals from anywhere from 6 to 11 of those satellites in the sky, all transmitting their unique codes and locations. A GPS receiver works by comparing the signals from four different GPS satellites

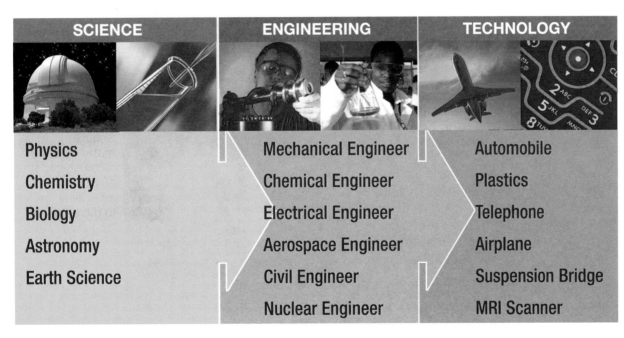

SCIENCE	ENGINEERING	TECHNOLOGY
Physics	Mechanical Engineer	Automobile
Chemistry	Chemical Engineer	Plastics
Biology	Electrical Engineer	Telephone
Astronomy	Aerospace Engineer	Airplane
Earth Science	Civil Engineer	Suspension Bridge
	Nuclear Engineer	MRI Scanner

Engineering

The career of engineering

Engineers are people who design, create, and work with technology. Engineers have to know science facts, but they also learn how to *use* science to do practical things. **Engineering** is a very creative, fun, and well-paying career. Following are descriptions of just a few areas of engineering (there are many others).

Electrical engineering

Cell phones are designed by *electrical engineers* using the physics of electricity and light waves. Computers, televisions, generators, and everything around you that uses electricity was probably designed by an electrical engineer.

Mechanical engineering

Mechanical engineers design the parts of a cell phone and all the machinery used to make cell phones. Mechanical engineers use concepts of geometry, force, motion, energy, and power to design things that are practical to build and that work correctly.

Civil engineering

Civil engineers design buildings, bridges, dams, and other structures (Figure 1.6). They need to understand how forces and materials impact structures. They also need to know about water and land. Some types of land, like wetlands, are not suitable for building on.

Chemical engineering

The batteries that make electric cars run were invented by *chemical engineers*. Chemical engineers use knowledge of chemistry to create new materials. Developing a nonpolluting fuel, such as alcohol made from corn and prairie grass, is another important new challenge that today's chemical engineers are working on.

Biomedical engineering

Biomedical engineers work with technology that is applied to the human body. One biomedical development is an artificial knee which has allowed thousands of injured people, who otherwise would be confined to a wheelchair, to walk, and even run again (Figure 1.7).

Genetic engineering

Genetic engineering is a relatively new area of both science research and technology. Genetic engineers use knowledge of DNA, chemistry, and biology to change how living organisms grow and develop. Someday, many human diseases may be cured by genetic engineering.

VOCABULARY

engineering - a career that uses science to design, create, and work with technology.

Figure 1.6: *San Francisco's Golden Gate Bridge.*

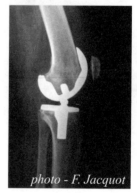

Special materials and careful design allow an artificial knee to recreate the same motion as a natural knee.

photo - F. Jacquot

Figure 1.7: *An x-ray showing an artificial knee joint.*

1.1 Section Review

Based on what you learned in this section, decide which of the following statements are *true* and which are *false*.

1. Understanding force and mass are part of the subject of physical science.
2. A truck with more mass always contains more matter than a car with less mass (Figure 1.8).
3. A car starts moving when the engine makes its mass smaller so the car feels less force from gravity.
4. Physical science applies to mechanical inventions such as a car but not to living creatures.

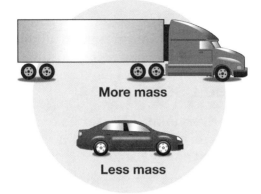

More mass

Less mass

Figure 1.8: *Question 2.*

Is this true?

Physical science applies   Physical science *does not* apply

5. Steel is matter because it is solid but water is not matter because water can flow and change its shape (Figure 1.9).
6. Matter can take the form of solid, liquid, or gas.
7. Air is not matter because you can't see air (Figure 1.10).
8. We eat food partly because it provides us with energy that our body uses to move.
9. Gasoline is a form of energy but it is not matter.
10. Glucose is a chemical fuel for living muscles.
11. Plants get some of their energy from sunlight but most from eating other plants.
12. Animals get most of their energy from sunlight, but also get a little energy from eating plants or other animals.

Steel   **Water**

Figure 1.9: *Question 5.*

Is air matter even though you can't see it?

Figure 1.10: *Question 7.*

1.2 Describing the Physical World

energy - the ability to change or to cause change.

To learn how the world works, we can start by describing exactly what we see and do. We can use three basic ideas to begin describing the world: (1) *what* things are made of (matter and energy); (2) *where* things are (in space); and (3) *when* things happen (in time).

Three useful ideas

Everything is matter and energy
Matter has mass and takes up space. In other words, matter is "stuff." Energy is harder to pin down. Think about changes you see every day. A thrown ball speeds up then slows down. Air gets warmer and colder. Water flows downhill. What explains these changes? The answer is *energy*. **Energy** is how the universe changes. A fast ball has more energy than a slow ball. Warm air has more energy than cold air. Water at the top of a hill has more energy than at the bottom.

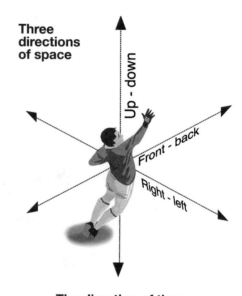

Space

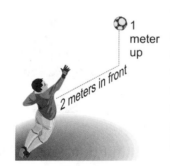

Up-down, right-left, and forward-backward are three directions of space (Figure 1.11). To completely understand the motion of a ball we need to know its exact path as it moves through space. For example, one second after tossing it, the ball might be 2 meters in front and 1 meter up from your chest. One second later it will be in a different place.

Time
Time is our reference for understanding change. As time goes on, each change causes other changes which cause still more changes. Time links things together in an endless chain of connections. For example, to understand how a ball moves, we think about what happened just before. Maybe somebody tossed it. To understand what the ball is doing *now* we need to know its past history over time.

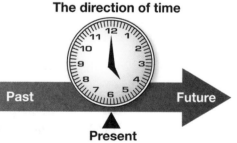

Figure 1.11: *Physical science explains how things change in space and time.*

Mass

Kilograms   Mass is measured in **kilograms** (kg) and **grams** (g). Most of the world uses kilograms for everyday measurement. An average-size adult has a mass of around 50 kg. A bicycle might be about 12 kg, a motorcycle about 200 kg, and a car about 1,500 kg. A bunch of bananas or a 1-liter bottle of water each have a mass of about 1 kg. Lift a full, 1-liter bottle of water to get a feeling of how much mass is in 1 kilogram.

Bunch of bananas
1 kilogram

Cat
5 kilograms

Person
55 kilograms

Motorcycle
200 kilograms

Electronic balance

Grams   For small amounts of mass, the gram is a more convenient measure. One gram (g) is one-thousandth of a kilogram. One grain of rice has a mass of about a gram, so a bag of 1,000 grains of rice has a mass of about 1 kilogram.

$$1 \; g = 0.001 \; kg \qquad 1 \; kg = 1,000 \; g$$

Using a mass balance   In the laboratory you will usually measure mass with a balance. The balance displays mass in grams. For example, the balance in Figure 1.12 shows the mass of six steel nuts to be 96.2 grams. Balances are sensitive and delicate instruments. Never drop things onto a balance; set them there gently!

Converting grams to kilograms   For many calculations you will need to convert mass from grams to kilograms. To convert a mass measured in grams to kilograms, you need to divide by 1,000 since there are 1,000 grams in a kilogram. In the example shown in Figure 1.12, 96.2 grams is equal to 0.0962 kilograms.

Converting from grams to kilograms

$$96.2 \; \cancel{g} \times \frac{1 \; kg}{1,000 \; \cancel{g}} = 0.0962 \; kg$$

$$96.2 \; g = 0.0962 \; kg$$

Figure 1.12: *A balance displays mass in grams. You may need to convert grams to kilograms when doing calculations.*

Length and distance

Distance is measured in units of length

Distance is measured in units of length. Some of the commonly used units of length include inches, feet, miles, centimeters, kilometers, and meters. The metric (or SI) system uses millimeters (mm), centimeters (cm), meters (m), and kilometers (km). The units in the metric system are based on multiples of 10. There are 10 millimeters in a centimeter, 100 centimeters in a meter, and 1,000 meters in a kilometer. Almost all fields of science use metric units because they are easy to work with and are used around the world.

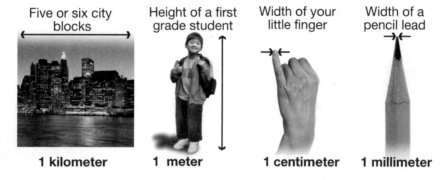

Five or six city blocks	Height of a first grade student	Width of your little finger	Width of a pencil lead
1 kilometer	**1 meter**	**1 centimeter**	**1 millimeter**

Always include units

When measuring, it is important to always say (or write) the unit you are using. Without a unit, measurements cannot be understood. For example, if you asked someone to walk 10, she would not know how far to go: 10 feet, 10 meters, 10 miles, or 10 kilometers. They are all 10, but the units are different and therefore the distances are also different. Units tell us how to understand numbers. Without units, we don't know what the numbers mean.

The meter stick

A meter stick is a good tool to use for measuring ordinary lengths in the laboratory. A meter stick is 1 meter long and is divided into millimeters and centimeters. The diagram in Figure 1.13 shows a meter stick along with objects of different lengths. Can you see how the meter stick is used to measure the length shown for each object?

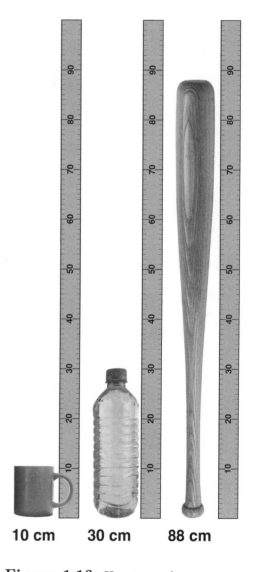

10 cm   **30 cm**   **88 cm**

Figure 1.13: *How to read a meter stick.*

Time

Time in science Time is very important in physical science. The concepts of *next* and *before* involve time. We often want to know how things change over time. For example, a car rolls down hill over time. A hot cup of coffee cools down over time. The laws of physical science tell us how things change over time.

What time is it? Time is used two ways (Figure 1.14). One way is to identify a particular moment. For example, saying someone was born on March 12, at 11:52 a.m. identifies a particular moment in time. This is the way "time" is usually used in everyday conversation.

How much time? The second way is to describe a *quantity* of time. For example, if a class lasts for 45 minutes then "45 minutes" is a quantity of time. The question "How much time?" is really asking for a quantity of time. A quantity of time is also called a *time interval*. A microwave oven with a built-in clock (Figure 1.15) displays both kinds of time: "time of day" and "time intervals." Any calculation involving time that you do in class will always use time intervals, *not* time of day.

What time is it?

11:52 a.m. March 12

How much time?

2 hours,
22 minutes, 42 seconds

Figure 1.14: *There are two different ways to understand time.*

Time in seconds

Hours   Minutes   Seconds

2 : 30 : 45

Many problems in science use time in seconds. For calculations, you may need to convert hours and minutes into seconds. For example, the timer (left) shows 2 hours, 30 minutes, and 45 seconds. To find out how many seconds this is, convert the hours and minutes into seconds.

There are 60 seconds in a minute, and 60 minutes in an hour. So, there are 3,600 (60 × 60) seconds in an hour. So, 2 hours = 7,200 seconds. 30 minutes = 1,800 seconds. Therefore, 2:30:45 = 7,200 + 1,800 + 45 = 9,045 seconds.

Figure 1.15: *A microwave oven can display time in either mixed units (minutes and seconds) or as a single unit (seconds). Both 1:30 and 0:90 will result in the same cooking time (90 seconds).*

1.2 Section Review

1. True or False: 35 centimeters is the same as 3.5 meters.
2. True or False: 1 kilogram is more mass than 10 grams.
3. True or False: There are 100 grams in one kilogram therefore, half a kilogram is 50 grams.
4. True or False: What happens now can only be affected by what happens in the future, not the past.
5. How many grams are in 2.5 kilograms?
6. The length of a sheet of standard (letter size) paper is closest to
    a. 0.11 meters.
    b. 11 centimeters.
    c. 29 centimeters.
    d. 279 millimeters.
7. The height of an average adult person is closest to
    a. 1.0 meters.
    b. 1.8 meters.
    c. 5.6 meters.
8. Someone who sells rope offers you 200 of rope for $10. What is wrong with this offer?
9. There are two ways to view time in science. One is historical time and the other is a time interval.
    a. Give an example of one way that both meanings are similar.
    b. Give an example of one way that both meanings are different.
10. Arrange the following intervals of time from shortest to longest.
    a. 160 seconds
    b. 2 minutes
    c. 1 minute 50 seconds
11. A bicyclist completes a race in 1 hour, 5 minutes, and 27 seconds. How many seconds did it take for the bicyclist to finish the race?

STUDY SKILLS

Using new words

Write sentences using each new vocabulary word from Sections 1.1 and 1.2. Using a new word helps you to remember what it means and how it is used. In fact, if you do not use a new word right away, you are very likely to forget it within a few hours!

Science assigns precise meanings to many common words

Many words in science are words you already know, like "force" or "energy." However, science defines these words in very precise ways that may be different from how they are used in everyday conversation. When you see a common word used in science, do not assume it means the same thing as it would it mean in casual conversation.

1.3 Energy, Matter, and Change

Physical science is all about how matter and energy change. Any matter that has energy can change itself or other matter. Matter can get hotter, colder, faster, higher, or change in many other ways. The world around us has a constant flow of energy between and through matter, creating changes as it goes.

Kinds of energy

The forms that energy can take Energy can exist in many forms, such as heat, motion, height, pressure, and electricity. Energy is also contained within matter itself, like the energy in food. The energy stored in food is an example of *chemical energy*. The diagram below shows some forms that energy can take. You have probably heard of many of them.

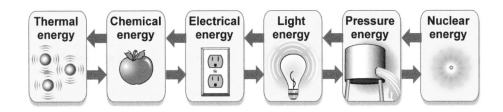

Creating change Energy can change from one form to another. Maybe you are reading this book under an electric light. It takes energy to make light. Where does this energy come from? Before it became light the energy was carried by electricity (Figure 1.16). Electricity is a modern way to transport energy from one place to another.

How power plants get energy The energy was changed into the form of electricity by your local power plant. But the energy itself was not made in the power plant! The power plant changed the chemical energy found in gas to heat energy (by burning the gas). The heat energy was used to turn water into steam, and the steam powered a machine called a turbine. The mechanical energy of the spinning turbine provided the power to run an electric generator, which produced the electrical energy.

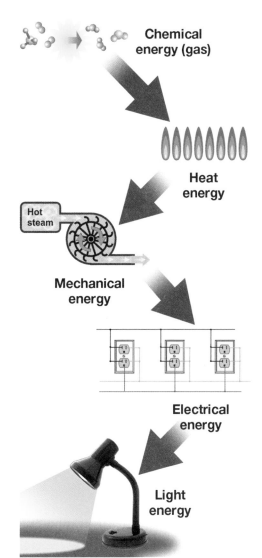

Figure 1.16: *Some of the steps energy takes on the way to your electric lamp.*

More about energy

Energy as nature's money

You can think of energy as nature's money. Any time anything changes, energy must be exchanged.

1. You use energy to throw a ball (change in speed).

2. The stove adds energy to a cup of tea (change in temperature).

3. Water loses energy as it flows downhill (change in height).

Each change "costs" a certain amount of energy. An object can only change as much as its energy allows. Bigger changes "cost" more energy. Smaller changes "cost" less energy. The amount of change you can have is limited by the amount of energy available.

Figure 1.17: *The energy from the Sun supports all living things on Earth.*

The Sun and energy

The energy in food starts with the Sun.

Both living creatures and products of technology get virtually all of their energy from the Sun. Without the Sun's energy, Earth would be a cold, icy place with a temperature of –273°C. As well as warming the planet, the Sun's energy drives the entire food chain (Figure 1.17). Plants use the energy in sunlight to make sugars from carbon dioxide in the air and water from the ground. Plants store the sugar as energy. Animals eat the plants to get energy. Other animals eat *those* animals for their energy. It all starts with the Sun.

Fossil fuels: gas and oil

A lot of the energy humans use comes from gas and oil. This energy also comes from the Sun! Over millions of years the Earth's surface has moved around. Some areas that were once vast jungles got pushed underground long ago. Gas and oil come from the decay of plant matter buried underground for millions of years. This plant matter was originally created with energy from sunlight. So, gas and oil are really a form of stored solar energy that was laid down over millions of years. We need to be concerned about using up gas and oil because once it is gone, there will be no more for millions of years to come.

Figure 1.18: *Mars is farther from the Sun than Earth and gets less energy. In fact, the average temperature on Mars is well below the freezing point of water. Can life exist on Mars?*

Forces

Example of force   What do you do when you want to move a box across the floor? You push it or pull it. Pushing and pulling are examples of force (Figure 1.19). Most of the changes that occur in the physical world are caused by forces. Sliding a box across the floor is a change in the position of the box. That change can only be caused through the action of a force.

What is force?   A force is a push or pull, or any action that is able to change motion. You need force to start things moving and also to make any change to their motion once they are moving. Forces can be used to make an object go faster or slower, or turn in a new direction. The thing to remember is that force is an *action*. Some forces act to cause things to change. Other forces act to keep things from changing.

What creates forces?   Forces are created in many different ways. Your muscles create force when you push a box. Earth's gravity creates forces that pull on everything around you. On a windy day, the movement of air can create forces. Each of these actions can create force and they all can change an object's motion.

Examples of forces

Figure 1.19: *Push and pull are examples of forces.*

Some of the many ways forces are created

Energy moves through forces   No matter what creates the force, forces require a source of energy. You use energy from food to create forces with your muscles. Lifting a book (against Earth's gravity) takes energy (Figure 1.20). If the book falls down again, its energy can make forces on anything it hits on the way down. The motion of the wind is caused by energy from the Sun being absorbed in the Earth's atmosphere. Energy moves through the action of forces! In fact, one simple way to think about energy is as the *stored ability to create forces*.

Figure 1.20: *When you use force to lift a book, you transfer some of your energy to the book by making it higher.*

Understanding changes

Thinking about changes

Science is about understanding how and why things change. Lots of different kinds of changes happen around you every minute. You can understand some changes by thinking about what you can actually see and touch. Other changes are harder to explain. Here is an example. Imagine being in the woods on a cold evening, stirring a pot of cocoa over a fire. Think about these three changes that happen.

1. The cocoa is moving as you stir it.

2. The cocoa in the pot is getting warmer.

3. The wood in the fire is burning to make heat.

An easy change to understand

The first change is the easiest to understand. Stirring makes a force on the cocoa in the pot, which makes it move. This kind of change can be explained with the ideas of force and motion, discussed in Unit 2.

Temperature and atoms

Getting warmer is a change in *temperature*. Temperature changes are also caused by forces and motion, only of a much *smaller size*. To understand temperature you need to know that matter is actually made of tiny particles called *atoms*. Atoms are so small that more than 200,000 of them fit in the thickness of a sheet of aluminum foil (Figure 1.21)! Temperature changes come from the forces and motion of the trillions of tiny atoms inside matter.

How matter changes

The third change is the hardest to understand. How does one kind of matter change into completely different kinds of matter? For example, once the wood in a fire has burned into ashes, it does not change back into wood again. The matter that started as wood has changed into another kind of matter that looks completely different (Figure 1.22). How? The answer to this question has to do with atoms. The forces between atoms sometimes cause them to combine with each other to form completely different kinds of matter!

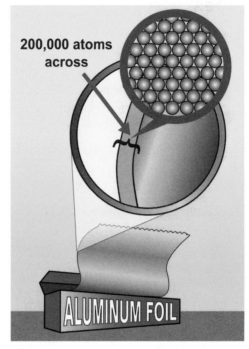

200,000 atoms across

Figure 1.21: *Even a thin sheet of aluminum foil is 200,000 atoms thick.*

What is fire?

How does fire change wood into ashes?

Figure 1.22: *How do we understand wood changing into ashes and smoke?*

Why are atoms so important?

Why learn about atoms?

For thousands of years, no one knew that atoms existed. Why is it important to know about atoms now? If atoms can't be seen, how do we know they exist?

Chemistry, physics, and technology

It's important to know about atoms because atoms explain all the properties of matter. We cannot understand chemistry or physics without atoms. Modern technology has become powerful enough that we can see and use atoms. For example, atoms are split for energy in nuclear power. Scientists can even move single atoms around and make structures out of atoms.

How does ice change to water?

Before people understood about atoms, the changing of ice to water was a mystery. Imagine an ice cube. Solid ice acts differently than liquid water. But ice can change into water and water into ice. How does this happen? The answer involves forces between atoms.

Atoms attract each other

Atoms attract each other when they are separated. In science, the word "attract" means a force. Each atom feels an attractive force pulling it toward every other atom. If the force is strong enough, the atoms all stick together in a *solid*, like the atoms in ice. Ice is solid because the atoms are stuck to each other by their attractive forces.

Temperature and energy

As the temperature of matter goes up, each atom starts to wiggle around. That's because heat is a kind of energy. When atoms absorb heat energy, they move. The higher the temperature gets, the more the atoms wiggle. As the temperature keeps rising, eventually the wiggling motion overcomes the attractive force sticking atoms together. When that happens, atoms are free to move around and switch places with each other and the ice *melts to a liquid*! Liquid water flows because its atoms are not stuck tightly to each other as they are in ice (Figure 1.23).

Hydrogen atom   Oxygen atom

Atoms feel attractive forces toward each other

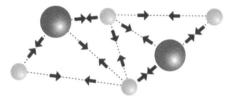

All the atoms in ice (solid) are stuck to each other

The atoms in liquid water can move around

Figure 1.23: *Solid water (ice) and liquid water are the same kind of matter. Only the connections between the atoms are different.*

Atoms and chemistry

The variety of matter

If you look around you can probably see over a hundred different kinds of matter: cloth, concrete, wood, metal, chalk, glass, leather, grass, etc. The list seems endless. Many kinds of matter, like plastic, are made from other kinds of matter, such as oil. Is it possible that the millions of different kinds of matter are all made from something simpler? Could water be a combination of other things just like a chocolate cake is a combination of ingredients like sugar, flour, and eggs?

Combinations of 26 letters make all the words in the dictionary.

Matter is made from different kinds of atoms

The answer is yes. Just as thousands of words can be made with only 26 letters, all the millions of different kinds of matter are made from about 90 different kinds of atoms (Figure 1.24). Each kind of atom is like a letter in the alphabet of matter. The word *water* is spelled with five letters. The water **molecule** is "spelled" with three atoms: hydrogen-oxygen- hydrogen, or H-O-H, usually written H$_2$O. Each molecule of water has one oxygen atom and two hydrogen atoms. Every different kind of matter has its own unique combination of the 90 basic kinds of atoms.

Combinations of about 90 different atoms make all the matter around you.

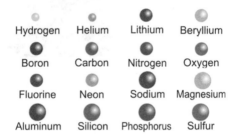

Each kind of atom is called an element

We call each kind of atom an **element**. An element (like gold) is a pure form of matter that cannot be broken down into other elements. All atoms of the same element are similar to each other and different from atoms of sother elements. If you examine a million atoms of carbon, they would all be similar to each other but different from sodium, aluminum, or oxygen atoms.

VOCABULARY

molecule - a group of atoms that are bonded together in a specific ratio.

element - a pure form of matter that cannot be broken down into other elements. There are about 90 elements that occur naturally.

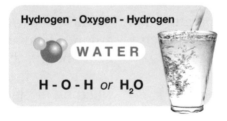

Figure 1.24: *The huge variety of matter around you is made from about 90 different kinds of atoms.*

1.3 Section Review

1. True or False: Earth receives a significant amount of its energy from the Moon and the other planets.
2. True or False: Nothing can change if there is no energy.
3. True or False: Mars is warmer than Earth because it receives more energy from the Sun than Earth does.
4. A large rock falls off a mountain and rolls downhill. The rock gains speed as it moves downhill. More speed means more energy. Where does the rock get the energy from?
   a. Earth's gravity
   b. the Sun's gravity
   c. the temperature difference between the top of the mountain and the bottom
5. What action causes motion to change?
6. The picture in Figure 1.25 shows salt, a common chemical. Is salt an element? Give a reason for your answer.
7. We can't ordinarily see individual atoms because
   a. they are invisible.
   b. they are only scientific ideas and really don't exist.
   c. they are extremely small.
8. Explain the difference between an atom and a molecule.
9. The difference between ice and liquid water is that
   a. atoms in ice are grouped together in molecules.
   b. molecules in liquid water can move around each other.
   c. ice is made of different elements than water.
10. Temperature is caused by
    a. the color of individual atoms.
    b. the motion of individual atoms and the forces between them.
    c. the presence of a thermometer.

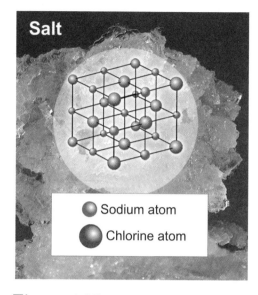

Salt

● Sodium atom
● Chlorine atom

Figure 1.25: *Question 4.*

Seeing individual atoms

STEM

It is now possible to actually "see" single atoms with a special instrument called an atomic force microscope. This image is of silicon atoms.

(*Photo courtesy Franz Giessibl.*)

How Do Hybrid Cars Work?

Gas-electric hybrid cars look and drive about like any other car, but use 20–30% less gas. For example, a hybrid car's gas mileage is about 50 miles per gallon. The gas mileage for standard cars ranges from 10 to 30 miles per gallon. To understand how hybrid cars get better gas mileage, we have to look at the engines. This is a great application of physical science concepts!

Cars powered by gasoline

The efficiency of a gasoline engine is about 13 percent. This means that when the car is in motion, it only uses about 13percent of the available energy from a tank of gas. The rest of the available energy from a tank of gas is lost as heat. The more energy that is lost as heat, the less efficient an engine or any system is. Although a gasoline engine produces many pollutants, gasoline is very energy-rich and easy for a car to carry. These two features made the gasoline engine the preferred choice when oil was inexpensive and there was less concern about polluting our environment.

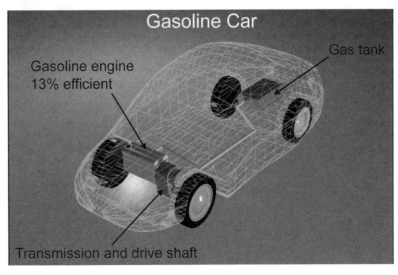

Gasoline Car

Gasoline engine 13% efficient

Gas tank

Transmission and drive shaft

Cars powered by electricity

Compared to gasoline-powered cars, electric motors are very efficient—up to 80 percent—and they produce no pollutants. To run an electric car, the batteries need to be charged. This is often done by plugging in the car during the night. Unfortunately, batteries are heavy and (per kilogram) don't have as much energy as gasoline. For instance, the available energy in a typical 20-kilogram car battery is equivalent to only about a small cupful of gasoline. Until there is a better electrical storage system, cars powered by electricity from a battery must be small and only used for short trips.

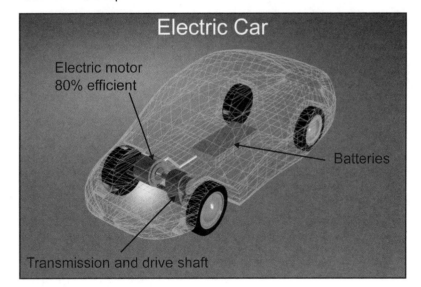

Electric Car

Electric motor 80% efficient

Batteries

Transmission and drive shaft

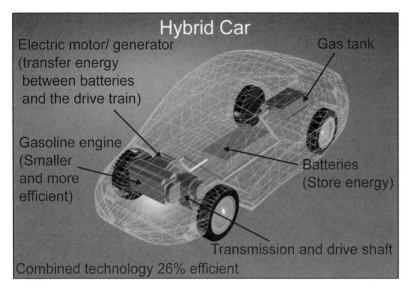

Hybrid Car

Electric motor/ generator (transfer energy between batteries and the drive train)

Gas tank

Gasoline engine (Smaller and more efficient)

Batteries (Store energy)

Transmission and drive shaft

Combined technology 26% efficient

The best of both technologies

A hybrid car uses the best of both worlds—a gasoline-powered engine and an electric motor. By combining technologies, the overall efficiency is improved from 13 percent to about 26 percent. The electric motor helps the gas-powered system be more efficient by using electricity to transfer energy within the system.

How do hybrids compare?

In a hybrid car, the gasoline engine and electric motor work together to accelerate the car. This allows the gasoline engine to be smaller and more efficient. Every time a standard car slows down, kinetic energy is lost as the brakes heat up. In contrast, the hybrid's electric motor operates as a generator during braking. When the car slows down, kinetic energy is converted to electrical energy that charges the batteries. Then, to speed up the car, the stored energy in the batteries is converted into useful kinetic energy by the motor. In addition to getting great gas mileage, hybrid cars are rated as ulta-low emissions vehicles (ULEVs). This means that they do not produce as many pollutants as standard cars. Hybrid cars produce less pollution because the engine is smaller and simply uses less gasoline. Also, when a hybrid car comes to a stop, the engine automatically shuts off to save gas. When it is time to go again, the car turns on instantly. At very low speeds, as when you are driving in a city, the electric motor runs the car instead of the gasoline engine. When the electric motor is used, there is less pollution.

Hybrid technology is just a beginning

The gas-electric hybrid is only one of the many types of more efficient motor-powered vehicles that are being developed today. Driving this development is an interest in decreasing our use of fossil fuels for transportation. Interest in developing alternative transportation technologies will continue because they are potentially more efficient and less polluting. In the meantime, since we all need to travel and often use gasoline-powered vehicles, how can you reduce your use of fossil fuels so that you save money and reduce pollution? Here are some options: share rides, take public transportation, and drive a medium-sized or small car that has high gas mileage.

QUESTIONS

1. If you only need to drive two miles per day, which kind of car would be the best to use? Justify your answer.

2. Why is the efficiency of gasoline-powered cars so low?

3. Some hybrid cars have efficiency meters—a gauge that shows your miles per gallon—so you can monitor and improve your driving habits. Make a list of driving habits that help you save gas.

Guess the Gram

Mass is the measure of the amount of matter an object contains. An object's mass is related to its size (volume) and the density of the material from which it is made. Common units for measuring mass include the gram and kilogram. One kilogram is equal to 1,000 grams. In this activity you will be using a triple beam balance to measure mass and estimate the masses of everyday objects.

Materials:

- balance capable of measuring 300 grams +/– 0.1 grams
- assorted items such as coins, paperclips, rubber bands, washers, marbles, popcorn kernels, etc.

Two kinds of mechanical balances

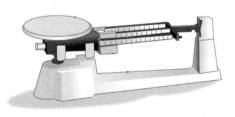 

What you will do

1. Make sure your balance is calibrated properly and shows a reading of zero when it is empty. Make adjustments to the thumb screw if necessary.

2. Copy the table shown to the right.

3. Choose an object from your assortment that you believe has a mass close to one gram. Record the name of the object in the first row of the table.

4. Use the balance to measure the mass of the object to the nearest tenth of a gram. Record the mass in the table in the first try column.

5. Unless your mass was exactly one gram, make a second attempt to find one or more objects with a mass of one gram. Record the object(s) you selected, measure the mass, and record the mass.

6. Repeat with all the other masses in the table.

Mass (g)	Object(s)	Mass (g) first try	Object(s)	Mass (g) second try
1				
5				
10				
25				
50				
100				
200				

Applying your knowledge

a. Did the accuracy of your estimations increase as the activity went on?

b. Calculate your error in estimating the mass of the 10 gram object on your first try. Calculate your error in estimating on your second try.

c. Estimate the mass of the following objects in grams:
   - your textbook
   - an unsharpened pencil
   - a sheet of notebook paper
   - a compact disc

d. Estimate your mass in grams and in kilograms.

e. If you wanted to estimate the mass of a car, would you use grams or kilograms?

Chapter 1 Assessment

Vocabulary

Select the correct term to complete the sentences.

element	energy	force
gram	kilogram	mass
matter	engineering	molecule
technology		

Section 1.1

1. Everything that has mass and takes up space is called ____.

2. A push or a pull is an example of a(n) ____.

3. ____ includes all the inventions and techniques humans have developed by applying science.

4. A career that uses science to design, create, and work with technology is ____.

5. The amount of matter an object contains is called ____.

Section 1.2

6. The "stored ability to create forces" is a description of ____.

7. A one liter bottle of soda has a mass about equal to one ____.

8. If 1,000 dollar bills have a mass of one kilogram, 1 dollar bill has a mass of one ____.

Section 1.3

9. The name for a pure form of matter that cannot be chemically broken down is ____.

10. A group of atoms that are bonded together in a specific ratio is a ____.

Concepts

Section 1.1

1. Describe five ways that physics and chemistry affect your life.

2. You have an idea for making a new type of backpack that is more comfortable to wear. Describe how you would use the design cycle to turn your idea into a practical solution.

3. Choose a technology invention and describe how it makes life easier for people.

4. Write the letters L (liquid), S (solid), or G (gas) to indicate the phase of matter of each of the following examples.
   a. ____ Window glass
   b. ____ Air in a balloon
   c. ____ Oil in a car's engine

Section 1.2

5. Name the four basic ideas required to describe the world around you.

6. Use the letters E (energy) and M (matter) to identify each of the following:
   a. ____ gasoline
   b. ____ light
   c. ____ electricity
   d. ____ air

7. How could you give a bottle of water more energy?

8. Your friend, Dayana, says air is not matter. How could you convince her that air is matter?

9. How many dimensions are needed to describe the location of a stationary baseball?

10. How does time help us to describe our physical world?

11. List whether the gram (g) or the kilogram (kg) would be most convenient for measuring each of the following objects.
   a. ____ 1-liter bottle of soda
   b. ____ penny
   c. ____ bicycle

12. A friend offers you a piece of candy that is 200. What is wrong with his offer?

13. Indicate whether the length of each object listed below is closest to a kilometer (km), a meter (m), a centimeter (cm), or a millimeter (mm).

   a. ____ length of a baseball bat
   b. ____ thickness of a sewing needle
   c. ____ width of a drinking straw
   d. ____ 10 football fields connected end-to-end

14. Identify each of the following as a moment in time (*M*) or as a quantity of time (*Q*).

   a. ____ Your 15ᵗʰ birthday
   b. ____ Six days until July 4
   c. ____ 15 minutes from home to school by bus
   d. ____ 3:15 on Friday afternoon

Section 1.3

15. A local power plant begins with a quantity of coal. Describe the changes in energy that you need in order to use energy from the power plant in your house.

16. What is the source of nearly all energy used by living things and by technology?

17. "Race cars run on solar energy." Explain why this is an accurate statement.

18. How does energy move?

19. Explain how energy and forces are related to all changes.

20. Name two ways that scientists use atoms to make our lives easier and more convenient.

21. How are the atoms in water affected by forces?

Problems

Section 1.1

1. The same force is applied to a ping-pong ball and a bowling ball. Both balls are free to roll along a level floor. Describe the differences between the motion of the two balls.

2. Describe a common substance that you have experienced as a solid, liquid, and gas.

Section 1.2

3. Convert 54 grams to kilograms.

4. Convert 26 kilograms to grams.

5. Convert 1,200 meters to millimeters.

6. How many seconds are in 2 hours and 14 minutes?

7. Write 3,800 seconds in hours, minutes, and seconds.

Section 1.3

8. Write three observations you could make to indicate that an object has an increased amount of energy.

9. You melt a pan of ice into water by heating it up on a stove.

   a. Name a change made to the ice.
   b. Which has more energy, the ice or the water?

10. Describe the energy transformations or changes for each of the pictures below.

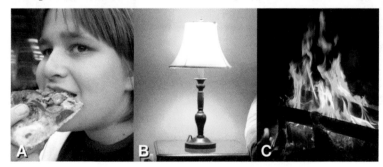

Science and Measurement

In 2014, on Mont Ventoux in France, Guy Martin of the United Kingdom climbed into a gravity race car with no motor. With one push, he raced downhill with nothing else but gravity for energy, and set a world record of 85.6 mph! His fiercely competitive engineering team had created the slipperiest low-friction car they could in four months' time, using high-tech materials and parts. At the speeds he was traveling, the car also had to be safe so safety features were designed such as roll-cage protection, a safety harness, and an energy-absorbing steering column.

How did his car reach such high speeds without using a motor? How did the engineering team design his car to be so fast? Answers to these questions involve experiments and variables. Read on and you will find out how engineers learn to make things better, faster, and more efficient.

Key Questions:

1. How do scientists know when they are right?

2. How is motion described in science?

3. What are experiments and what do they tell us?

2.1 Inquiry and the Scientific Method

ã VOCABULARY

Scientists believe everything in the universe works by a set of rules called **natural laws**. Everything that happens everywhere obeys the same natural laws. Unfortunately, the natural laws are not written down nor are we born knowing them. *The primary goal of science is to discover what the natural laws are.* Over time, we have found the most reliable way to discover natural laws is called *scientific inquiry*.

natural laws - the set of rules that are obeyed by every detail of everything that occurs in the universe.

inquiry - a process of learning that starts with asking questions and proceeds by seeking the answers to the questions.

deduce - to figure something out from known facts using logical thinking.

What "inquiry" means

Inquiry is learning through questions

How is science like solving a mystery?

Learning by asking questions is called **inquiry** (Figure 2.1). An inquiry is like a crime investigation with a mystery to solve. Something illegal happened and the detective must figure out who did it. Solving the mystery means accurately describing who did what, when they did it, and how. The problem is that the detective never actually *saw* what happened. The detective must **deduce** what happened in the past from information collected in the present.

Theories In the process of inquiry, the detective asks lots of questions related to the mystery. The detective searches for evidence and clues that help answer the questions. Eventually, the detective comes up with a theory about what happened. The theory is a description of what must have occurred in the crime, down to the smallest details.

How you know you have learned the truth At first, the detective's theory is only one possible explanation among several of what *might have happened*. The detective must have evidence that a theory describes what actually *did happen*. To be accepted, a theory must pass three demanding tests. First, it must be supported by enough evidence. Second, there cannot be even a *single* piece of evidence that contradicts the theory. Third, the theory must be unique. If two theories both fit the facts equally well, you cannot tell which is correct. When the detective arrives at a theory that passes all three tests, he believes he has "solved" the mystery by using the process of inquiry.

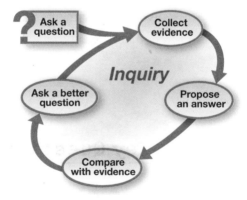

Figure 2.1: *The steps in learning through inquiry.*

Scientific evidence

What counts as scientific evidence?

In science, the only way to know you are right is to compare what you think against real evidence. However, what types of evidence qualify as *scientific* evidence? Do feelings or opinions count as scientific evidence? Does what other people think qualify as scientific evidence? The answer to both questions is no. Because evidence is so important in science, there are careful rules defining what counts as scientific evidence.

An example of scientific evidence

Scientific evidence may include numbers, tables, graphs, words, pictures, sound recordings, or other information. The important thing is that the evidence accurately describes what happens in the real world (Figure 2.2). Scientific evidence may be collected without doing experiments in a laboratory. For example, Galileo used his telescope to look at the moon. He recorded what he saw by sketching in his notebook. Galileo's sketches are considered scientific evidence.

When is evidence considered scientific?

Scientific evidence must be **objective** and **repeatable**. "Objective" means the evidence should describe *only what actually happened* as exactly as possible. "Repeatable" means that others who look the same way at the same thing will observe the same results. Galileo's sketches describe in detail what he actually saw through the telescope. That means the sketches are *objective*. Others who looked through his telescope saw the same thing. That makes the sketches *repeatable*. Galileo's sketches are good scientific evidence because they are both objective and repeatable. Galileo's sketches helped convince people that the Moon was actually a world like the Earth with mountains and valleys. This was not what people believed in Galileo's time.

Communicating scientific evidence

It is important that scientific evidence be clear, with no room for misunderstanding. For this reason, scientists define concepts like "force" and "weight" very clearly. Usually, the scientific definition is similar to the way you already use the word, but more exact. For example, your "weight" in science means the force of gravity pulling on the mass of your body.

VOCABULARY

objective - describes evidence that documents only what actually happened as exactly as possible.

repeatable - describes evidence that can be seen independently by others if they repeat the same experiment or observation in the same way.

Examples of scientific evidence

Pictures or sketches that show actual observations

Time (s)	Speed (m/s)	Position (m)
0.0	0.00	0.00
0.2	0.83	0.08
0.4	1.66	0.33
0.6	2.50	0.75
0.8	3.33	1.33
1.0	4.16	2.08

Measurements and data

Figure 2.2: *Some examples of scientific evidence.*

Scientific theories and natural laws

How theories are related to natural laws
A scientific **theory** is a human attempt to describe a natural law. For example, if you leave a hot cup of coffee on the table eventually it will cool down. Why? There must be some natural law that explains what causes the coffee to cool. A good place to start looking for the law is by asking what it is about the coffee that makes it hot. Whatever quality creates "hot" must go away or weaken as the coffee gets cold (Figure 2.3). The question of what causes hot and cold puzzled people for a long time.

The theory of caloric
Before 1843, scientists believed a theory that heat was a kind of fluid (like water) that flowed from hotter objects to colder objects. They called this fluid *caloric*. People thought hot objects had more caloric than cold objects. When a hot object touched a cold object, the caloric flowed between them until the temperatures were the same.

Testing the theory
The caloric theory explained what people knew at the time. However, a big problem came up when people learned to measure weight accurately. Suppose caloric really did flow from a hot object to a cold object. Then an object should weigh more when hot compared to its weight when cold. Experiments showed this was not true. Precise measurements showed that objects have the same weight, hot or cold. The caloric theory was soon given up because it could not explain this new evidence.

How theories are tested against evidence
Scientists are always testing the theories we believe against new experiments and new evidence. One of two things can happen when new evidence is found:

1. The current theory correctly explains the new evidence. This gives us confidence that the current theory is the right one;

2. or the current theory does *not* explain the new evidence. This means there is a new (or improved) theory waiting to be discovered that can explain the new evidence (as well as all the old evidence).

VOCABULARY

theory - a scientific explanation supported by a lot of evidence collected over a long period of time.

What makes these two cups of coffee different?

Hot coffee 70°C   Cold coffee 21°C

Figure 2.3: *A question that might begin inquiry into what "heat" really is.*

CHALLENGE

Humans understood much less about science 1,000 years ago. That doesn't mean that people didn't know about things like temperature. Ancient people certainly knew the difference between hot and cold. What they didn't know was the scientific reason for why things were hot or cold. Research a theory about something in science that was believed in the past, but no longer believed. What convinced people to change their minds?

Theories and hypotheses

The hypothesis   Based on observations and evidence, a good detective evaluates many different theories for what might have happened. Each different theory is then compared with the evidence. The same is true in science, except that the word *theory* is reserved for a single explanation supported by lots of evidence collected over a long period of time. Instead of *theory*, scientists use the word **hypothesis** to describe a possible explanation for a scientific mystery.

VOCABULARY

hypothesis - a possible explanation that can be tested by comparison with scientific evidence. Early hypotheses are rarely correct and are often modified as new evidence becomes available.

Hypothesis
Suppose heat is really a form of energy. Then it would not have any mass.

Many experiments are done to see if heat might be energy.

Theory
Heat is a form of energy.

Theories in science are hypotheses that correctly explain every bit of evidence   Theories in science start out as hypotheses. The old explanation that heat was the fluid caloric was an incorrect hypothesis, one of many leading up to the modern theory of heat. The first hypothesis that heat is a form of energy was made by a German doctor, Julius Mayer, in 1842, and confirmed by experiments done by James Joule in 1843. Energy has no weight so Mayer's hypothesis explained why an object's weight remained unchanged whether it was hot or cold. After many experiments, Mayer's hypothesis that heat was a form of energy became the accepted *theory* of heat we believe today (Figure 2.4).

More energy   *Less energy*

Hot coffee 70°C   Cold coffee 21°C

Figure 2.4: *A hot cup of coffee has more heat energy than a cold cup of coffee. As coffee cools, its heat energy is transferred to the air in the room. As a result, the air is warmed.*

Hypotheses must be testable to be scientific   A scientific hypothesis must be testable. That means it must be possible to collect evidence that proves whether the hypothesis is true or false. This requirement means *not all hypotheses* can be considered by science. For instance, it has been believed at times that creatures are alive because of an undetectable "life force." This is not a scientific hypothesis because there is no way to test it. If the "life force" is undetectable, that means no evidence can be collected that would prove whether it exists or not. Science restricts itself only to those ideas which may be proved or disproved by actual evidence.

The Scientific Method

Learning by chance
At first, humans learned about the world by trial and error. Imagine a small child trying to open a jar. She will try what she knows: biting the lid, pulling on it, shaking the jar, dropping it, until, by chance, she twists the lid. It comes off. She puts it back and tries twisting it again—and the lid comes off again. The child learns by trying many different things and then *remembering what works*.

Learning by the scientific method
It takes a long time to learn by randomly trying everything. What is worse, you can never be sure you tried *everything*. The **scientific method** is a much more dependable way to learn.

VOCABULARY

scientific method - a process of learning that begins with a hypothesis and proceeds to prove or change the hypothesis by comparing it with scientific evidence.

The Scientific Method

1. Scientists observe nature, then develop or revise hypotheses about how things work.

2. The hypotheses are tested against evidence collected from observations and experiments.

3. Any hypothesis that correctly accounts for all of the evidence from the observations and experiments is a potentially correct theory.

4. A theory is continually tested by collecting new and different evidence. Even one single piece of evidence that does not agree with a theory will force scientists to return to step one.

Why the scientific method works
The scientific method is the underlying logic of science. It is a careful and cautious way to build an evidence-based understanding of our natural world. Each theory is continually tested against the results of observations and experiments. Such testing leads to continued development and refinement of theories to explain more and more different things. The way people came to understand the solar system is a good example of how new evidence leads to new and better theories (Figure 2.5).

Early civilizations thought Earth was covered by a dom on which the Sun, stars, and planets moved.

In the Middle Ages, people thought the Sun, stars, and planets circled Earth which sat in the center.

Today we know Earth and planets orbit around the Sun, and the stars are very far away.

Figure 2.5: *Three different models for Earth and the solar system that were believed at different times in history.*

2.1 Section Review

1. Which of the following is an example of deduction?
   a. Hector calls the weather service to find out if the temperature outside is below freezing.
   b. Caroline looks out the window and concludes that the temperature is below freezing because she sees that the puddles in her neighbor's driveway are frozen.
2. Describe the relationship between a hypothesis, a theory, and a natural law.
3. To be correct, a scientific theory must be everything *except*
   a. supported by every part of a large collection of evidence.
   b. believed by a large number of reputable people.
   c. testable by comparison with scientific evidence.
   d. an explanation of something that actually occurs within the natural world or within man-made technology.
4. Julie, a third grade student, believes that the moon disappears on certain days every month. Explain why the following information is or is not scientific evidence which can be used to evaluate Julie's hypothesis.
   a. Julie sometimes cannot see the moon all night even though the sky is clear.
   b. Anne, Julie's older sister, thinks the phases of the moon are caused by the moon's position in its orbit around the Earth.
5. When describing scientific evidence, what is the meaning of the word *repeatable*?
6. Which of the following is an example of learning through inquiry?
   a. Miguel is told that hot objects, like a cup of coffee, cool off when left on the table in a cooler room.
   b. Enrique wonders what happens to hot objects if you remove them from the stove. He puts a thermometer in a pot of boiling water and observes that the water cools off once it's removed from the heat source.

Paper wasp nest

Keep your eyes and ears open

A great many discoveries were made almost by accident! For example, paper used to be made of cotton or linen, which are costly plant fibers. Inventors searched for a less expensive way to make paper. In 1719, French scientist and inventor Rene de Reaumer was walking in the woods when he noticed that wasp nests were made from something a lot like paper! How did the wasps do it? In 1840, Friedrich Keller made the first all wood paper and today nearly all paper is made from wood. Reaumer's curiosity and alert eyes lead directly to the paper we use today.

2.2 **Distance, Time, and Speed**

Imagine you are in a submarine exploring the deepest part of the ocean. How can you tell the rest of your team where you are? You need to describe where you are in such a way that your fellow team members know exactly what you mean. When scientists need to communicate precise information they use **variables**. A variable is a well-defined piece of information with a name and a **value**. The *depth* of a submarine is a variable that describes how far a submarine is below the surface (Figure 2.6).

Speed

Speed is a motion variable We use the variable **speed** to describe how quickly something moves. Saying a race car, runner, or plane is "fast" is not enough to accurately describe its speed scientifically. To understand speed we need to be more specific and define speed so we can measure it and give it a precise value. As you will learn in the next section, speed equals distance divided by time.

An example of speed Imagine two bicycles moving along the road at different speeds. The illustration below shows the position of each bicycle at one-second intervals. The fast bicycle (bottom) moves 3 meters each second, while the slow bicycle (top) moves only 1 meter each second. The fast bicycle moves three times the speed of the slow one.

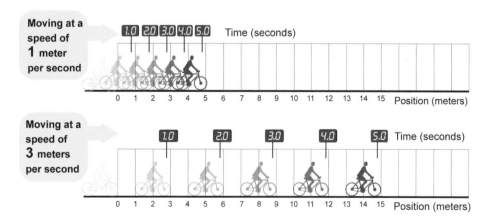

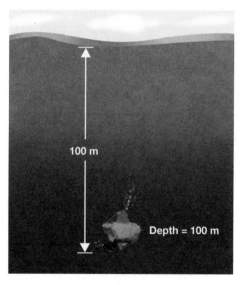

Figure 2.6: *The variable* depth *represents all possible values for the distance between the surface and the submarine. At any moment, the submarine has a specific value of depth. At the moment shown in the picture, the depth is 100 meters.*

VOCABULARY

variable - a quantity that can change, often with a numerical value. For example, position and speed are variables.

value - the particular number (with units) that a variable may have. For example, 20 feet is a value.

speed - the distance an object travels divided by the time it takes.

Measuring speed

Speed is distance divided by time

Speed is a ratio of the distance traveled divided by the time taken. To measure speed you need two values: distance and time. Suppose you drive 150 kilometers (km) in 1.5 hours (h). Your **average speed** is 150 km divided by 1.5 h, or 100 km per h (km/h) (Figure 2.7).

Why "average"?

The speed above is the *average* speed because it really doesn't tell you how fast you are going at any moment during the trip. If you watch the speedometer as you drive, you will see that you are going faster than average some times and slower than average other times. You might even be stopped (speed = 0) for part of the trip. The only way your average speed and actual speed would be the same during the whole trip is if you traveled at a **constant speed**. *Constant* means "does not change," so constant speed is speed that does not change.

What does "per" mean?

The word *per* means "for every" or "for each." Saying "100 kilometers per hour" is the same as saying "100 kilometers *for each* hour." You can also think of *per* as meaning "divided by." The quantity before the word *per* is divided by the quantity after it. To calculate speed in kilometers per hour, you divide the number of kilometers by the number of hours—150 km divided by 1.5 h equals 100 km/h.

Units for speed

Since speed is a ratio of distance over time, the units for speed are distance units over time units. If distance is in kilometers and time in hours, then speed is in kilometers per hour (km/h). Other metric units for speed are cm per second (cm/s) and meters per second (m/s). Your family's car probably shows speed in miles per hour (mph). Table 2.1 shows different units commonly used for speed.

Table 2.1: Common units for speed

Distance	Time	Speed	Abbreviation
meters	seconds	meters per second	m/s
kilometers	hours	kilometers per hour	km/h
centimeters	seconds	centimeters per second	cm/s
miles	hours	miles per hour	mph

average speed - the total distance divided by the total time for a trip.

constant speed - speed that stays the same. Moving at a constant speed means you travel the same distance each second (like perfect cruise control).

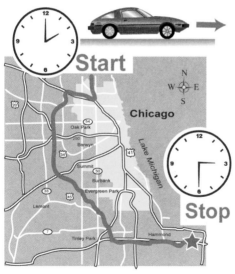

$$\frac{150 \text{ kilometers}}{1.5 \text{ hours}} = 100 \text{ kilometers per hour (km/h)}$$

Figure 2.7: *A driving trip with an average speed of 100 km/h.*

Relationships between distance, speed, and time

Mixing up distance, speed, and time

A common type of question in physics is: "How far do you go if you drive for two hours at a speed of 100 km/h?" You know how to get speed from time and distance. How do you get distance from speed and time? The answer is the reason mathematics is the language of physics. An *equation* (also called a *formula*) shows you how to get speed, distance, or time if two of the three values are known.

Calculating speed

Let the letter d stand for "distance traveled" and the letter t stand for "time taken." The letter v is used to represent "speed" because it refers to the word *velocity* (later we will learn that velocity is speed plus direction). There are three ways to arrange the variables to find either distance, time, or speed. You should be able to calculate any one of the three if you know the other two (Figure 2.8).

Using formulas

To use a formula, remember that the words or letters stand for values that the variables have (Figure 2.9). You can think of each letter as a box that will eventually hold a number. Maybe you don't know what the number will be yet, but once you get everything arranged according to the rules, you can fill the boxes with the numbers that belong in each one. The last box left will be your answer.

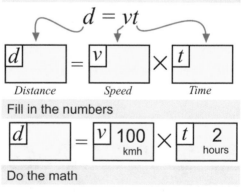

SPEED

$$v = \frac{d}{t}$$

Speed (cm/s) — Distance (cm), Time (s)

Word Formula	Equation
speed = distance ÷ time	$v = \dfrac{d}{t}$
distance = speed x time	$d = vt$
time = distance ÷ speed	$t = \dfrac{d}{v}$

Figure 2.8: *Different forms of the speed equation.*

Each letter (variable) is a box for a number (value)

$$d = vt$$

d		v		t
Distance	=	Speed	×	Time

Fill in the numbers

d		v 100 kmh		t 2 hours

Do the math

$$200 = 100 \times 2$$

Figure 2.9: *Using a formula.*

Calculating distance from time and speed

How far do you go if you drive for two hours at a speed of 100 km/h?

1. Looking for: You are asked for the distance.

2. Given: You are given the speed and the time.

3. Relationships: distance = speed × time

4. Solution: distance = (100 km/h) × (2 h) = 200 km

Your turn...

a. What is the speed of a snake that moves 20 m in 5 s. **Answer:** 4 m/s

b. A train is moving at a speed of 50 km/h. How many hours will it take the train to travel 600 kilometers? **Answer:** 12 hours

Comparing variables

You can't compare values in different units
Which is faster: 95 km/h or 75 mph? One speed could get you a speeding ticket and the other might not! In order to compare speeds (or any variables) they must be in the same units. Otherwise it's like asking how many oranges make ten grapes. Oranges and grapes are not the same, so this question has no sensible answer.

Units are like languages
Both 95 km/h and 75 mph are speeds per *hour*. That means we only need to convert kilometers to miles to find out which is faster. How many kilometers are in 1 m? A distance of 1 m is the same as 1.609 km. *The distance is the same*, only the values and units are different. Think about finding the word that means "dog" in both Spanish and English. The animal (dog) is the same, only the words are different. Metric and English are two different languages for describing the same things.

Conversion factors
To convert between units, you multiply and/or divide by **conversion factors**. A conversion factor is a ratio that has the same amount on the top and bottom, *but in different units* (Table 2.2). Any fraction with the same thing on top and bottom has a value of exactly one. That means you can multiply or divide by a conversion factor without changing the actual quantity; *you only change the unit*. Conversion factors are *translators* between one language of units and another.

conversion factor - a ratio used to convert from one unit to another, such as from feet to meters.

Table 2.2: Conversion factors

Time	Distance	Speed
$\dfrac{1 \text{ min}}{60 \text{ s}}$	$\dfrac{1 \text{ meter}}{3.28 \text{ ft}}$	$\dfrac{1 \text{ mph}}{1.609 \text{ kmh}}$
$\dfrac{1 \text{ hour}}{60 \text{ min}}$	$\dfrac{1 \text{ in}}{2.54 \text{ cm}}$	$\dfrac{1 \text{ m/s}}{2.24 \text{ mph}}$
$\dfrac{1 \text{ hour}}{3,600 \text{ s}}$	$\dfrac{1 \text{ mile}}{1.609 \text{ km}}$	$\dfrac{1 \text{ m/s}}{100 \text{ cm/s}}$

Using conversion factors

$$\frac{95 \text{ km}}{\text{hour}} \times \left(\frac{1 \text{ mile}}{1.609 \text{ km}}\right) = \left(\frac{95}{1.609}\right)\frac{\text{miles}}{\text{hour}} = \boxed{59 \text{ mph}}$$

Arrange the conversion factor so the units cancel → *Divide or multiply the numbers* → *Get the answer!*

Using conversion factors
The units are your clue as to whether to multiply or divide. We want to convert 95 kilometers to miles (Figure 2.10). That means we need to get rid of the units of kilometers and end up with units of miles. We flip the conversion factor upside down *so the units of km cancel out!* That tells us we divide 95 by 1.609 to get 59 miles. We now know 95 km/h is the same speed as 59 mph, which is slower than 75 mph.

Figure 2.10: *The speeds 95 km/h and 59 mph are really the same because they are the same distance (59 miles) divided by the same time (1 hour).*

How to solve science problems

Physics problems Problem solving means using what you already know to figure out something you want to know. Many problems involving speed, distance, and time ask you to calculate something using formulas. Other problems ask you to explain something based on your knowledge of science.

A four-step technique The technique for solving problems has four steps. Follow these steps and you will be able to see a way to the answer most of the time. You will at least make progress toward an answer every time. The diagram in Figure 2.11 shows the four steps. The table below explains each one.

Table 2.2: Steps to solving physics problems

Step	What to do
1	What is the problem asking for? If you can, figure out exactly what variables or values need to be in the answer.
2	What information are you given? Sometimes this includes numbers or values. Other times it includes descriptive information you must interpret. Look for words like *constant* or *at rest*. In a physics problem, saying something is constant means it does not change. The words "at rest" in physics mean the speed is zero. You may need conversion factors to change units.
3	What relationships exist between what you are asked to find and what you are given? For example, suppose you are given a speed and time and asked to find a distance. The relationship $v = d \div t$ relates what you are asked to find to what you are given.
4	Combine the relationships with what you know to find what you are asked for. Once you complete steps 1–3, you will be able to see how to solve most problems. If not, start working with the relationships you have and see where they lead.

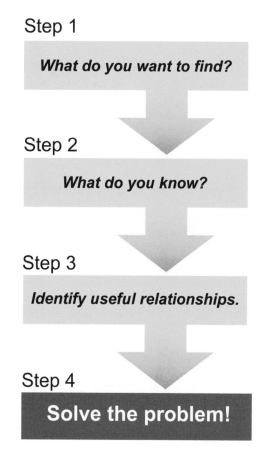

Step 1

What do you want to find?

Step 2

What do you know?

Step 3

Identify useful relationships.

Step 4

Solve the problem!

Figure 2.11: *Follow these steps and you will be able to find the answer to a problem most of the time.*

How to solve design problems

Different kinds of problems

Consider the following two problems.

1. How far do you travel in 2 hours at 60 mph on a straight road?

2. Create a container that will protect a raw egg from breaking when dropped 10 meters onto a sidewalk.

"Book" problems

The first problem has a single answer, you go 120 miles in 2 hours at 60 mph. You apply what you know (distance = speed × time) to take what you are given and find the answer.

Design problems

The second problem is much more challenging (and fun too). You have to use what you know to design a solution that solves the problem. Unlike "book problems," design problems have many correct solutions limited only by your creativity, ingenuity, skill, and patience (Figure 2.12). The important thing is to create something that "does the job" and fits the requirements. In the egg-drop problem, typical requirements are that the container must weigh less than 1 kg, and cannot be something simply purchased "off the shelf."

Solving design problems

Here are some useful steps to help you solve design problems.

1. Write down very clearly everything your solution needs to accomplish.

2. Write down every *constraint* that must also be met. Constraints are limits on cost, weight, time, materials, size, or other things.

3. Think up an idea that *might* work. Talking with others, doing research, and trying things out are all ways to help.

4. Follow the engineering cycle (shown right).

Engineering Cycle

The egg drop rocket

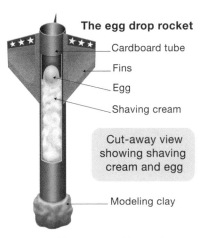

Cardboard tube

Fins

Egg

Shaving cream

Cut-away view showing shaving cream and egg

Modeling clay

The egg and hoop frame

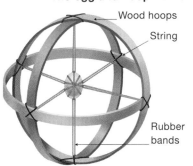

Wood hoops

String

Rubber bands

The cotton-filled shoebox

Egg   Cotton

Figure 2.12: *Some successful solutions to the egg drop problem.*

2.2 Section Review

1. Explain how a bicycle can be fast compared to walking and slow compared to driving. How can two opposite words (fast and slow) describe the same speed?

2. If something moves at a constant speed, what do you know about the distance it moves each second?

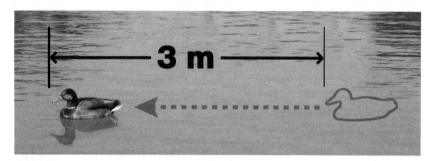

3. What is the speed of the duck swimming in the picture above if it takes 15 seconds to move the distance shown?

4. Calculate the average speed (in km/h) of a car that travels 280 kilometers in 4 hours.

5. You ride your bicycle at an average speed of 15 km/h for 2 hours. How far did you go?

6. How long (in seconds) will it take you to run 100 meters if you run at 5 m/s?

7. A boat sails at an average speed of 20 km/h for two days. How far does the boat go?

8. The distance between two cities is 300 kilometers. Is this longer or shorter than 200 miles?

9. Can you go 500 kilometers in 8 hours without driving faster than 55 mph?

10. Two students measure the time it takes for a race to finish. One measures 75.5 seconds. The other measures 1 minute and 15.5 seconds. Both students are correct. Why?

You leave your house at 7:30 a.m. to go to school. You arrive at 7:50 a.m. The school is 3 miles away from your house.

What was your average speed in miles per hour?

If the speed limit on the road was 40 mph, how long should it have taken you?

Explain why your calculated time does not match the actual time it took you to get to school.

Solved example problems can be very helpful when you are studying for a test. Cover up the solution to the example problem and then try to solve it on your own. Fully write out the steps you follow.

Look at the answer to see if you are correct. If your solution is wrong, compare your steps to those in the example problem. Figure out where you made a mistake. Then try to solve the additional problems below the example problem.

2.3 Experiments and Variables

An **experiment** is a situation specially set up to investigate something. Experiments are one of the best ways scientists learn about the physical world. You may do an experiment in your class to investigate how fast a car moves going down hill on a ramp. In the experiment you set the ramp at different angles. At each angle you measure how long it takes the car to roll a certain distance (Figure 2.13).

Experiments

Experiments tell us how variables are related   The goal of any experiment is to understand the relationship between variables. For example, what is the relationship between the speed of the car and the angle of the ramp? To answer the question, you set up the experiment with the ramp attached to different holes in the stand. Each hole puts the ramp at a different angle. You measure the speed of the car at different ramp angles to see how (and if) the speed changes when the angle is changed.

Changing one variable at a time   In an ideal experiment *only one variable is changed at a time.* Then you can assume any changes you see in other variables were caused by the variable you changed. If you change more than one variable at the same time, you can't tell which one caused the changes in the other. You would not learn much from the results of that experiment.

The experimental variable   The variable you change in an experiment is called the **experimental variable**. This is usually the variable that you have direct control over. Going back to the experiment with a car on a ramp, the angle of the ramp is the experimental variable.

Control variables   The variables that you keep the same are called **control variables**. If you are changing the angle of the ramp, you want to keep the mass of the car the same each time you roll the car. You also want to keep the photogate (timing device) distance and position the same. If you want to test different angles, then the ramp angle is the experimental variable and it should be *the only variable you change.*

ă VOCABULARY

experiment - a situation specially set up to investigate relationships between variables.

experimental variable - a variable that changes in an experiment.

control variable - a variable that is kept constant (the same) in an experiment.

Hole (#)	Time (s)
5	0.0286
7	0.0220
9	0.0198
11	0.00160
13	0.0125

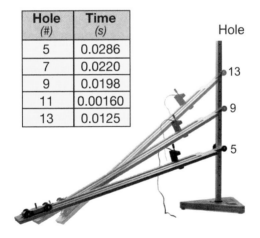

Figure 2.13: *A car rolling downhill can be an experiment.*

Measurement, accuracy, and errors

The value of a measured variable

How many marbles are in the picture at the left? There are exactly seven, no more and no less. Unfortunately, measuring most variables in science is not that easy. The reason is that most variables can have values that are not limited to whole numbers. For example, what is the length of the screw under the marbles? Is it 5.1 cm, or 5.13 cm or 5.1342 cm? Because you can always add more decimal places, you can *never* know the *exact* value of a variable like length!

Measurements and errors

In your experiments with motion you will use a photogate timer to make measurements to the nearest 0.0001 second. You will notice that you rarely get the exact same number three times in a row even if you always do the same thing. This is because *any real measurement always contains some error*. **Error** is the difference between a measurement and the (unknown) exact value of what you are trying to measure. This kind of error does not mean you made a mistake! It is impossible to measure a real variable with zero error. The best you can do is to estimate the error and make it as small as possible.

The average

When you make many measurements of the same thing you will notice that the measurements cluster around an **average** value. Some measurements are more than the average and some are less. To calculate the average, you add up all the measurements and divide by the total number of measurements you have. For example, the average of the times shown in Figure 2.14 is 0.1253 seconds.

Accuracy and averages

Accuracy describes how close a measurement is to the exact value. *The average is usually more accurate than any single measurement.* That's because most errors cancel each other out when you take the average. The more measurements you include in the average, the better the errors cancel out. A word of caution: some kinds of errors do not cancel when many measurements are averaged.

VOCABULARY

error - the difference between a measurement and the true value.

average - a mathematical process in which you add up all the values, then divide the result by the number of values.

accuracy - describes how close a measurement is to the true value.

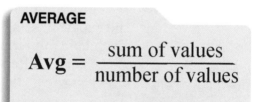
AVERAGE

$$\text{Avg} = \frac{\text{sum of values}}{\text{number of values}}$$

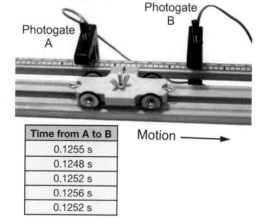

Time from A to B
0.1255 s
0.1248 s
0.1252 s
0.1256 s
0.1252 s

Figure 2.14: *The average time from A to B in these five trials is 0.1253 s.*

Significance: When are results really different?

When are different results "the same"?

Earlier we learned that scientific evidence should be *repeata.ble*. This means an experiment gives the same result if you or any one else does it again the same way. This brings up a key question: How can you tell if results are the same when all measurements contain error?

The meaning of significance

The word *same* when applied to real measurements does not mean what it does in ordinary conversation. When comparing scientific results, *same* means "not significantly different." **Significant differences** are differences that are much larger than the estimated error in the results. That means two results are "the same" unless their difference is much greater than the estimated error. *This is important to remember.*

> *Two results are considered the same unless their difference is much greater than the estimated error.*

How to estimate the error

How can we know the error if we don't know the exact value of a quantity? The way scientists estimate the error is to *assume the average is the exact value*. The estimated error is roughly the largest difference between the average and a typical measured value.

An example of estimating error

Consider two groups doing identical experiments (Figure 2.15). Each group does four trials of the experiment and calculates the average. The table shows Group 1's average to be 0.3352 seconds. Group 2's average is 0.3349 seconds. In this example, the results from the two different groups are considered the same because the estimated error (the largest difference between the average and a measured value) is 0.0004 seconds, whereas the difference between between the group averages (0.3352 – 0.3349) is 0.0003 seconds. As you can see, the difference between the averages is less than the estimated error, so we must conclude that the results from both groups are within the expected error. There is no significant difference between the groups' results, and the experiment is repeatable.

significant difference - two results are only significantly different if their difference is much larger than the estimated error.

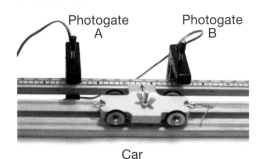

Two groups of students measure the time it takes a car to roll between two photogates. Each group makes four measurements and takes the average. One group claims its results are the same. The other group claims its results are different. Who is right?

Group 1	Group 2
Time *(s)*	Time *(s)*
0.3356	0.3346
0.3351	0.3353
0.3349	0.3350
0.3352	0.3349
Average	**Average**
0.3352	0.3349
Error	**Error**

Figure 2.15: *Group data.*

Drawing conclusions from data

We do experiments to reach conclusions
The point of an experiment is to produce data that allows a scientist (like you) to come to a conclusion. The conclusion tells whether your idea, the hypothesis, is right or not. You need to know about errors before you can make a conclusion. For example, suppose you think that pointy cars roll faster down a hill than blunt cars. An experiment tests cars with different shapes by measuring the time between two photogates. Your hypothesis (pointy cars roll faster) predicts that the time between photogates should be less for the pointy car.

A sloppy experiment
One group rolls each car once and records the time in a data table (Figure 2.16). Their results show a shorter time for the pointy car. This seems to confirm the hypothesis. Are they right? Have they proved that pointy cars go faster? They have not! They only did one trial, so they don't know how big their error is. Without an error estimate, they can't tell if the difference in times is *significant* or not.

A better experiment
The same experiment is repeated by a second group. The second group does five identical trials for each shape car. Doing identical trials allows the second group to get an estimated error. The largest difference between the average and a measured value is 0.0007 s for the blunt car and 0.0006 s for the pointy car.

When differences are significant
The second group can say that, scientifically, the data do *not* show that pointy cars are faster. At the speeds in their experiment, the shape of the car made no *significant* difference. In fact, shape only starts to become an important factor at speeds at least five times higher than those you will observe in your investigations.

How numbers can be different but still the same
Two results are significantly different only when the difference between them is greater than the error. This is an important consideration because experiments rarely produce exactly the same numbers twice in a row. Numbers that are "different" in a mathematical sense may not be *significantly* different in a scientific sense.

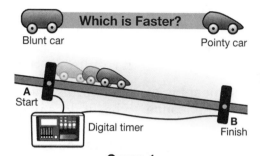

Group 1

Blunt	Pointy
0.3545 s	0.3542 s

Group 2

Blunt	Pointy
0.3540 s	0.3542 s
0.3550 s	0.3548 s
0.3541 s	0.3538 s
0.3539 s	0.3540 s
0.3546 s	0.3541 s

Averages

0.3543 ± 0.0007	0.3542 ± 0.0006

Figure 2.16: *An experiment to test whether the shape of a car has an effect on its speed going downhill. Group 1 does only one trial, but Group 2 does five trials of the experiment.*

2.3 Section Review

1. Georgiana has the idea that salt water heats up faster than fresh water. Which of the following would be acceptable scientific proof of her hypothesis?

   a. Three of her friends believe it.

   b. She read on an Internet Web site that it was so.

   c. She did an experiment that showed it.

2. A careful description of how an experiment is conducted is called

   a. a data table.

   b. a procedure.

   c. an analysis.

   d. a conclusion.

3. Explain why all variables but one should be controlled in a well-designed experiment.

4. Is it possible to measure the true value of a physical property, such as mass? Explain why or why not.

5. Three groups do the same experiment, rolling a car through two photogates. The track is set at the same angle and all other variables are kept the same for each group. The data is shown in Figure 2.17. The first group does the experiment in the daylight. The second group does it under a magnet. The third group does the experiment in the dark. Group 2 claims that its experiment shows that magnets make the car go faster. Is their claim supported by the evidence? Explain why or why not.

6. Which of these sets of data has an average of 10.5?

   a. 8.5, 9.5, 10.5, 11.5

   b. 9.0, 10.0, 11.0, 12.0

   c. 10.0, 10.5, 11.0, 11.5

   d. 10.5, 10.6, 10.7, 10.8

7. What does it mean when two values are different but not *significantly* different?

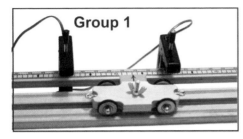

Group 1	Group 2	Group 3
Time A to B	Time A to B	Time A to B
0.343 s	0.339 s	0.341 s
0.346 s	0.338 s	0.338 s
0.341 s	0.345 s	0.343 s
0.340 s	0.341 s	0.340 s
0.349 s	0.339 s	0.339 s

Figure 2.17: *Question 5.*

Amazing Infrared

How do you measure the time it takes a small car to go from the top of a ramp to the bottom? A stopwatch isn't the best choice. What about an electronic timer? Many experiments found in this science program will use devices called photogates to time motion events. It turns out that this technology is used for other things too—some may surprise you!

How do photogates work?

Photogates use the same technology that your TV remote uses to control the TV. On one side of the small slot is an LED (like a small light bulb) that emits a beam of infrared light. On the other side is a detector that sees infrared light. You can't see the light beam because human eyes cannot see infrared light. However, the electronic detector instantly senses when anything blocks the light beam. That is how the clock is started and stopped.

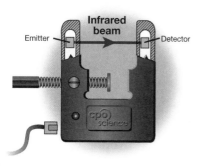

Olympic timing

Have you ever seen an Olympic sledding event? Bobsleds can hurtle down the track at speeds of over 80 miles per hour! Because they move so fast, the difference between finish times can be as little as one-thousandth of a second (0.001 s). A human-controlled stopwatch will not have enough precision or accuracy to time this event. Guess what is used? Yes, an infrared beam similar to the one used in the CPO Timer IIe photogates is used to time Olympic sledding events. The start and finish lines of the bobsled track both have an infrared beam that is about 1 inch wide. The infrared beam is focused at a receiver that starts the

clock when the beam is broken at the starting line, and the clock is stopped when the beam is broken at the finish line. This is very similar to how the CPO photogates are used to time intervals of motion between photogate A (starting line) and photogate B (finish line).

Your TV remote

Human eyes cannot see infrared light. Infrared (commonly called IR for short) is light that is just a bit redder than the reddest light your eyes can see. Check out your TV, DVD, or stereo remote control device. There is something in the front of the remote that looks like a small light bulb. This part of the remote sends a series of short IR pulses each time you push one of the control buttons. Your TV has an IR detector. When you point the remote control at the front of the TV and push one of the buttons, the IR pulses reach the TV's detector. Each button has its own special sequence of IR pulses, so the TV "knows" which button was pushed.

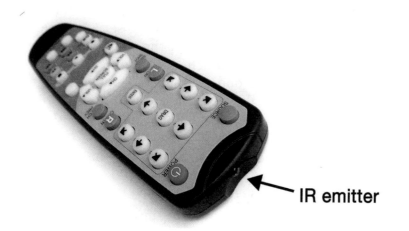

IR emitter

Garage door safety

Infrared beam technology is not just used for timing and remote controls. Garage doors that open and close automatically also use IR. Suppose a garage door is open, and you want to close it. You can do this by hitting the button on a remote (which sends an IR signal to the door opener), or by using

Infrared beam

the switch in the garage next to the door. But what if an object or a person is in the way? The garage door can be fairly heavy, and could cause serious injury or damage if someone or something gets in the way. What prevents this from happening? You guessed it. There is an IR emitter and receiver located on the floor on either side of the garage door opening. If that beam is blocked, the door will not close. This is an important safety feature!

Focusing a camera

Did you know that IR is used in some cameras that have an automatic focus feature? Cameras, especially digital cameras, are very popular. Many people don't want to take the time to manually move the lens in and out until the subject looks focused

in the viewfinder. Most people just want to quickly push a button and take a clear, sharp, focused picture. Well, how does the camera focus itself? Yes, it uses IR. Most all cameras nowadays use IR for the auto focus feature (except the

more expensive cameras that have interchangeable lenses). For most cameras, if you look near the viewfinder, you will see the IR emitter and receiver. When you push the camera's shutter release button halfway, IR pulses are sent out to the subject.

When the IR bounces back to the camera, the circuitry "tells" the motor to move the lens in or out to focus on the subject. There are a few problems to avoid when using an IR focusing camera. Be sure there is a clear path between the camera and the subject, so the auto focus IR beam isn't blocked. A source of infrared energy, like birthday candles or a fire, can confuse the IR sensing device. Bright lights or a very brightly lit subject can also confuse the IR sensing device. Avoiding these situations will make the auto focus feature on your camera work a lot better!

QUESTIONS

1. What is infrared light?

2. What is the purpose of the infrared light beam in a photogate?

3. You can do some fun experiments with your TV remote control. Try holding different materials in front of the IR emitter on the remote control, and then see if the beam still makes it to the TV to control it. Is there anything that will block the beam? What will allow the beam to pass right through? Can you bounce the IR beam off anything, like a mirror?

4. Name four things that you or someone in your family owns that uses IR technology. There are things that use IR that this article did not mention. Can you find any of them?

Make a Water Clock

A clock is a tool used to measure time. Inside a clock are parts that move with a constant repetition. We can record a quantity of time by counting how many "movements" of our clock occur during an interval of time that has a beginning and an end. The number of movements gives us our time measurement. In this activity, you and a partner will make your own clock and measure time with it.

Trial	Time (seconds)
1	
2	
3	
4	
5	
6	
Average	

Materials

two empty 2-liter soda bottles; 400 mL beaker; water; duct tape; stopwatch

Making your clock

1. Pour three beakers of water (1,200 mL) into one of the empty soda bottles.

2. Attach the mouths of the two soda bottles together and seal them with duct tape.

3. Turn the two attached soda bottles upside down so that the water runs from one soda bottle to the other.

4. Seal your bottles with more duct tape if you have any leaks.

Measuring time with your clock

5. One partner should hold the stopwatch, while the other partner holds the soda bottle clock.

6. One partner turns the soda bottle clock upside down at the same time the other partner starts the stopwatch.

7. Stop the stopwatch as soon as all the water has emptied from the top bottle to the bottom bottle. Record your data in the table.

8. Repeat the procedure two more times, and record your data in the table.

9. Switch roles and repeat the activity three more times. Record your data in the table.

Discussion Questions

a. The new unit of time you created was the time it took the water to run from one bottle completely into the other. Give this unit of time a name.

b. Using the data from your six trials, find the average number of seconds in your new unit of time and record it in the table.

c. Maurice Greene could run 100 meters in about 9.8 seconds. How many of your new units did it take?

d. How many of your new units do you think it would take you or your partner to walk from one end of your classroom to the other? Try it and see how close you are.

e. Why is the water clock much more difficult to use than a stopwatch?

f. Compare the times from your six trials. How precise are these times? How accurate is your water clock? Propose a change in the design that could make it more accurate.

Engineering Cycle

Chapter 2 Assessment

Vocabulary

Select the correct term to complete the sentences.

accuracy	average	value
constant	control	conversion factor
deduce	error	experiment
experimental	hypothesis	inquiry
natural laws	objective	repeatable
scientific method	variables	average speed
theory		

Section 2.1

1. To work out the answer to a problem using logical thinking, you ____ the answer to the problem.

2. Learning by asking questions is called ____.

3. Evidence that can be seen by others if they do the same experiment in the same way is said to be ____.

4. Evidence that describes only what actually happened as exactly as possible is labeled ____.

5. Rules that describe the behavior of things in the universe are called ____.

6. A process of learning that begins with a hypothesis and leads to a conclusion supported by scientific evidence is known as the ____.

7. A preliminary explanation that can be tested and compared to scientific evidence is called a(n) ____.

8. A scientific explanation supported by much evidence collected over an extended period of time is called a(n) ____.

Section 2.2

9. Position and speed are examples of ____.

10. The number or size that a variable may have is its ____.

11. Speed that stays the same is known as ____ speed.

12. The total distance of a trip divided by the total time taken is known as ____.

13. A ratio used to change one unit of measurement to another is called a(n) ____.

Section 2.3

14. A situation specially set up to investigate relationships between variables is called a(n) ____.

15. The difference between a measurement and the true value is what you're trying to measure is called ____.

16. If you add up all the different values for a measurement and divide by the number of values, you calculate the ____.

17. ____ describes how close a measurement is to the true value.

18. The variable that you change in an experiment is the ____ variable.

19. In an experiment, variables that are *not* allowed to change are ____ variables.

Concepts

Section 2.1

1. List the steps you should follow when using the inquiry method of learning.

2. For each example, write whether it could be considered scientific evidence (*S*) or not (*N*).

   a. _____ A drawing of an oak leaf

   b. _____ The time for a car to drive once around a track

   c. _____ A description of Atlanta's beauty in the spring

   d. _____ Photographs of a beach

   e. _____ The number of white cars compared to the number of blue cars in a parking lot

3. Indicate which of the following hypotheses are testable and scientific (*S*) and which are not (*N*).

   a. _____ Your brain produces undetectable energy waves.
   b. _____ Life forms do not exist in other galaxies.
   c. _____ Red apples taste better than green apples.
   d. _____ Earth revolves around the Sun every 24 hours.

4. A student notices that some plants in her class have grown faster than others and wants to know why. Unscramble the steps of the scientific method she might use to investigate. Place them in a logical order from the first step to the last.

   a. She thinks it might be light (a hypothesis).
   b. She wonders why (a question).
   c. She concludes that it is not light (a conclusion).
   d. She grows similar plants under different amounts of light (an experiment).
   e. She compares the plants' growth (analyzes data).

Section 2.2

5. If you take a one hour drive at an average speed of 65 mph, is it possible for another car with an average speed of 55 mph to pass you? Explain your answer.

6. What is the speed of an object that is standing still?

7. Name three common units for measuring speed.

8. Write the form of the speed equation that you would see in each of the following scenarios. Let v = speed, t = time, and d = distance.

   a. You know distance and speed and want to find the time.
   b. You know time and distance and want to find the speed.
   c. You know speed and time and want to find the distance.

9. In a formula, what do the letters or words represent?

10. Summarize the four steps for solving physics problems mentioned in the text.

11. Explain why a conversion factor always has a value of "1" when the fraction does not equal "1."

Section 2.3

12. You and your lab partners are investigating how the speed of a cart rolling down a ramp is affected by the height of the ramp. You calculate the speed of the cart at the bottom of the ramp for five different ramp heights and find that the speed is different for each height.

   a. Name the experimental variable.
   b. Name a possible control variable.
   c. When another lab group repeats your investigation, they get *different* speed values from your group. Your teacher says the values are not *significantly* different. What does she mean?

Problems

Section 2.1

1. You are getting ready for a camping trip. When you turn your flashlight on, it doesn't work.

   a. Make a hypothesis as to why your flashlight isn't working.
   b. How could you test your hypothesis?

2. You want to find out whether the birds near your school prefer thistle seed or sunflower seed. You have a bag of thistle seed, a bag of sunflower seed, and two bird feeders. Describe the experiment you would do to see which type of seed birds prefer. Write down your question, your hypothesis, and the procedure you would follow when doing your experiment.

Section 2.2

3. A high-speed train in France travels at 300 km/h. How long (in hours) would it take the train to travel 1,500 km at this speed?

4. A biker in the 15th stage of the Tour de France had an average speed of 33.63 km/h over 4 hours. How far (in kilometers) did he travel?

5. It takes Brooke 10 minutes to run 1 mile. What is her speed in miles per minute?

6. You are traveling on the interstate highway at a speed of 65 mph. What is your speed in km/h? The conversion factor is: $\frac{1.0 \text{ mph}}{1.6 \text{ km/h}}$.

7. Use the speed equation to complete the following chart:

distance (m)	speed (m/s)	time (s)
	10	6
45	5	
100		2

8. A pelican flies at a speed of 52 km/h for 0.25 hours. How many *miles* does the pelican travel? Be sure to list your conversion factor.

9. A mountain rises 830 feet above the surrounding plain. Calculate the height of the mountain in meters. The conversion factor is: $\frac{1 \text{ meter}}{3.28 \text{ feet}}$.

10. A snail crawls 300 cm in 1 hour. Calculate the snail's speed in each of the following units:

    a. centimeters per hour (cm/h)

    b. centimeters per minute (cm/min)

    c. meters per hour (m/h)

11. If it takes 500 seconds for the light from the Sun to reach Earth, what is the distance to the Sun in meters? (The speed of light is 300,000,000 m/s.)

Section 2.3

12. If the width of a machine part should be 4.00 cm with an acceptable error of +/– 0.03 cm, which of the following lengths is significantly different?

    a. 4.04   b. 3.98   c. 4.29

13. Given a ruler, a stopwatch, a tennis ball, a 1-meter long piece of string, a rubber band, tape, and 10 pieces of paper, design an experiment. List a question, a hypothesis, the independent variable, the dependent variable, the control variables, and the procedure for your experiment.

14. The table shows data collected by two different lab groups for the same experiment.

Times (s) for Group 1	Times (s) for Group 2
2.21	2.23
2.53	2.51
2.54	2.50
2.72	2.74
2.60	2.64
2.52	2.44

    a. What is the average time for Group 1?
    b. What is the estimated error for Group 1?
    c. What is the average time for Group 2?
    d. What is the estimated error for Group 2?
    e. Is there a significant difference in their results? Explain your answer.

UNIT 2

MOTION AND FORCE

CHAPTER 3
Motion

CHAPTER 4
Forces

position   distance   velocity

FORCE

Speed vs. Time

meters per second

Time (sec)

1   2

STEM

Exploring on Your Own

How many vehicles drive past your school on an average day? Does the traffic flow smoothly or is it congested? Suppose a developer wants to build a shopping center on an empty lot across the street from your school. What problems could this cause? Civil engineers resolve transportation issues. Create a model to present solutions to the problems you identified.

Chapter 3

Motion

How long can you stand perfectly still? Ten seconds? A minute? Are you sure you're really not moving? Even when you stand still, organs, cells, and fluids inside your body are moving. And even fast asleep, your body is not at rest compared to other objects in the universe. The 24-hour rotation of Earth on its axis moves you in a circle at several hundred miles per hour. And every 365 days, Earth completes a 584-million-mile circle around the Sun. During this trip, you are rushing through space at the astounding speed of 67,000 miles per hour!

Objects are always moving. To understand how the world works, we must think about motion. How do we describe going from here to there? Whether we're discussing a toy car rolling down a ramp or Earth rushing through space, the ideas in this chapter apply to all motion.

67,000 mph

Key Questions:

1. How do we accurately describe motion?

2. What kinds of motion are there?

3. How does motion change?

3.1 Position and Velocity

The concept of motion is related to knowing where things are (position) and how they move (speed). The variables position and speed apply to vehicles, people, and many other things around you—from the tiny atoms inside of matter to the planets and stars. We start our discussion of motion with a precise method for describing where something is.

The position variable

Position as a variable
You may do an experiment in your class that involves a toy car on a ramp. How can you describe exactly where the car is? You can do this by measuring the car's **position**. Position is a variable. The position of the car is where it is located. In the diagram below, the position of the car is 50 centimeters (cm). That means the center of the car is at the 50 cm mark on the ramp.

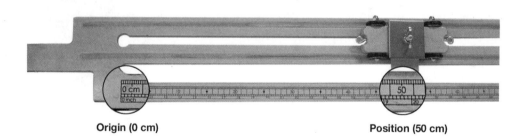

Origin (0 cm)   Position (50 cm)

Position and distance
Position and distance are related but not the same. Both use units of length. However, position is given relative to an **origin**. The origin is the place where position = 0. Here's an example of the difference between position and distance. Suppose a car moves 20 cm from one photogate to the next (Figure 3.1). Is this enough information to describe the car's new position? You know the *distance* the car moved (20 cm) but you still don't know its exact location on the track. You could describe the motion better by saying the car moved from a position of 50 cm to a position of 70 cm.

VOCABULARY

position - a variable that gives your location relative to an origin.

origin - the place where the position has a value of zero.

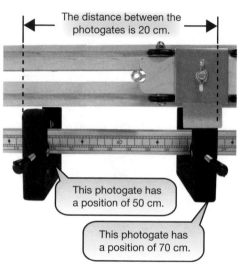

The distance between the photogates is 20 cm.

This photogate has a position of 50 cm.

This photogate has a position of 70 cm.

Figure 3.1: *The difference between position and distance on the ramp.*

Forward and backward

Telling "in front" from "behind"   Some variables, like distance, can have only positive values. The distance between two of the ants in Figure 3.2 can only be positive (or zero). Position is different. Like distance, position is measured in units of length (meters, inches, etc.). The difference is that you can be in front of the origin or behind it. How can you tell the difference between one meter in front of the origin and one meter behind the origin?

Using positive and negative numbers   The answer is to use positive and negative numbers. Positive numbers are for positions to the right (in front) of the origin. Negative numbers are for positions to the left (or behind) the origin.

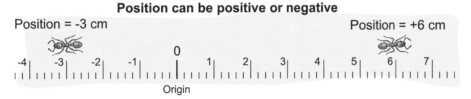

Vectors   Many variables can be positive or negative. These include position, speed, and force. These variables are called **vectors** because they can have a direction as well as a value. When the only directions are forward and backward, using positive and negative numbers is enough information. When up–down and right–left are also possible directions, vectors get more complicated.

Velocity   Motion can be going right or left, forward or backward. We use the term **velocity** to mean speed with direction. Velocity is positive when moving to the right, or forward. Velocity is negative when moving to the left, or backward (Figure 3.3).

The difference between velocity and speed   In conversation you might use "speed" and "velocity" to mean the same thing. In science, they are related but different. Speed is a positive number value that tells you how many meters you go each second (or miles each hour). Velocity is speed *and* a positive or negative sign, or other information that tells whether you are going *forward* or *backward*. Velocity is a vector, speed is not.

vector - a variable which gives direction information included in its value.

velocity - a variable that tells you both speed and direction.

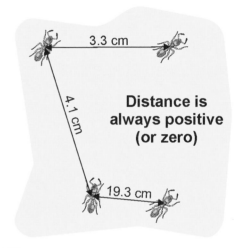

Figure 3.2: *A distance can have only positive values. A position can have either positive or negative values.*

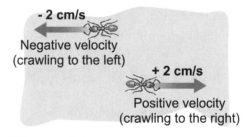

Figure 3.3: *Positive and negative velocity.*

Keeping track of where you are

How a robot uses vectors
Sojourner is a small robot sent to explore Mars (Figure 3.4). As it moves, Sojourner needs to keep track of its position. How does Sojourner know where it is? It keeps track of its velocity vector and uses a clock.

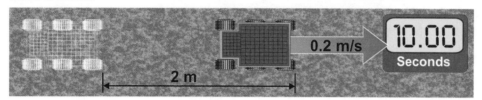

Figure 3.4: *Sojourner is a robot explorer which landed on Mars in 1997 (NASA/JPL).*

Position, velocity, and time
Suppose Sojourner moves forward at 0.2 m/s for 10 seconds. Its velocity is +0.2 m/s. In 10 seconds, its position changes by +2 meters. In other words, Sojourner is 2 meters in front of where it was. *The change in position is velocity × time* (Figure 3.5). This is just like saying "distance is speed × time." Only we are now using velocity and position instead of speed and distance. We use velocity instead of speed to include the *direction* of motion.

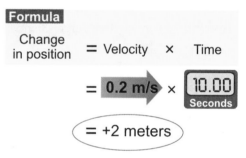

Figure 3.5: *The change in position is the velocity multiplied by the time.*

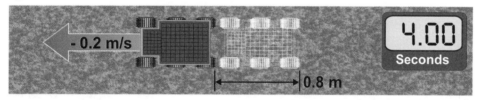

Backward motion
Now suppose Sojourner goes backward at 0.2 m/s for 4 seconds. Where is it now? We can use the same relationship: Change in position equals velocity × time. This time the velocity is –0.2 m/s. The velocity is negative because Sojourner is moving backward. The change in position is –0.8 meters.

Adding up a series of movements
The computer in Sojourner adds up +2 m and –0.8 m to get +1.2 m. After these two moves, Sojourner is 1.2 meters in front of where it was. Sojourner knows where it is by keeping track of each move it makes. It adds up each change in position using positive and negative numbers to come up with a final position (Figure 3.6).

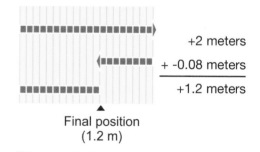

Figure 3.6: *Each change in position is added up using positive and negative numbers.*

Maps and coordinates

Two dimensions If Sojourner was crawling on a straight board, it would have only two choices for direction. Positive is forward and negative is backward. Out on the surface of Mars, Sojourner has more choices. It can *turn and go sideways*! The possible directions include north, east, south, and west, and anything in between. A flat surface is an example of *two dimensions*. We say *two* because it takes two number lines to describe every point (Figure 3.7).

North, south, east, and west One common way to describe two dimensions is to use north–south, as one number line, or **axis**. Positive positions are north of the origin. Negative positions are south of the origin. The other axis goes west–east. Negative positions on this axis are west of the origin. Positive positions are east of the origin.

Coordinates describe position

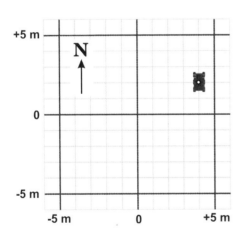

Sojourner's exact position can be described with two numbers. These numbers are called **coordinates**. The graph at the left shows Sojourner at coordinates of (4, 2) m. The first number gives the position on the west–east axis. Sojourner is 4 m east of the origin. The second number gives the position on the north–south axis. Sojourner is 2 m north of the origin.

Maps A graph using north–south and east–west axes can accurately show where Sojourner is. The graph can also show any path Sojourner takes, curved or straight. This kind of graph is called a *map*. You have surely used one before! Many street maps use letters on the north–south axis and numbers for the east–west axis. For example, the coordinates F-4 identify the square that is in row F, column 4 of the map shown in Figure 3.8.

 **VOCABULARY**

axis - one of two (or more) number lines that form a graph.

coordinates - values that give the position relative to an origin.

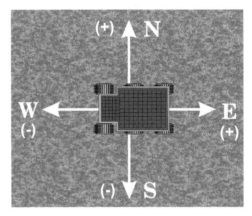

Figure 3.7: *A flat surface has two perpendicular dimensions: north–south, and west–east. Each dimension has positive and negative directions.*

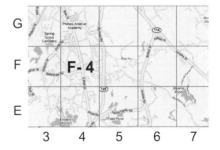

Figure 3.8: *Street maps often use letters and numbers for coordinates.*

Vectors on a map

A trip with a turn Suppose you run east for 10 seconds at a speed of 2 m/s. Then you turn and run south at the same speed for 10 more seconds (Figure 3.9). Where are you compared to where you started? To get the answer, you figure out your east–west changes and your north–south changes separately.

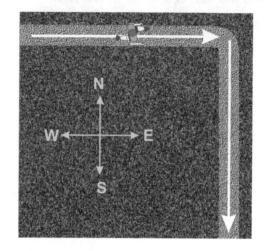

Figure 3.9: *A running trip with a turn.*

Figure each direction separately

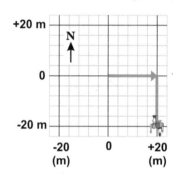

Your first movement has a velocity vector of +2 m/s east–west. After 10 seconds your change in position is +20 meters (east). There are no more east-west changes because your second movement is north–south only. Your second movement has a velocity vector of –2 m/s north–south. In 10 seconds you move –20 meters. The negative sign means you moved south.

Figuring your final position Now add up any east-west changes to get your final east-west position. Do the same for your north-south position. Your new position is (+20 m, –20 m).

Velocity vector

A train travels at 100 km/h heading east to reach a town in 4 hours. The train then reverses and heads west at 50 km/h for 4 hours. What is the train's position now?

1. Looking for: You are asked for position

2. Given: You are given two velocity vectors and the times for each

3. Relationships: change in position = velocity × change in time

4. Solution: The first change in position is (+100 km/h) × (4 h) = +400 km
                      The second change in position is (–50 km/h) × (4 h) = –200 km
                      The final position is (+400 km) + (–200 km) = +200 km, the train is 200 km east of where it started.

Your turn...

a. A ship needs to sail to an island that is 1,000 km south of where the ship starts. If the captain sails south at 30 km/h for 30 hours, will the ship make it? **Answer:** No, because 30 km/h × 30 h = 900 miles. The island is still 100 km away.

3.1 Section Review

1. What two pieces of information do you need to know to get from one location to another?
2. What is the difference between *distance* and *position*?
3. You start at the origin and walk 3 meters east, 7 meters west, and 6 meters east. Where are you now?
4. Give an example of a situation in which you would describe an object's position in
   a. one dimension.
   b. two dimensions.
   c. three dimensions.

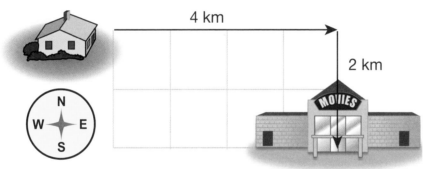

5. A movie theater is 4 kilometers east and 2 kilometers south of your house.
   a. Using your house as the origin, give the coordinates of the movie theater.
   b. After leaving the movie theater, you drive 5 kilometers west and 3 kilometers north to a restaurant. What are the coordinates of the restaurant? Use your house as the origin.
6. Does the origin of an object always have to be at zero on a number line or map? Why or why not?
7. What velocity vector will move you 200 miles east in 4 hours traveling at a constant speed?

How a Compass Works

Imagine you are at sea far from sight of land. There are clouds overhead and you cannot see the Sun. How do you know which way to steer?

You may know that the north pole of one magnet attracts the south pole of another magnet. A simple compass has a magnetic needle that can spin. The north magnetic pole of the compass needle points toward the south magnetic pole of any nearby magnet.

Earth itself is a large magnet! You can tell direction with a compass because the compass needle always points toward the same place on Earth. Can you figure out where the magnetic north pole of the compass needle points and why?

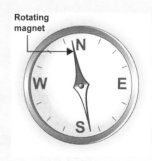

Rotating magnet

3.2 Graphs of Motion

Motion graphs are an important tool used to show the relationships between position, speed, and time. For example, meteorologists use graphs to show the motion of hurricanes and other storms. A graph can show the location and speed of a storm at different points in time. The graph can be used to help predict the path of the storm and the time when it will reach a certain location.

The position vs. time graph

Recording data
Imagine you are helping a friend who is training for a track meet. She wants to know if she is running at a constant speed. You mark the track every 50 meters. Then you measure her time at each mark as she runs. The data for your experiment is shown in Figure 3.10. This is position vs. time data because it tells you her position at different points in time. She is at 50 meters after 10 seconds, 100 meters after 20 seconds, and so on.

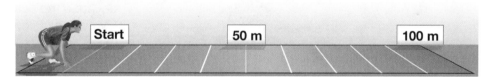

Graphing the data
To graph the data, you put position on the vertical (*y*) axis and time on the horizontal (*x*) axis. Each row of the data table makes one point on the graph. Notice the graph goes over 10 seconds and up 50 meters between each point. This makes the points fall exactly in a straight line. The straight line tells you the runner moves the same distance during each equal time period. *An object moving at a constant speed always creates a position vs. time graph that is a straight line.*

Calculating speed
The data shows that your friend took 10 seconds to run each 50-meter segment. Because the time was the same for each segment, you know her speed was the same for each segment. You can use the formula $v = d/t$ to calculate the speed. Dividing 50 meters by 10 seconds tells you her speed was 5 meters per second.

Position and Time Data for a Runner

Time (s)	Position (m)
0	0
10	50
20	100
30	150

Runner's Position vs. Time

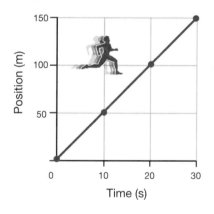

Figure 3.10: *A data table and a position vs. time graph for a runner.*

Graphs show relationships between variables

Relationships between variables
Physical science is all about relationships between variables. Think about rolling a car down a ramp. You suspect that steeper angles on the ramp will make the car go faster. How do you find out if your suspicion is correct? You need to know the relationship between the variables *angle* and *speed*.

Patterns on a graph show relationships
A good way to show a relationship between two variables is to use a **graph**. A graph shows one variable on the vertical (or *y*) axis and a second variable on the horizontal (or *x*) axis. Each axis is marked with the range of values the variable has. In Figure 3.11, the *x*-axis (angle) has values between 0 and 60 degrees. The *y*-axis (time) has values between 0 and 0.3 s. You can tell there is a relationship because all the points on the graph follow the same curve that slopes down and to the right.

Recognizing a relationship from a graph
The relationship between variables may be strong, weak, or no relationship at all. In a strong relationship, large changes in one variable make similarly large changes in the other variable, like in Figure 3.11. In a weak relationship, large changes in one variable cause only small changes in the other. The graph on the right (below) shows a weak relationship. When there is no relationship, the graph looks like scattered dots (below left). The dots do not make an obvious pattern (a line or curve).

Angle (degrees)	Time (s)
10	0.3286
20	0.2431
30	0.1937
40	0.1708
50	0.1565

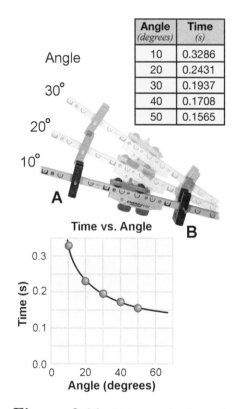

Figure 3.11: *This graph shows how quickly the car gets from A to B as the angle of the track is changed. What kind of relationship does the graph show?*

No relationship between variables

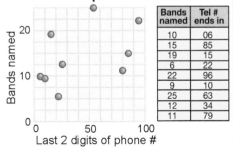

Bands named	Tel # ends in
10	06
15	85
19	15
6	22
22	96
9	10
25	63
12	34
11	79

Weak relationship between variables

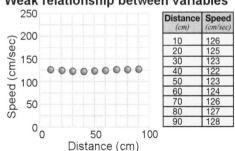

Distance (cm)	Speed (cm/sec)
10	126
20	125
30	123
40	122
50	123
60	124
70	126
80	127
90	128

Designing a graph: Dependent and independent variables

What to put on the *x*- and *y*-axes To a scientist, a graph is a language that shows the relationship between two variables. Graphs are drawn a certain way, just like words are spelled a certain way. The first rule in drawing a proper graph is to choose which variable to put on which axis.

The independent variable Graphs are usually made to show a cause-and-effect relationship between two variables. A graph makes it easy to see if changes in one variable *cause* changes in the other variable (the *effect*). The variable that causes the change is called the **independent variable**. In an experiment, this is the variable that the experimenter is free to change. *By agreement among scientists, the independent variable goes on the* x-*axis*. In the example below, mass is the independent variable, so mass goes on the *x*-axis (horizontal).

The dependent variable The **dependent variable** shows the effect of changes in the independent variable. *The dependent variable goes on the* y-*axis*. In the example, temperature is the dependent variable and therefore goes on the *y*-axis (vertical).

Dependent variable
This is the variable that responds to changes in the independent variable.

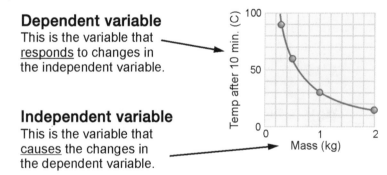

Independent variable
This is the variable that causes the changes in the dependent variable.

If time is a variable Like many rules, there are important exceptions. Time is an exception to the rule about which variable goes on which axis. *When time is one of the variables on a graph it usually goes on the* x-*axis*. This is true even though you may not think of time as an independent variable.

Reading a graph

Using a graph to make a prediction
Suppose you measure the speed of a car at four places on a ramp. Can you figure out the speed at other places without having to actually measure it? As long as the ramp and car are set up the same, the answer is yes! A graph can give you an accurate answer even without doing the experiment. Look at the example below to see how. The students doing the experiment measured the speed of the car at 20, 40, 60, and 80 cm. They want to know the speed at 50 cm.

1) Start by finding 50 cm on the *x*-axis.

2) Draw a line vertically upward from 50 cm until it hits the curve that fits the points that were measured.

3) Draw a line across horizontally to the *y*-axis.

4) Use the scale on the *y*-axis to read the predicted speed.

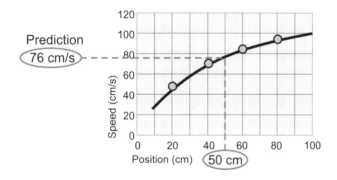

Large graphs are more precise
For this example, the graph predicts the speed to be 76 cm/s. You will get the best predictions when the graph is big enough to show precise measurements. That's why you should draw your graphs so they fill as much of the graph paper as possible.

A graph is a form of a model
A graph is a simple form of a model. Remember, a model is a relationship that connects two or more variables. Scientists use models to make and test predictions.

Graph for a rainy day

A student measures the mass of water collected every five minutes on a rainy day. Design a graph to show the student's data. Once the graph is complete, estimate how many seconds it took for 20 grams of water to be collected.

Time (min)	Mass (g)
0	0
5	17
10	26
15	38
20	49

Time is the independent variable, therefore mass is the dependent variable. The mass axis should go from 0 to at least 50 grams. The time axis should go from 0 to at least 20 minutes. The graph shows that 20 grams of rainwater fell in the first 7.5 minutes.

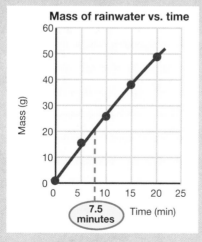

Slope

Comparing speeds You can use position vs. time graphs to quickly compare the speeds of different objects. Figure 3.12 shows the position vs. time graph for two people running along a jogging path. Both runners start at the beginning of the path (the origin) at the same time. Runner A (blue) takes 100 seconds to run 600 meters. Runner B (red) takes 150 seconds to go the same distance. Runner A's speed is 6 m/s (600 ÷ 100) and runner B's speed is 4 m/s (600 ÷ 150). Notice that the line for runner A is steeper than the line for runner B. A steeper line on a position vs. time graph means a faster speed.

A steeper line on a position vs. time graph means a faster speed.

Calculating slope The "steepness" of a line is called its *slope*. The **slope** is the ratio of the "rise" (vertical change) to the "run" (horizontal change). The diagram below shows you how to calculate the slope of a line. Visualize a triangle with the slope as the hypotenuse. The rise is equal to the height of the triangle. The run is equal to the length along the base of the triangle. Here, the x-values represent time and the y-values represent position. The slope of a position vs. time graph is therefore a distance divided by a time, which equals speed. The units for the speed are the units for the rise (meters) divided by the units for the run (seconds), meters per second, or m/s.

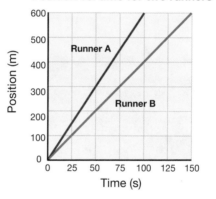

Figure 3.12: *A position vs. time graph for two runners.*

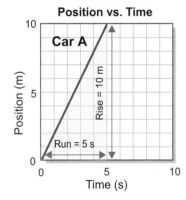

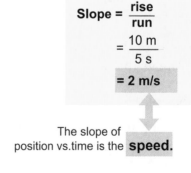

Speed vs. time graphs

Constant speed on a speed vs. time graph   The speed vs. time graph has speed on the *y*-axis and time on the *x*-axis. The bottom graph in Figure 3.13 shows the speed versus time for the runner. The top graph shows the position vs. time. Can you see the relationship between the two graphs? The blue runner has a speed of 5 m/s. The speed vs. time graph shows a horizontal line at 5 m/s for the entire time. On a speed vs. time graph, constant speed is shown with a straight horizontal line. At any point in time between 0 and 60 seconds the line tells you the speed is 5 m/s.

Another example   The red runner's line on the position vs. time graph has a less steep slope. That means her speed is lower. You can see this immediately on the speed vs. time graph. The red runner shows a line at 4 m/s for the whole time.

Calculating distance   A speed vs. time graph can also be used to find the *distance* the object has traveled. Remember, distance is equal to speed multiplied by time. Suppose we draw a rectangle on the speed vs. time graph between the *x*-axis and the line showing the speed. The area of the rectangle (shown below) is equal to its length times its height. On the graph, the length is equal to the time and the height is equal to the speed. Therefore, the area of the graph is the speed multiplied by the time. This is the distance the runner traveled.

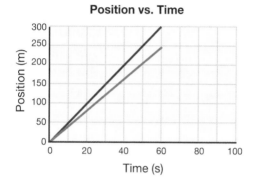

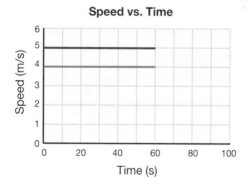

Figure 3.13: *The position vs. time graph (top) shows the exact same motion as the speed vs. time graph (bottom).*

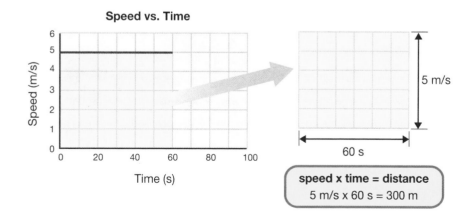

3.2 Section Review

1. What does the slope of the line on a position vs. time graph tell you about the object's speed?
2. On a graph of position vs. time, what do the *x*-values represent? What do the *y*-values represent?
3. The graph in Figure 3.14 shows the position and time for two runners in a race. Who has the faster speed, Robin or Joel? Explain how to answer this question without doing calculations.
4. Calculate the speed of each runner from the graph in Figure 3.14.
5. Maria walks at a constant speed of 2 m/s for 8 seconds.
   a. Draw a speed vs. time graph for Maria's motion.
   b. How far does she walk?
6. What is the difference between speed and velocity?
7. A ball rolls along the ground at a constant velocity. Describe the path it follows.
8. What type of speed does the *v* in the formula $v = d/t$ represent?
9. Which of the three graphs below corresponds to the position vs. time graph in Figure 3.15?

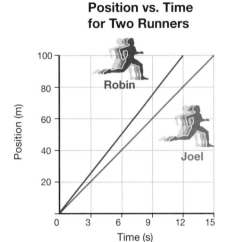

Figure 3.14: *Questions 3 and 4.*

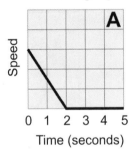 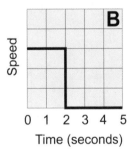 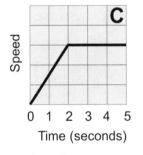

10. Between which times is the speed zero for the motion shown on the position vs. time graph in Figure 3.15?

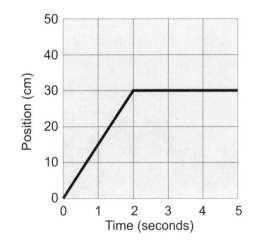

Figure 3.15: *Question 9 and 10.*

3.3 Acceleration

Constant speed is easy to understand. However, almost nothing moves with constant speed for long. When a driver steps on the gas pedal, the speed of the car increases. When the driver brakes, the speed decreases. Even while using cruise control, the speed goes up and down as the car's engine adjusts for hills. Another important concept in physics is *acceleration*. Acceleration is how we describe changes in speed or velocity.

ǎ *VOCABULARY*

acceleration - the rate at which velocity changes.

An example of acceleration

Definition of acceleration
What happens if you coast down a long hill on a bicycle? At the top of the hill, you move slowly. As you go down the hill, you move faster and faster—you accelerate. **Acceleration** is the rate at which your velocity changes. If your speed increases by 1 meter per second (m/s) each second, then your acceleration is 1 m/s per second.

Time (s)	Speed (m/s)
1	1
2	2
3	3
4	4
5	5

Time (s)	Speed (m/s)
1	2
2	4
3	6
4	8
5	10

Steeper hills
Your acceleration depends on the steepness of the hill. If the hill is a gradual incline, you have a small acceleration, such as 1 m/s each second. If the hill is steeper, your acceleration is greater, perhaps 2 m/s per second. On the gradual hill, your speed increases by 1 m/s every second. On the steeper hill, it increases by 2 m/s every second.

Acceleration on a speed vs. time graph
Acceleration is easy to spot on a speed vs. time graph. If the speed changes over time then there is acceleration. Acceleration causes the line to slope up on a speed vs. time graph (Figure 3.16). The graph on the top shows constant speed. There is zero acceleration at constant speed because the speed does not change.

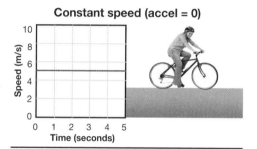

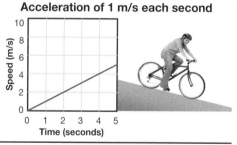

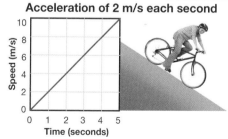

Figure 3.16: *Speed vs. time graphs showing constant speed (top) and acceleration (middle and bottom).*

Speed and acceleration

The difference between speed and acceleration

Speed and acceleration are not the same thing. You can be moving (non-zero speed) and have no acceleration (think *cruise control*). You can also be accelerating and not moving! Think about dropping the car down the ramp. In the instant you release it, the car has zero speed because it is not moving yet. But, it is *accelerating* because its speed is already changing.

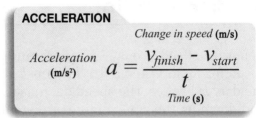

ACCELERATION

$$\underset{\text{(m/s}^2)}{\text{Acceleration}} \quad a = \frac{\overset{\text{Change in speed (m/s)}}{v_{finish} - v_{start}}}{\underset{\text{Time (s)}}{t}}$$

Example: acceleration in cars and trucks

Acceleration is the change in speed divided by the change in time. Acceleration describes how quickly speed changes. High acceleration means speed changes rapidly. A powerful sports car can change its speed from 0 to 60 mph in 5 seconds (Figure 3.17). The car has an acceleration of 12 mph/s. Low acceleration means speed changes slowly. A loaded garbage truck takes 15 seconds to get up to a speed of 60 mph. It has an acceleration of 4 mph/s.

Sports car

Speed goes from 0 to 60 mph in 5 seconds

$$\text{Acceleration} = \frac{\text{Change in speed}}{\text{Change in time}}$$

$$= \frac{60 \text{ mph}}{5 \text{ seconds}}$$

= 12 mph/sec

Acceleration in metric units

To calculate acceleration, you divide the change in speed by the amount of time it takes for the change to happen. If the change in speed is in meters per second, and the time is in seconds, then the acceleration is in m/s/s or *meters per second per second*. An acceleration of 50 m/s/s means that the speed increases by 50 m/s *every second*.

Garbage truck

Speed goes from 0 to 60 mph in 15 seconds

What does "units of seconds squared" mean?

An acceleration in m/s/s is often written as m/s^2 (meters per second squared). The steps below show you how to simplify the fraction m/s/s to get m/s^2. Saying *seconds squared* is just a math-shorthand way of talking. It is better to think about acceleration in units of speed change per second (that is, meters per second *per second*).

$$\text{Acceleration} = \frac{\text{Change in speed}}{\text{Change in time}}$$

$$= \frac{60 \text{ mph}}{15 \text{ seconds}}$$

= 4 mph/sec

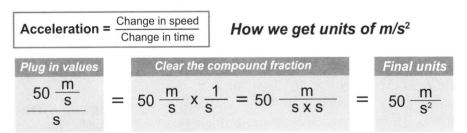

$\boxed{\text{Acceleration} = \dfrac{\text{Change in speed}}{\text{Change in time}}}$ **How we get units of m/s²**

Plug in values	Clear the compound fraction	Final units
$\dfrac{50 \frac{m}{s}}{s}$	$= 50 \frac{m}{s} \times \frac{1}{s} = 50 \frac{m}{s \times s}$	$= 50 \frac{m}{s^2}$

Figure 3.17: *The acceleration of a sports car and a garbage truck.*

Acceleration on motion graphs

Acceleration on a speed vs. time graph
A speed vs. time graph is useful for showing how the speed of a moving object changes over time. Think about a car moving on a straight road. If the line on the graph is horizontal, then the car is moving at a constant speed (top of Figure 3.18). The upward slope in the middle graph shows increasing speed. The downward slope of the bottom graph tells you the speed is decreasing. The word *acceleration* is used for any change in speed, up or down.

Positive and negative acceleration
Like velocity, acceleration can be positive or negative. Positive acceleration adds more speed each second; things get faster. Negative acceleration subtracts some speed each second; things get slower. People sometimes use the word *deceleration* to describe slowing down.

Acceleration on a position vs. time graph
The position vs. time graph is a *curve* when there is acceleration. Think about a car that is accelerating (speeding up). Its speed increases each second. That means it covers more distance each second. The position vs. time graph gets steeper each second. The opposite happens when a car is slowing down. The speed decreases so the car covers less distance each second. The position vs. time graph gets shallower with time, becoming flat when the car is stopped.

Speed is constant when there is zero acceleration.

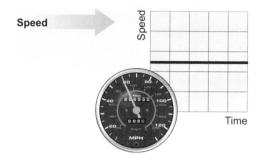

Speed increases with positive acceleration.

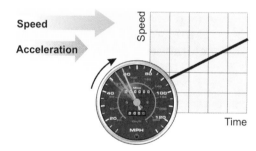

Speed decreases with negative acceleration.

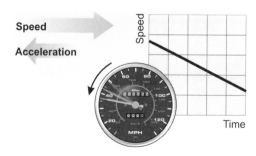

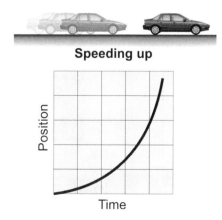

Speeding up

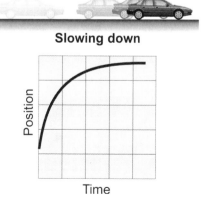

Slowing down

Figure 3.18: *Three examples of motion showing constant speed (top) and acceleration (middle, bottom).*

Free fall

The definition of free fall An object is in **free fall** if it is accelerating due to the force of gravity and no other forces are acting on it. A dropped ball is in free fall from the instant it leaves your hand until it reaches the ground. A ball thrown upward is also in free fall after it leaves your hand. Although you might not describe the ball as "falling," it is still in free fall. Birds, helicopters, and airplanes are *not* normally in free fall because forces other than gravity act on them.

The acceleration of gravity Objects in free fall on Earth accelerate downward, increasing their speed by 9.8 m/s every second (Figure 3.19). The value 9.8 m/s^2 is called the **acceleration due to gravity**. The small letter *g* is used to represent its value. When you see the letter *g* in a physics question, you can substitute the value 9.8 m/s^2.

Constant acceleration The speed vs. time graph below is for a ball in free fall. Because the graph is a straight line, the speed increases by the same amount each second. This means the ball has a *constant acceleration*. Make sure you do not confuse constant speed with constant acceleration! Constant acceleration means an object's *speed* changes by the same amount each second.

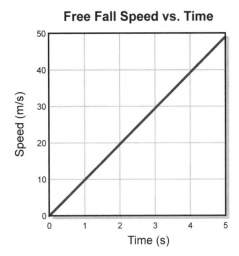

Time (s)	Speed (m/s)
0	0
1	9.8
2	19.6
3	29.4
4	39.2
5	49.0

Free Fall Speed vs. Time

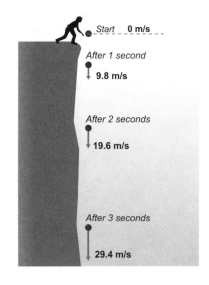

Figure 3.19: *A dropped ball increases its speed by 9.8 m/s each second, so its acceleration is 9.8 m/s^2.*

Acceleration and direction

A change in direction is acceleration
If an object's acceleration is *zero*, the object can only move at a constant speed *in a straight line* (or be stopped). A car driving around a curve at a constant speed is accelerating (in the "physics sense") because its direction is changing (Figure 3.20). Acceleration occurs whenever there is a change in speed, direction, or both.

What "change in direction" means
What do we mean by "change in direction"? Consider a car traveling east. Its velocity is drawn as an arrow pointing east. Now suppose the car turns southward a little. Its velocity vector has a new direction.

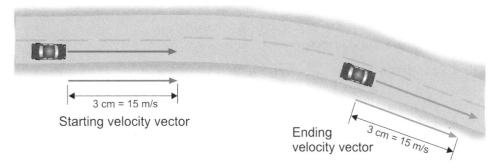

3 cm = 15 m/s
Starting velocity vector

Ending velocity vector   3 cm = 15 m/s

Drawing vectors
When drawing velocity arrows, the length represents the speed. A 2 cm arrow stands for 10 m/s (22 mph). A 4 cm arrow is 20 m/s, and so on. At this *scale*, each cm stands for 5 m/s. You can now find the change in velocity by measuring the length of the arrow that goes from the old velocity vector to the new one.

Start
End
} Change in velocity

The change in velocity is 5 m/s sideways

1 cm = 5 m/s

Turns are caused by sideways accelerations
The change in velocity is the small pink arrow that connects the old velocity and the new velocity. This arrow represents the difference in velocity before and after the turn. The change vector is 1 cm long, which equals 5 m/s. Notice the speed is the same before and after the turn! However, the change in direction is a *sideways* change of velocity. This change is caused by a *sideways acceleration*.

2 results of acceleration

Speed can change.

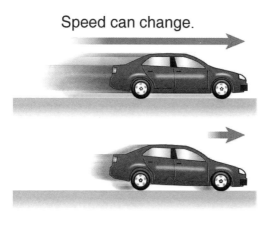

Direction can change.

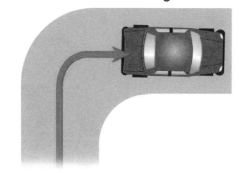

Figure 3.20: *A car can change its velocity by speeding up, slowing down, or turning.*

Curved motion

Acceleration and curved motion Curved motion is caused by sideways accelerations. Like velocity, acceleration has direction and is a vector. Sideways accelerations cause velocity to change direction, which results in turning. Turns create curved motion.

An example of curved motion As an example of curved motion, imagine a soccer ball kicked into the air. The ball starts with a velocity vector at an upward angle (Figure 3.21). Gravity accelerates the ball downward as it flies. The acceleration of gravity bends the velocity vector more toward the ground during each second the ball is in the air. Near the end of the motion, the ball's velocity vector is angled down toward the ground. The path of the ball makes a bowl-shaped curve called a *parabola*.

Projectiles A soccer ball is an example of a **projectile**. A projectile is an object moving under the influence of only gravity. The action of gravity is to constantly turn the velocity vector more and more downward. Flying objects such as airplanes and birds are *not* projectiles, because they are affected by forces generated from their own power.

Circular motion

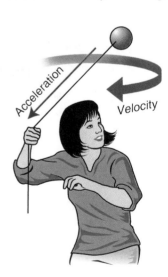

Circular motion is another type of curved motion. An object in circular motion has a velocity vector that constantly changes direction. Imagine whirling a ball around your head on a string. You have to pull the string to keep the ball moving in a circle. Your pull accelerates the ball toward you. That acceleration is what bends the ball's velocity into a circle with you at the center. Circular motion always has an acceleration that points toward the center of the circle. In fact, the direction of the acceleration changes constantly so it *always* stays pointed toward the center of the circle.

projectile - an object moving through space and affected only by gravity.

Projectile motion -------------
Velocity vector ⟶

The shape of the ball's path is called a parabola.

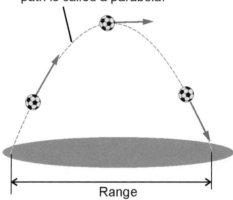

Range

Figure 3.21: *A soccer ball in the air is a projectile. The path of the ball is a bowl-shaped curve called a parabola.*

3.3 Section Review

1. Nearly all physics problems will use the unit m/s^2 for acceleration. Explain why the seconds are squared. Why isn't the unit given as m/s, like speed?

2. Suppose you are moving left (negative) with a velocity of −10 m/s. What happens to your speed if you have a *negative* acceleration? Do you speed up or slow down?

3. A rabbit starts from a resting position and moves at 6 m/s after 3 seconds. What is the acceleration of the rabbit? (Figure 3.22)

4. You are running a race and you speed up from 3 m/s to 5 m/s in 4 seconds.

   a. What is your change in speed?

   b. What is your acceleration?

5. Does a car accelerate when it goes around a corner at a constant speed? Explain your answer.

6. A sailboat increases its speed from 1 m/s to 4 m/s in 3 seconds. What will the speed of the sailboat be at 6 seconds if the acceleration stays the same? (Figure 3.23)

7. The graph at the right shows the speed of a person riding a bicycle through a city. Which point (A, B, or C) on the graph is a place where the bicycle has speed but no acceleration? How do you know?

8. What happens to the speed of an object that is dropped in free fall?

9. A ball is in free fall after being dropped. Will the speed of the ball be greater than 30 m/s in 2 seconds? Why or why not?

10. What happens when the velocity and acceleration are not in the same direction? What kind of motion occurs?

11. Earth moves in a nearly perfect circle around the Sun. Assume the speed stays constant. Is Earth accelerating or not?

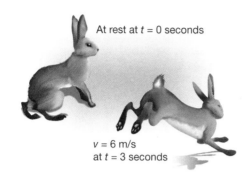

At rest at $t = 0$ seconds

$v = 6$ m/s
at $t = 3$ seconds

Figure 3.22: *Question 3.*

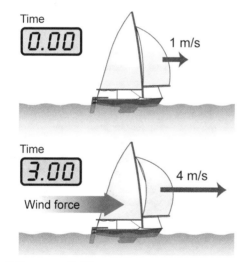

Time

0.00

1 m/s

Time

3.00

4 m/s

Wind force

Figure 3.23: *Question 6.*

Moments in Motion

Some things move too quickly for us to see what is really happening. Have you ever seen a hummingbird in flight? A little hummingbird can beat its wings about 10 times every second. Our eyes can't see individual wing beats—their wings just look like a blur! Special photography can capture fast action in still images that reveal a whole new world to our eyes.

Splashy motion

What does a milk drop splashing onto a plate really look like close-up? Suppose you could take a photograph of what the milk drop looks like at the exact moment when it splashes onto the plate. This is possible with a special kind of photography called strobe photography. Study the photograph of the milk splash (below). Our eyes can't see this happen, but the photograph shows it! This is not ordinary picture-taking.

Blurry motion

Have you ever tried to take a photo from a car or bus window while moving quickly down the highway? When an ordinary camera takes a picture of a moving object, the image can be blurry. The blur happens because it takes a certain minimum amount of light to capture the image. If the object moves while the camera is still collecting light, the image will be blurry.

Capturing motion

To make a sharp, fast-action photo, the camera can only see light for a short time compared to the object's movement time. This can be done two different ways. One way is to open the shutter for a very short time. Better cameras are able to do this. Another way is to let the shutter stay open but turn the light on and off very quickly. If you use a very bright, short pulse of light while the shutter is open, motion can be captured without creating a blurry image. This short, bright pulse of light is a *strobe*.

Stop-action strobes

Maybe you've seen strobe lights used as a special effect at a school dance, concert, or other live performance. A strobe light flashes continuously at regular intervals. When dancers move where strobe lights are flashing, their movements look jerky, almost as if their motion is being "stopped" over and over again. Why does it look like that? The answer is that you only see the dancers when the light is turned on! Instead of seeing the continuous movement, you see a sequence of "snapshots" of the dancers in different places. During the short periods without the bright light, you don't see the movements (because it's dark). This tricks your eyes into seeing the continuous movements as "stop action" segments. The effect can be hilarious!

Strobe photography

A strobe light can be used to produce a sharp "stop action" image of a fast moving object, like a milk splash. To do this, the strobe is flashed only once with a very bright, short pulse of light. The flash is so short that the object hardly moves at all during the light pulse. The single rapid flash gives enough light to capture the fast motion on film without blurring. Dr. Harold Edgerton is famous for perfecting strobe photography. Many discoveries have been made using Edgerton's strobe technique to photograph moving objects.

Many marbles or one?

The photograph at right of a marble rolling along a hilly track was taken with a digital camera and a strobe light. When the photographer hit the camera button, the shutter stayed open for 2 seconds while a strobe light pulsed about 10 times every second. At the same time, the marble was released from the top of the track. The photograph you see makes it look like there are 20 marbles on the track, when there is really only one. There are 20 in the photo because as the marble moved, the strobe light flashed, and the camera captured the same marble in 20 different places as it moved along the track. Study the photo carefully.

Why are the marble's images closer together in some places than others? How does this relate to the shape of the track?

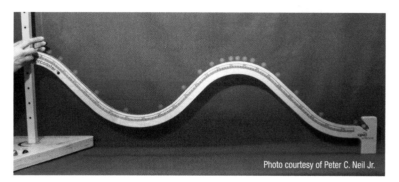

Photo courtesy of Peter C. Neil Jr.

Motion facts revealed

The marble images are closer together at the top of the first hill and second hill because it is going slower at these places. The marble images are farther apart at the bottom of each hill because it is moving faster at these places. Does this make sense? You will investigate the marble's motion on this same hilly track in Chapter 6.

How Fast Are You?

Speed is how fast something moves in relation to a reference point without regard to the direction. Speed is found by dividing the distance traveled by the total time the object has traveled. An object can travel at a constant rate or the speed may vary.

When speed varies during a trip, you can find the average speed for the entire trip. In this activity you and a partner will each calculate your average speed in different units.

Materials

tape measure, meterstick, or ruler; stopwatch or watch with a second hand; pieces of tape

What you will do

Origin

1. Decide how you and your partner will be moving. You can walk, run, roll, or move in any other way you choose.

2. Find an open area outside, in a hallway, or in another location where you can do this activity.

3. Mark your starting point (origin) with a piece of tape.

4. Measure at least five evenly spaced positions in meters along the path you are going to follow. Mark these

positions with tape. For example, if you are running 60 meters, place a piece of tape at the starting point and at every 10 meters. If you are crawling only 5 meters, mark off every 1 meter.

5. Start at the origin and move along the length of your path. Your partner will start the timer once you start moving. Your partner should record the time for each marked position. For example, at the origin time is zero. At the 1-meter mark the time might be 2 seconds, at the 2-meter mark the time might be 4 seconds, and so on.

6. Record your data in a table like this:

Position (m)	Time (s)

7. Switch roles and repeat the activity with the other person moving. Record your data in the table.

8. Make a position vs. time graph to show each person's motion. Put both sets of data on the same graph. It might be helpful to use two different colors to plot the points.

Applying your knowledge

a. Explain how you can use your graph to figure out who had the faster average speed.

b. Explain how you can use your data table to figure out who had the faster average speed.

c. Look at each person's line on the graph. How can you use the graph to tell whether you moved at a constant speed? Did you move at a constant speed? Did your partner?

d. Calculate each person's average speed in meters per second and in centimeters per second.

Chapter 3 Assessment

Vocabulary

Select the correct term to complete the sentences.

acceleration	free fall	dependent variable
graph	origin	independent variable
position	slope	projectile
velocity	vectors	acceleration due to gravity

Section 3.1

1. Speed with direction is called ____.

2. Variables that are described using both a number and a direction are called ____.

3. The ____ is the place where position equals zero.

4. The ____ of an object is given relative to an origin.

Section 3.2

5. A mathematical diagram using two axes to represent the relationship between variables is a(n) ____.

6. The ____ of a line is the ratio of rise to run.

7. The variable usually represented on the *x*-axis of a graph is the ____.

8. The variable usually represented on the *y*-axis of a graph is the ____.

Section 3.3

9. The rate at which velocity changes is defined as ____.

10. An object moving in a curved path and affected only by gravity is called a(n) ____.

11. An object accelerating under only the force of gravity is said to be in ____.

12. An object in free fall will accelerate toward Earth at 9.8 m/s^2, the ____.

Concepts

Section 3.1

1. Write whether each of the following directions usually are considered positive (+) or negative (–).
   a. ____ up
   b. ____ down
   c. ____ left
   d. ____ right
   e. ____ north
   f. ____ south
   g. ____ east
   h. ____ west

2. If you are given *x-y* axes coordinates of (4, 9), which axis is represented by the number 9?

Section 3.2

3. Sort the following words into two groups. Explain what categories you used to divide them.
   x-axis, *y*-axis, dependent variable, independent variable, horizontal axis, vertical axis

4. A graph is made of the speed vs. time of a plane as it flies from San Francisco to the Kahului Airport on Maui. How could the distance traveled by the plane be calculated from the graph?

5. When comparing two different lines on a position vs. time graph, how can you tell which object is faster?

6. Which of the graphs below shows an object that is stopped?

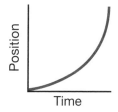 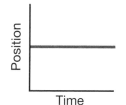 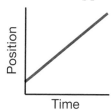

7. Which of the graphs above shows an object moving at a constant speed?

Section 3.3

8. A ball is thrown straight up into the air. As it moves upward, its speed ____ by ____ each second. As it falls back down, its speed ____ by ____ each second.

9. How would it be possible for an object to be traveling with constant speed and still be accelerating?

10. Can an object have a speed of zero while it has an acceleration that is not zero? Explain.

Problems

Section 3.1

1. Starting from school, you bicycle 2 km north, then 6 km east, then 2 km south.
   a. How far did you cycle?
   b. What is your final position compared to your school?
   c. How far and in what direction must you travel to return to school?

2. If you walk 8 blocks north and then 3 blocks south from your home, what is your position compared to your home? What distance did you walk?

3. You use an *x-y* plane to represent your position. Starting at (+150 m, –50 m), you walk 20 meters west and 30 meters north. What are your new coordinates?

4. A bird flies from its nest going north for 2 hours at a speed of 20 km/h and then goes west for 3 hours at 15 km/h. What are the distance coordinates for the bird relative to its nest?

Section 3.2

5. Draw the position versus time graph for a person walking at a constant speed of 1 m/s for 10 seconds. On the same axes, draw the graph for a person running at a constant speed of 4 m/s.

6. Calculate the speed represented by each position versus time graph below.

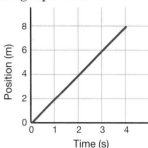 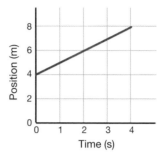

7. Draw the speed vs. time graph that shows the same motion as each position versus time graph above.

Section 3.3

8. When a ball is first dropped off a cliff in free fall, it has an acceleration of 9.8 m/s^2. What is its acceleration as it gets closer to the ground? Assume no air friction.

9. Why is the position vs. time graph for an object in free fall a curve?

10. Draw a speed vs. time graph for an object accelerating from rest at 2 m/s^2.

11. Draw a speed vs. time graph for a car that starts at rest and steadily accelerates until it is moving at 40 m/s after 20 seconds then answer the following questions.
    a. What is the car's acceleration?
    b. What distance did the car travel during the 20 seconds?

12. Draw a speed vs. time graph for each of the following situations.
    a. A person walks along a trail at a constant speed.
    b. A ball is rolling up a hill and gradually slows down.
    c. A car starts out at rest at a red light and gradually speeds up.

Chapter 4

Forces

On May 27, 1931, a train called Empire Builder encountered the amazing force of a tornado as it moved across Minnesota. The tornado's force was so great that as the train moved along the tracks at 60 miles per hour, five of its 60-ton cars were lifted from the rails! One car was lifted and thrown 80 feet away into a ditch. Moving heavy railroad cars requires a tremendous amount of force.

Forces are created and applied every time anything moves. Forces such as weight are even present when things are not moving. Your body uses forces every moment of your life, for every action, from the beating of your heart to walking up stairs. Understanding how forces are created and described is fundamental to understanding nature. Read this chapter to learn more about how forces are created, measured, described, and used in daily life.

Key Questions:

1. What is a force?

2. How are forces measured?

3. What is friction, and is friction ever useful?

Images courtesy of NOAA

4.1 Forces

We have talked about *forces* since Chapter 1. However, since force is such an important idea, this whole chapter is about forces. You will learn where forces come from, how they are measured, and how they are added and subtracted.

The cause of forces

What are forces? A force is a push or pull, or any action that has the ability to change motion. The key word here is *action*. Force is an action. You need force to start things moving. You also need force to make any change to an object's motion once it is moving. Forces can increase or decrease the speed of an object. Forces can also change the direction in which an object is moving.

How are forces created? Forces are created in many ways. For example, your muscles create force when you swing a tennis racket. Earth's gravity creates a force called **weight** that pulls on everything around you. On a windy day, the movement of air can create forces. Each of these actions can create force because they all can change an object's motion.

Some causes of force

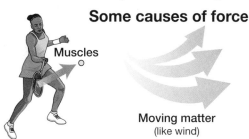
Muscles

Moving matter
(like wind)

Massive objects
(like planets)

The four elementary forces All of the forces we know in the universe come from four elementary forces (Figure 4.1). You are most familiar with the force of gravity but if you have ever felt a zap of electricity or have played with magnets you have experienced an electromagnetic force. Strong and weak forces occur inside atoms and are studied by scientists.

The Four Elementary Forces

Strong nuclear force
This force holds the nucleus of an atom together. This force is very strong but only reaches a very short distance.

Electromagnetic force
This force acts between positive and negative charges. This force holds atoms together in molecules.

Weak force
This force causes some kinds of radioactivity.

Gravity
This force causes all masses to attract one another. Your weight comes from the mass of Earth attracting the mass of your body.

Figure 4.1: *All forces in the universe come from only four elementary forces.*

Measuring force

Pounds Suppose you are buying some apples at the grocery store. How does the cashier know how much to charge you? You are charged a certain amount for every pound of weight. The **pound** (lb) is a unit of force commonly used in the United States. When you measure weight in pounds on a postal scale, you are measuring the force of gravity acting on an object (Figure 4.2). For smaller amounts, pounds are divided into ounces (oz). There are 16 ounces in 1 pound.

The origin of the pound The word *pound* comes from the Latin *pondus*, meaning "weight." So why is "lb" the abbreviation for pound? The reason is that the pound is based on the Roman *libra*, which means "balance." If you speak Spanish, you know that *libra* is also the Spanish word for pound.

Newtons Although we use pounds all the time in our everyday life, scientists prefer to measure forces in newtons. The **newton** (N) is a metric unit of force. We call the SI unit of force the *newton* because force is defined by Newton's laws. A newton is the amount of force needed to accelerate a 1-kg object at a rate of 1 m/s². As shown below, a 1-kg object will increase speed by 1 m/s each second if a 1-N force acts on it.

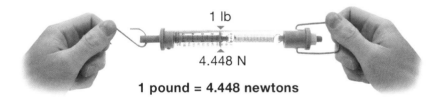

1 pound = 4.448 newtons

Converting newtons and pounds The newton is a smaller unit of force than the pound. One newton is approximately the weight of a medium-sized apple, or roughly one-quarter of a pound. One pound of force equals 4.448 newtons. As another example, a 100-pound person weighs 444.8 newtons.

pound - the English unit of force equal to 4.448 newtons.

newton - the metric unit of force, equal to the force needed to make a 1-kg object accelerate at 1 m/s².

Pound
One pound (lb) is about the weight of 0.454 kg of mass

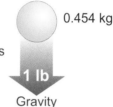

Newton
One newton (N) is the force it takes to change the speed of a 1 kg mass by 1 m/s in 1 second.

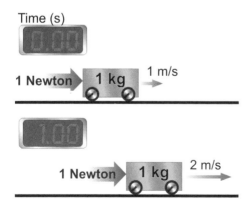

Figure 4.2: *The definitions of the newton and pound.*

Gravity and weight

Gravity's force depends on mass
The force of gravity on an object is called *weight*. At Earth's surface, gravity exerts a force of 9.8 N on every kilogram of mass. That means a 1-kilogram mass has a weight of 9.8 N, a 2-kilogram mass has a weight of 19.6 N, and so on. On Earth's surface, the weight of any object is its mass multiplied by 9.8 N/kg. Because weight is a force, it is measured in units of force such as newtons and pounds.

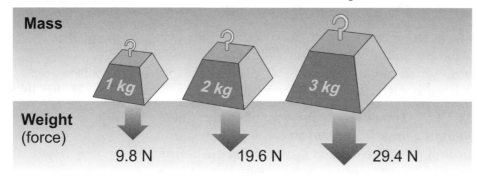

At Earth's surface each kg of mass feels 9.8 N of weight from Earth's gravity.

Weight and mass are not the same thing
People often confuse *weight* and *mass* in conversation. However, *weight and mass are not the same*. Mass is a fundamental property of matter measured in kilograms (kg). Weight is a *force* caused by mass. You have weight because the huge mass of Earth is right next to you. It is easy to confuse mass and weight because heavy objects (more weight) have lots of mass and light objects (less weight) have little mass. Always remember the difference when doing physics. Weight is a *force* measured in *newtons* (N) that depends on mass and gravity.

Weight is a force measured in newtons.

Weight is less on the Moon
A 10-kilogram rock has the same mass no matter where it is in the universe. A 10-kilogram rock's weight however, depends completely on where it is. On Earth, the rock weighs 98 newtons. But on the Moon, it only weighs 16 newtons (Figure 4.3)! The same rock weighs six times less on the Moon because gravity is weaker on the Moon.

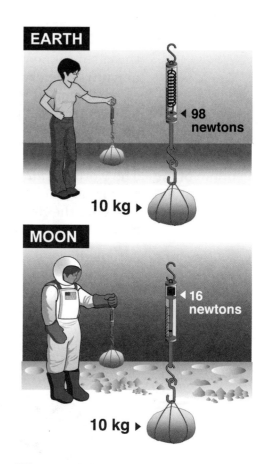

Figure 4.3: *A 10-kilogram rock weighs 98 newtons on Earth but only 16 newtons on the Moon.*

Calculating weight

The weight formula The weight formula (Figure 4.4), weight = mass × strength of gravity, can be rearranged into three forms. You can use this formula to find weight, mass, or the strength of gravity if you know any two of the three values.

Use. . .	if you want to find. . .	and you know. . .
$W = mg$	weight (W)	mass (m) and strength of gravity (g)
$m = W/g$	mass (m)	weight (W) and strength of gravity (g)
$g = W/m$	strength of gravity (g)	weight (W) and mass (m)

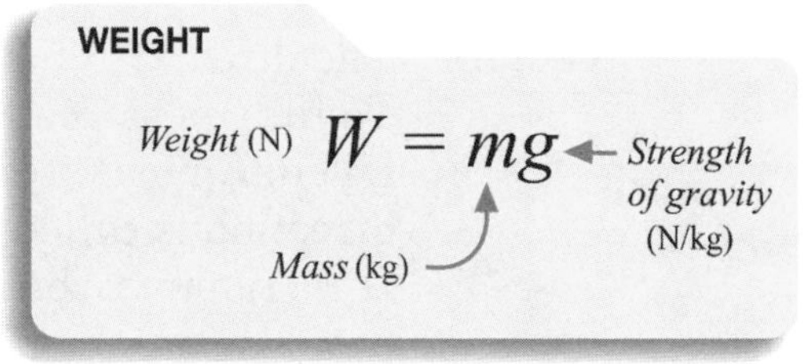

WEIGHT

Weight (N) $W = mg$ ← Strength of gravity (N/kg)

Mass (kg)

Figure 4.4: *The weight formula.*

Weight and mass

Calculate the weight of a 60-kilogram person (in newtons) on Earth and on Mars ($g = 3.7$ N/kg).

1. Looking for: You are asked for a person's weight on Earth and Mars.

2. Given: You are given the person's mass and the value of g on Mars.

3. Relationships: $W = mg$

4. Solution: For the person on Earth:
$W = mg$
$W = (60 \text{ kg})(9.8 \text{ N/kg}) = 588$ newtons

For the person on Mars:
$W = mg$
$W = (60 \text{ kg})(3.7 \text{ N/kg}) = 222$ newtons

Notice that while the masses are the same, the weight is much less on Mars.

Your turn...

a. Calculate the mass of a car that weighs 19,600 newtons on Earth. **Answer:** 2,000 kg

b. A 70-kg person travels to a planet where he weighs 1,750 N. What is the value of g on that planet? **Answer:** 25 N/kg

The force vector

Vectors The direction of a force makes a big difference in what the force does. To fully describe a force, both its strength and its direction must be given. A measurement that has both a number meaurement and a direction is called a vector. Strength is usually measured in newtons. Direction may be given in words (such as 5 newtons down or 10 newtons east), or can also be given using an arrow in a diagram.

Positive and negative numbers Forces may be assigned positive and negative values to tell their directions. Suppose a person pushes with a force of 10 newtons to the right (Figure 4.5). The force is +10 N. A person pushing with the same force to the left would create a force vector of –10 N. The negative sign indicates the –10 N force is in the opposite direction from the +10 N force. We usually choose positive values to represent forces directed up, to the right, to the north, or to the east. When drawing a force vector, the arrow shows the direction so the negative sign is not needed.

Drawing vectors Force vectors are drawn with an arrow that shows both the strength and direction of the force. The length of the arrow represents the strength of the force. The arrow points in the direction of the force. Vectors are drawn using a scale, with each centimeter representing a certain amount of force.

Choosing a scale When drawing a force vector to show its strength, you must choose an appropriate scale. For example, suppose you want to draw a force of 50 N to the east. The vector would be too big if you used a scale of 1 cm = 1 N. You should choose a bigger scale, such as 1 cm = 5 N or 1 cm = 10 N.

10 N right or +10 N

+10 N

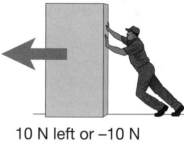

10 N left or –10 N

–10 N

Figure 4.5: *Positive and negative numbers are used to indicate the direction of force vectors.*

Two ways to draw a force of 50 newtons

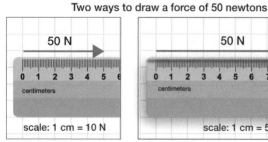
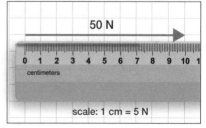

Forces from springs and ropes

Types of forces Ropes and springs are often used to make and apply forces. Ropes are used to transfer forces or change their direction. Springs are used to make and control forces.

Tension forces

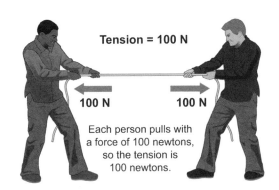

Tension = 100 N

100 N   100 N

Each person pulls with a force of 100 newtons, so the tension is 100 newtons.

The pulling force carried by a rope is called **tension**. *Tension always acts along the direction of the rope.* A rope carrying a tension force is stretched tight and pulls with equal strength on either end. For example, the two people in the diagram at the left are each pulling on the rope with a force of 100 newtons. The tension in the rope is 100 newtons. Ropes or strings do *not* carry pushing forces. This is obvious if you have ever tried pushing a rope!

The force from springs

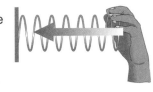

Stretch a spring and the spring exerts an opposite force back on your hand.

Compress a spring and the spring also exerts an opposite force back on your hand.

Springs are used to make or control forces. A spring creates a force when you stretch it or squeeze it away from its natural shape. The force created by a spring always acts to push or pull the spring back to its natural length. When you stretch a spring, it pulls back on your hand. When you squeeze a spring, called **compression**, the spring gets shorter. As it gets shorter, the spring pushes back on your hand.

Spring forces vary in strength The force created by a spring is proportional to the amount the spring is stretched or compressed. If you stretch a spring twice as much, it makes a force that is twice as strong.

Springs

STEM

Springs are used in many devices to make controlled amounts of force. Two of the many kinds of springs are extension springs and compression springs. Extension

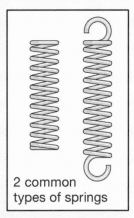

2 common types of springs

springs are designed to be stretched. They often have loops on either end. Compression springs are designed to be squeezed. They are usually flat on both ends. Can you find both types in springs in your classroom?

1. What is the spring used for?
2. What would happen if the spring broke?

4.1 Section Review

1. Name three situations in which force is created. Describe the cause of the force in each situation.
2. Which of the following are units of force?
   a. kilograms and pounds
   b. newtons and pounds
   c. kilograms and newtons
3. Which is greater: a force of 10 N or a force of 5 lbs?
4. Does the mass of an object change if the object is moved from one planet to another? Explain your answer.
5. What is the weight (in newtons) of a bowling ball which has a mass of 3 kilograms?
6. If the strength of gravity is 9.8 newtons per kilogram, that means:
   a. each newton of force equals 9.8 pounds.
   b. each pound of force equals 9.8 newtons.
   c. each newton of mass weighs 9.8 kilograms.
   d. each kilogram of mass weighs 9.8 newtons.
7. An astronaut in a spacesuit has a mass of 100 kilograms. What is the weight of this astronaut on the surface of the Moon where the strength of gravity is approximately 1/6 that of Earth?
8. A rope is used to apply a force to a box. Which drawing shows the force vector drawn correctly?

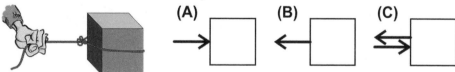

9. A spring is stretched as shown. Which drawing shows the force exerted *by the spring*? (*Hint*: *Not* the force *on* the spring.)

Calculating mass from weight

What is the mass of an object with a weight of 35 newtons? Assume the object is on the Earth's surface.

1. Looking for: Mass

2. Given: Weight = 35 N

3. Relationships: The weight equation
                    $W = mg$

4. Solution: $m = W/g$
                    $= (35 \text{ N})/$
                    (9.8 N/kg)
                    $= 3.57 \text{ kg}$

Your turn...

a. Which is greater: A force of 100 N or the weight of 50 kilograms at Earth's surface? **Answer**: The weight of 50 kg is greater.
b. The mass of a potato is 0.5 kg. Calculate its weight in newtons. **Answer**: 4.9 N

4.2 Friction

Friction is a force that resists motion. Friction is found everywhere in our world. You feel the effects of friction when you swim, ride in a car, walk, and even when you sit in a chair. Friction can act when an object is moving or when it is at rest. Many kinds of friction exist. Figure 4.6 shows some common examples.

Some causes of friction

The cause of friction   Imagine looking through a microscope at two smooth surfaces touching each other. You would see tiny hills and valleys on both sides. As surfaces slide (or try to slide) across each other, the hills and valleys grind against each other and cause friction. The tiny hills may change shape or wear away. If you rub sandpaper on a piece of wood, friction affects the wood's surface and makes it either smoother (hills wear away) or rougher (they change shape).

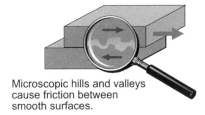

Microscopic hills and valleys cause friction between smooth surfaces.

Two surfaces are involved   Friction depends on *both* of the surfaces in contact. The force of friction on a rubber hockey puck is very small when it is sliding on ice. But the same hockey puck sliding on a piece of sandpaper experiences a large friction force. When the hockey puck slides on ice, a thin layer of water between the rubber and the ice allows the puck to slide easily. Water and other liquids, such as oil, can greatly reduce the friction between surfaces.

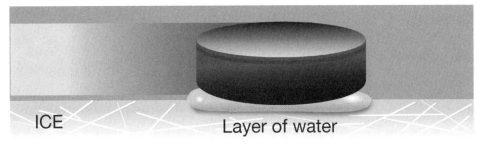

ICE   Layer of water

friction - a force that resists motion.

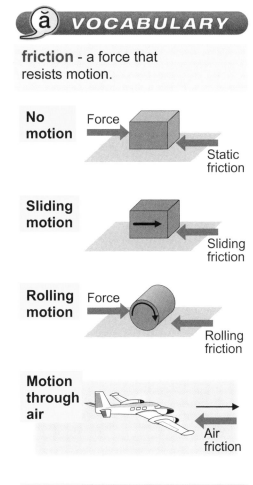

No motion   Force   Static friction

Sliding motion   Sliding friction

Rolling motion   Force   Rolling friction

Motion through air   Air friction

Motion through water   Viscous friction

Figure 4.6: *There are many types of friction.*

Identifying friction forces

Resisting motion
Friction is a force and can be drawn with a force vector. To figure out the direction of the vector, always remember that friction *resists motion between surfaces*. The force of friction acting *on* a surface always points opposite the direction of the motion *of that surface*. Imagine pushing a heavy box across the floor (Figure 4.7). If the box is moving to the right, then friction acts to the left against the surface of the box touching the floor. If the box were moving to the left instead, the force of friction would point to the right. This is what we mean when we say friction resists motion.

Sliding friction
Sliding friction is a force that resists dry sliding motion between any two surfaces. If you push a box across the floor toward the right, sliding friction acts toward the left. The friction force acts between the floor and the bottom surface of the box. If you stop pushing the box, sliding friction keeps causing a force as long as the box is moving. Sliding friction is what eventually slows the box to a stop when you stop pushing.

Static friction
Static friction keeps an object that is standing still (at rest) from moving. Imagine trying to push a heavy box with a small force. The box stays at rest because the static friction force acts against your force and cancels it out. As you increase the strength of your push, the static friction also increases. Eventually your force becomes strong enough to overcome static friction and the box starts to move (Figure 4.7). The force of static friction balances your force up to a limit. The limit of the static friction force depends on the types of surfaces and the weight of the object you are pushing.

Comparing sliding and static friction
How does sliding friction compare with static friction? If you have ever tried to move a heavy sofa or refrigerator, you probably know the answer. It is harder to get something moving than it is to keep it moving. This is because static friction is almost always greater than sliding friction at slow speeds.

VOCABULARY

sliding friction - the friction force that resists the motion of an object moving across a surface.

static friction - the friction force that resists the motion between two surfaces that are not moving.

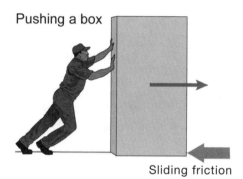
Pushing a box

Sliding friction

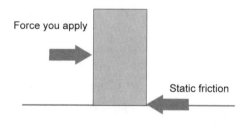
Force you apply

Static friction

Figure 4.7: *The direction of friction is opposite the direction the box is pushed.*

A model for friction

Different amounts of friction The amount of friction generated when a box is pushed across a smooth floor is very different from when it is pushed across a carpet. Friction depends on materials, roughness, how clean the surfaces are, and other factors. Even the friction between two identical surfaces changes as the surfaces are polished by the sliding motion. No single formula can accurately describe all types of friction.

An example An easy experiment to measure friction is to pull a piece of paper across a table with a force scale. The paper slides smoothly, and the scale measures almost no force. Now put a brick on the piece of paper (Figure 4.8). Friction increases and you must pull with a greater force to keep the paper moving.

Friction depends on the force between surfaces Why does the brick have an effect on friction? The two surfaces in contact are still the paper and the tabletop. The brick causes the paper to press harder into the table's surface. The tiny hills and valleys in the paper and in the tabletop are pressed together with a much greater force, so the friction increases. The same is true of most dry sliding friction. Increasing the force that pushes surfaces together increases the amount of friction.

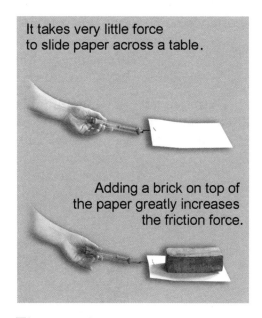

It takes very little force to slide paper across a table.

Adding a brick on top of the paper greatly increases the friction force.

Figure 4.8: *Friction increases greatly when a brick is placed on the paper.*

The greater the force squeezing two surfaces together, the greater the friction force.

Why sliding friction increases with weight The friction force between two smooth, hard surfaces is approximately proportional to the force squeezing the surfaces against each other. Consider sliding a heavy box across a floor. The force between the bottom of the box and the floor is the weight of the box. Therefore, the force of friction is proportional to the weight of the box. If the weight doubles, the force of friction also doubles.

Other kinds of friction act differently This rule is *not* true if the surfaces are wet, or if they are soft. Rubber is soft compared to pavement. The friction between rubber and pavement also depends on how much rubber is contacting the road. Wide tires have more friction (traction) than narrow tires.

Reducing the force of friction

All surfaces experience some friction
Unless a force is constantly applied, friction will slow all motion to a stop eventually. For example, bicycles have low friction, but even the best bicycle slows down as you coast on a level road. It is impossible to completely eliminate friction. However, many clever inventions have been devised to reduce friction. You use them every day.

Lubricants reduce friction in machines
Putting a liquid such as oil between two sliding surfaces keeps them from touching each other. The tiny hills and valleys don't become locked together, so there is less friction. The liquid also keeps the surfaces from wearing away as quickly. You add oil to a car's engine so that the moving parts slide or turn with less friction. Even water can be used to reduce friction between objects if they are not too hot.

Ball bearings

A ball bearing you might find in a machine

Ball bearings reduce friction in rotating motion (Figure 4.9). Ball bearings change sliding motion into rolling motion, which has much less friction. For example, a metal shaft rotating in a hole rubs and generates a lot of friction. Ball bearings that go between the shaft and the inside surface of the hole allow the shaft to spin more easily. The shaft rolls on the bearings instead of rubbing against the walls of the hole. Well-oiled bearings rotate easily and greatly reduce friction.

Magnetic levitation
Another method of decreasing friction is to separate the two surfaces with a cushion of air. A hovercraft floats on a cushion of air created by a large fan. Magnetic forces can also be used to separate surfaces. A magnetically levitated (or maglev) train uses magnets that run on electricity to float on the track once the train is moving (Figure 4.10). There is no contact between train and track, so there is far less friction than with a standard train on tracks. The ride is smoother, so maglev trains can move at very fast speeds. Maglev trains are not widely used yet because they are much more expensive to build than regular trains. They may become more popular in the future.

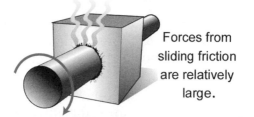

Forces from sliding friction are relatively large.

Rolling balls

Forces from rolling friction are much smaller.

Figure 4.9: *The friction between a shaft (the long pole in the picture) and the inner surface of the hole produces a lot of heat. Friction can be reduced by placing ball bearings between the shaft and the hole surface.*

Figure 4.10: *With a maglev train, there is no contact between the moving train and the rail—and thus there is little friction.*

Using friction

Friction is useful for brakes and tires

There are many times when friction is very useful. For example, the brakes on a bicycle create friction between the brake pads and the rim of the wheel. Friction makes the bicycle slow down or stop. Friction is also needed to make a bicycle go. Without friction, the bicycle's tires would not grip the road.

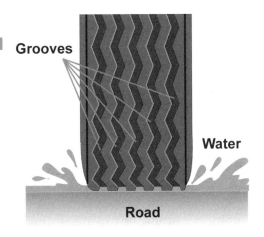

Figure 4.11: *Grooved tire treads allow space for water to be channeled away from the road–tire contact point, allowing for more friction in wet conditions.*

Tires designed for bad weather   Friction is also important to anyone driving a car. Tires are specially designed to maintain friction on pavement in rain or snow. Tire treads have grooves that allow space for water to be channeled away where the tire touches the road (Figure 4.11). This allows good contact between the rubber and the road surface. Special groove patterns, along with tiny slits, are used on snow tires to increase traction in snow. These grooves and slits keep snow from getting packed into the treads.

Nails   Friction keeps nails in place (Figure 4.12). When a nail is hammered into wood, the wood pushes against the nail on all sides. The force of the wood against the nail surface creates a lot of friction. Each hit of the hammer pushes the nail deeper into the wood. The deeper the nail goes, the more surface there is for friction to grab onto.

Cleated shoes

Shoes are designed to increase the friction between your foot and the ground. Many athletes, including football and soccer players, wear shoes with cleats. Cleats are like teeth on the bottom of the shoe that dig into the ground. Players wearing cleats can apply much greater force against the ground to help them move and to keep them from slipping.

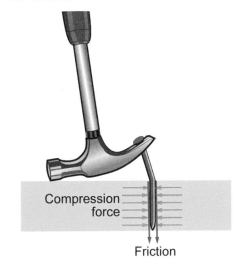

Figure 4.12: *Friction is what makes nails hard to pull out, and what gives nails the strength to hold things together.*

Friction and energy

Friction changes energy of motion into heat

Why does rubbing your hands together make them warmer?

Earlier we learned that energy moves through the action of forces. Energy also changes into different forms. Friction changes energy of motion into heat energy. You may have noticed that rubbing your hands together quickly can make them warmer on a cold day. You are feeling the effect of friction changing energy of motion into heat.

Heat in machines

Friction is always present in any machine with moving parts. If the machine is small, or the forces are low, the amount of heat produced by friction may also be small. A sewing machine gets warmer as it runs, but usually not so hot that parts melt or break. Larger machines have more problems with heat. In many machines, oil is pumped around moving parts. The oil does two important things. First, oil reduces friction so less heat is generated. Second, the oil absorbs the heat and carries it away from the moving parts. Without the flow of cooling oil, moving parts in an engine would quickly heat up and melt.

Friction causes wear

Which rocks have been worn by friction and which have not?

Another way friction changes energy is by wearing away moving parts. You have probably noticed that objects that slide against each other often get rounded or smoothed. Each time two moving surfaces touch each other, tiny bits of material are broken off by friction. Breaking off bits of material uses energy. Sharp corners and edges are rounded off and flat surfaces may be scratched or even polished smooth and shiny. This is why water flowing over stones in a stream causes the stones to be rounded and smooth.

Dealing with the heat

STEM

Every machine releases heat from friction. The faster the parts move, and the larger the forces inside the machine, the more heat is released. Electronic machines, like computers, are no exception, even though they may have no moving parts! Electricity moving though wires also creates friction.

If a machine gets too hot, parts may melt and the machine may stop working. Because of this, many machines have special systems, parts, and designs to get rid of unwanted heat energy.

Computer

Vacuum cleaner

Car engine

Here are three machines you probably see every day. How does excess heat get removed from each one?

4.2 Section Review

1. Name three devices or inventions that are designed to decrease friction.
2. Name three devices or inventions that are designed to increase friction.
3. If the force squeezing two surfaces together is decreased, the force of friction between the two surfaces will most likely
   a. increase.
   b. decrease.
   c. stay about the same.
4. True or False: A well-oiled machine has no friction. Explain your answer.
5. The difference between static friction and sliding friction is that
   a. sliding friction is always greater.
   b. static friction is always greater.
   c. sliding friction occurs at rest and static friction occurs in motion.
   d. static friction occurs at rest and sliding friction occurs in motion.
6. A box is sliding across the floor from left to right. Which diagram correctly shows the force of friction acting on the box?

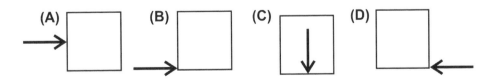

7. True or False: Friction makes energy vanish. Explain your answer.

4.3 Forces and Equilibrium

We almost never feel only one force at a time. Friction and weight are two forces that might act on you at the same time. To figure out how (or if) things move, we need to add up all of the forces that are acting on them. This section is about how forces add up.

Adding forces

Net force   The sum of all the forces on an object is called the **net force**. The word *net* means "total." *Net force* also means the direction of the forces has been taken into account. Consider a flying airplane (Figure 4.13). Four forces act on the plane: weight, drag (air friction), the thrust of the engines, and the lift force caused by the flow of air over the wings. For a plane to fly at a constant speed in a level path, the forces must all balance. **Balanced forces** result in a net force of zero.

Changing motion

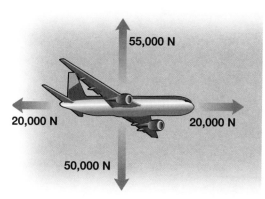

A pilot must always be aware of these four forces and know how to change them in order to speed up, slow down, lift off, and land. For example, to speed up there must be a net force in the forward direction. The thrust must be greater than the drag. To climb, there must be an upward net force. The lift force must be greater than the weight.

Calculating net force   To calculate the net force on an object, you must add the forces in each direction separately. Remember to define positive and negative directions for both the *x*-direction and *y*-direction. In the diagram above, +*x* is to the right and +*y* is up. The net force in the *x*-direction is zero because the +20,000 N and −20,000 N add up to zero. The net force in the *y*-direction is +5,000 N (+55,000 N − 50,000 N). The plane climbs because there is a positive (upward) net force.

net force - the sum of all forces acting on an object.

balanced forces - combined forces that result in a zero net force on an object.

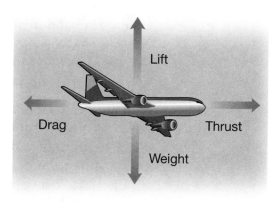

Figure 4.13: *Four forces act on a plane as it flies.*

Equilibrium

Net force can be zero or not zero

Two things can be true when many forces act on the same object. One or the other is always true (Figure 4.14).

1. The net force is zero, or

2. the net force is *not* zero.

Definition of equilibrium

When the net force is zero, an object at rest will stay at rest.* When the net force is zero, we say an object is in **equilibrium**. Equilibrium does *not* mean there are no forces! Equilibrium means all forces cancel each other out leaving zero net force. Interestingly, an object can be in motion at constant speed and still be in equilibrium. This happens when a pushing force and a friction force are equal but opposite in direction so the object does not speed up or slow down.

Using equilibrium to find unknown forces

The idea of equilibrium is often used in reverse. Instead of thinking "an object in equilibrium stays at rest" we think "an object at rest must be in equilibrium." If an object is at rest, *the net force on it must be zero*. This fact often allows us to find the strength and direction of forces that must be there even if we don't directly cause them.

When net force is not zero

If the net force is *not* zero, then the motion of an object will change. An object at rest will start moving. An object that is moving will change its velocity. In Chapter 5, we will learn about how unbalanced forces cause *acceleration*.

equilibrium - the state in which the net force on an object is zero.

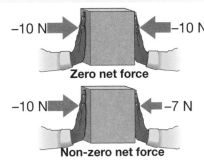

Figure 4.14: *The two possibilities for the net force.*

* The exception!

An object moving at a constant speed in a straight line is also in equilibrium! See Newton's First Law in the next chapter.

Finding an unknown force

A person with a weight of 150 N is sitting motionless in a swing. What is the tension force in each rope holding up the swing?

1. Looking for: You are asked for an unknown tension force.

2. Given: You are given the weight in newtons and you know the swing is at rest (equilibrium).

3. Relationships: The net force on the swing is zero.

4. Solution: The upward force from the ropes must exactly cancel the downward force of weight. That means the upward force from both ropes must be 150 N, so the force in each rope is 75 N.

Normal force

Definition of normal force
Imagine a book sitting on a table (Figure 4.15). Gravity pulls the book downward with the force of the book's weight. The book is at rest, so the net force must be zero. But what force balances the weight? The table exerts an upward force on the book called the **normal force**. The word *normal* here has a different meaning from what you might expect. In mathematics, *normal* means "perpendicular." The force that the table exerts is perpendicular to the table's surface. The normal force is also sometimes called the *support force*.

When normal force is created
A normal force is created whenever an object is in contact with a surface. The normal force has *equal strength* to the force pressing the object into the surface, which is often the object's weight. The normal force has *opposite direction* to the force pressing the object into the surface. For example, the weight of a book presses down on the table surface. The normal force is equal in strength to the book's weight but acts upward on the book, in the opposite direction from the weight.

What normal force acts on
The normal force acts on the object pressing into the surface. That means, in this example, the normal force *acts on the book*. The normal force is created by the book *acting on the table*.

Strength of the normal force
What happens to the normal force if you put a brick on top of the book? The brick makes the book press harder into the table. The book does not move, so the normal force must be the same strength as the total weight of the book and the brick (Figure 4.16). The normal force increases to keep the book in balance.

How the normal force is created
How does a table "know" how much normal force to supply? The answer is that normal force is very similar to the force exerted by a spring. When a book sits on a table, it squeezes the atoms in the table together by a tiny amount. The atoms resist this squeezing and try to return the table to its natural thickness. The greater the table is compressed, the larger the normal force it creates. The matter in the table acts like a bunch of very stiff springs. You don't see the table compress because the amount of compression is very small.

normal force - the force that a surface exerts on an object that is pressing on it.

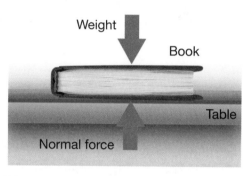

Figure 4.15: *The normal force and the weight are equal in strength and opposite in direction.*

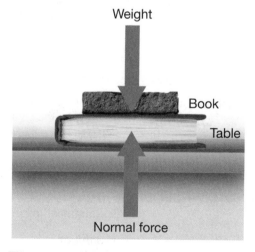

Figure 4.16: *The normal force is greater if a brick is placed on the book.*

The free-body diagram

Forces on a free-body diagram

How can you keep track of many forces with different directions? The answer is to draw a **free-body diagram**. A free-body diagram contains only a single object, like a book or a table. All connections or supports are taken away and replaced by the forces they exert on the object. An accurate free-body diagram includes *every* force acting on an object, including weight, friction, and normal forces.

An example

As an example of a free-body diagram, consider a stack of books weighing 30 newtons resting on a table that weighs 200 newtons. The books are on one corner of the table so that their entire weight is supported by one table leg. Figure 4.17 shows a free-body diagram of the forces acting on the table.

Finding the forces

Because the table is in equilibrium, the net force on it must be zero. The weight of the books acts on the table making the 30 N force. The weight of the table acts on the floor. At every point where the table touches the floor (each leg) a normal force is created. The correct free-body diagram shows six forces. The normal force at each of three legs is one-quarter the weight of the table (50 newtons). The leg beneath the book also supports the weight of the book (50 N + 30 N = 80 N).

The purpose of a free-body diagram

By separating an object from its physical connections, a free-body diagram helps you identify all forces and where they act. A normal force is usually present at any point an object is in contact with another object or surface. Forces due to weight may be assumed to act directly on an object, often at its center.

Positive and negative forces

There are two ways to handle positive and negative directions in a free-body diagram. One way is to make all upward forces positive and all downward forces negative. The second way is to draw all the forces in the direction you believe they act on the object. When you solve the problem, if you have chosen correctly, all the values for each force are positive. If one comes out negative, it means the force points in the opposite direction from what you guessed.

free-body diagram - a diagram showing all the forces acting on an object.

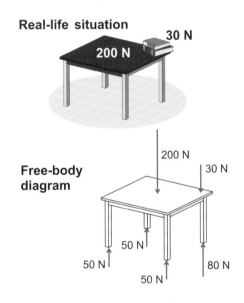

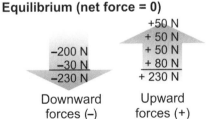

Figure 4.17: *A free-body diagram showing the forces acting on a table that has a stack of books resting on one corner.*

Solving equilibrium problems

Finding the net force For an object to be in equilibrium, all the forces acting *on the object* must add up to zero (Figure 4.18). The net force *in each direction* must be zero. That means the total force in the horizontal (*x*) direction must be zero and total force in the vertical (*y*) direction also must be zero. You cannot mix forces in the horizontal direction with forces in the vertical direction.

Balancing forces If you are trying to find an unknown force on an object in equilibrium, the first step is always to draw a free-body diagram. Then, use the fact that the net force is zero to find the unknown force. To be in equilibrium, forces must balance both horizontally and vertically. Forces to the right must balance forces to the left, and upward forces must balance downward forces.

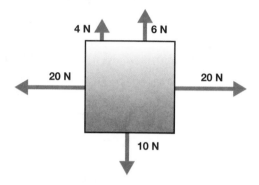

Figure 4.18: *An object is in equilibrium if the vertical forces balance and the horizontal forces balance.*

Equilibrium

Two chains are used to support a small boat weighing 1,500 newtons. One chain has a tension of 600 newtons. What is the force exerted by the other chain?

1. Looking for: You are asked for an unknown tension in a chain.

2. Given: You are given the boat's weight in newtons and the tension in one chain in newtons.

3. Relationships: The net force on the boat is zero.

4. Solution: Draw a free-body diagram.
The force of the two chains must balance the boat's weight.
$600 \text{ N} + F_{chain2} = 1,500 \text{ N}$ $F_{chain2} = 900 \text{ N}$

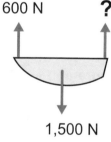

Your turn...

a. A heavy box weighing 1,000 newtons sits on the floor. You press down on the box with a force of 450 newtons. What is the normal force on the box? **Answer:** 1,450 newtons

b. A cat weighing 40 newtons stands on a chair. If the normal force on each of the cat's back feet is 12 newtons, what is the normal force on each front foot? (You can assume it is the same on each.) **Answer:** 8 newtons

4.3 Section Review

1. A vector is an example of a physical quantity that
   a. includes information about force and mass.
   b. includes information about temperature.
   c. includes information about quantity and direction.
   d. includes information about forces only.

2. The diagram in Figure 4.19 shows three forces acting on a pencil. What is the net force acting on the pencil?

3. If an object is in equilibrium, it means
   a. the net force on the object is zero.
   b. the object has zero total mass.
   c. no forces are acting on the object.
   d. only normal forces are acting on the object.

4. A train is climbing a gradual hill. The weight of the train creates a downhill force of 150,000 newtons. Friction creates an additional force of 25,000 newtons acting in the same direction (downhill) (Figure 4.20). How much force does the train's engine need to produce so the train is in equilibrium?

5. Draw a free-body diagram of your own body sitting on a chair. Include all forces acting on your body.

6. If a force has a negative value, such as –100 N, that means the force
   a. is less than 100 N in strength.
   b. acts in the opposite direction from a +100 N force.
   c. is a normal force.

7. A child weighing 200 newtons is sitting on a swing. The swing is supported by two ropes, one on each side. What is the tension in one of the ropes?

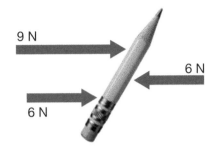

Figure 4.19: *Question 2.*

Weight = 150,000 N

Friction = 25,000 N

Figure 4.20: *Question 4.*

Defy Gravity? It Can Be Done

How can something that weighs almost a million pounds overcome the force of gravity and stay off the ground for hours? It almost sounds impossible. Yet it happens thousands of times every day, as large airplanes like the Boeing 747 fly all over the world.

When you see a 747 parked at an airport gate, the plane looks as big as a building. How does this enormous object manage to fly? Simple physics—really!

Newton's first law of motion states that an object will remain at rest unless external forces affect it. A 747 jet plane parked on the ground will not move until external forces make it move. For a plane to move and take off, four basic forces are at work: weight, lift, thrust, and drag.

Weight and lift

Weight is a force caused by gravity. The gravitational pull of Earth causes objects to have weight, which is a force. All forces have magnitude (size) and direction. The magnitude of weight varies from object to object, depending on mass. A suitcase has less magnitude than an airplane. The direction of weight in an airplane is down, toward Earth's center.

Lift is a force that goes in the opposite direction of weight. The magnitude of lift depends mainly on the size and shape of an airplane's wing, and the plane's speed through the air.

The combined effects of lift and weight will determine the motion of the airplane. If lift is much weaker than weight, the airplane will remain on the ground. But when the force of lift is stronger than the force of an airplane's weight, it will leave the ground and fly.

Controls allow the pilot to keep the airplane at a constant altitude once it is airborne. The forces of lift and weight are balanced, and the motion of the airplane does not change along its perpendicular axis, unless the pilot wants it to.

Thrust and drag

Thrust is the force that moves an airplane forward. This is the heavy work. On the ground, airplanes move on wheels, which reduce the force of friction from the ground. But to get a 747 rolling fast enough to take off requires a lot of thrust.

The direction of the thrust force is forward, opposite to the exhaust coming out of the engines. The magnitude of thrust depends on the number of engines and their power. Aircraft engines typically make more than 10,000 horsepower, 100 times more than an average car engine.

Drag is a force that goes in the opposite direction of thrust. Drag is horizontal, like thrust. But the direction of drag is toward the back of the airplane. The magnitude of drag depends mainly on the shape of the airplane and its wing, and the plane's velocity through the air.

When an airplane is airborne, air resistance causes drag. The more air resistance, the greater the magnitude of the drag. When you ride your bike, you feel the force of the wind in your face even on a calm day. This is air resistance, or drag. If you ride into a strong wind, or pedal faster, the magnitude of the drag increases. The same is true of the drag on an airplane flying into a heavy wind.

Once the airplane is airborne, controls allow the pilot to keep the airplane at a constant speed. At this point the forces of thrust and drag will remain balanced until the wind speed changes or the pilot reduces power.

Combining forces

A 747 has a lot of mass and requires an enormous amount of thrust to get it in motion. But how does all that relate to the airplane becoming airborne?

The answer lies in the motion of air over and under the wing. Airplane wings are shaped to make the airflow over the top of the wing different from the airflow under the bottom of the wing. The air flowing over the top of the wing travels a longer path than the air going under the wing. The air from the top and bottom must meet at the back edge of the wing. That means the air on top goes faster

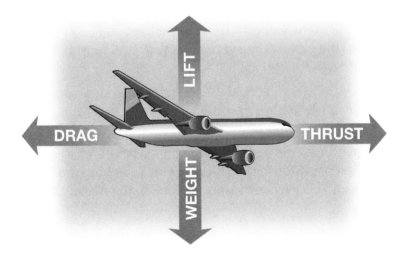

than the air on the bottom. Faster means higher kinetic energy. The kinetic energy has to come from somewhere, and it comes from pressure. Faster air on top of the wing has lower pressure than air underneath the wing. The difference in pressure is what produces the lift force.

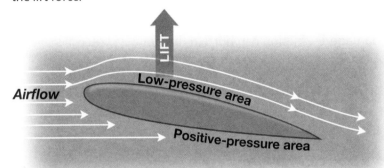

The strength of the lift force depends on the speed of air flowing over the wings. That is why a plane has to reach a minimum speed before it can take off. The plane accelerates along the runway until its speed reaches the minimum needed for the lift force to be greater than the plane's weight. When that speed is reached, the pilot changes the shape of the wings by moving the flaps at the wing's back edges. The plane then takes off!

QUESTIONS

1. How does an airplane "defy gravity"?

2. Describe how each of these four forces act on an airplane: weight, lift, thrust, and drag.

3. Some airports have been known to shut down temporarily if the outside air temperature gets too high. Can you think why this might be necessary? (*Hint*: Think about the force of lift and the importance of air density.)

4. How does the shape of an airplane's wing help the plane "defy gravity"?

Make It Work: Friction and Forces

Friction is a force that resists motion. Sometimes, friction is helpful. It is easier to walk on a rough road surface than it is to walk on smooth ice. Other times, friction is not helpful. If you fall down and slide across a rough road surface, your skin will be damaged—friction can hurt! In this activity, you will solve a problem by increasing and decreasing friction.

Materials (per group):

two textbooks; rubber band (cut so it is a straight piece); a table for a work surface

Set up the Problem

1. Cut the rubber band so that it is one flat straight piece.

2. Place one of the textbooks on the table.

3. Lay the piece of rubber band down on the top of the book, so some of it hangs down over the edge of the book.

4. Place the second book on top of the first. Part of the rubber band will be between the two books, and the other part will be hanging down over the side of the bottom book.

5. Grab the rubber band firmly and pull. *Warning*: The result might surprise you—be ready for a possibly painful *snap*!

Solve the Problem

Your job is to modify your system so you can use the rubber band to pull the books. Both books must move together across the table. You may not use tape, staples, or other fasteners. You may not push the books.

1. First, design a solution that involves *decreasing* friction somehow. Be creative!

2. Once your solution works, draw a diagram and explain what you did to decrease friction.

3. Next, design a different solution that involves *increasing* friction somehow. Be creative!

4. Once your solution works, draw a diagram and explain what you did to increase friction.

Applying your knowledge

a. Why did the flat piece of rubber band just snap right out from between the books when you pulled on it at first?

b. Explain why you could use the rubber band to pull the books when you set up your system with decreased friction.

c. Explain why you could use the rubber band to pull the books when you set up your system with increased friction.

d. Give an example of when friction is useful, and an example when friction is not useful. (Don't use the examples given in the introduction to this activity.)

Chapter 4 Assessment

Vocabulary

Select the correct term to complete the sentences.

balanced	compression	equilibrium
free-body diagram	friction	net force
newton	normal	pound
sliding	static	tension
weight		

Section 4.1

1. The English unit of force equal to 4.48 newtons is the ____.

2. The metric unit of force needed to accelerate a 1-kg mass at 1 m/s^2 is the ____.

3. A force that comes from the pulling of Earth's gravity is called ____.

4. The force created when you squeeze a spring is called ____.

5. A pulling force carried by a rope is called ____.

Section 4.2

6. A force that resists the motion of objects or surfaces over each other is ____.

7. A frictional force resisting motion as one surface slides over another is named ____ friction.

8. A frictional force between two non-moving surfaces that resists motion is known as ____ friction.

Section 4.3

9. A zero net force is established when all forces are ____.

10. When all forces on an object are balanced, the object is in ____.

11. The force a surface exerts on an object pressing on it is called the ____ force.

12. A diagram representing all forces acting on an object is called a(n) ____.

13. The sum of all forces acting on an object is called the ____.

Concepts

Section 4.1

1. Name three ways in which forces are created.

2. If you drop a feather and a baseball in a place where there is no air (a vacuum), how will their motions compare? Why?

3. Name the four fundamental forces of nature, the forces from which all others are created.

4. Forces cause changes to the motion of objects. Name a force and describe two changes it makes.

5. What information do you need to describe a force?

6. Draw the following force vectors on a piece of paper and show the scale you use.
   a. 20 N west
   b. 4 N southeast

7. Write a formula expressing the relationship between weight and mass. Explain the difference between weight and mass.

8. Identify which of the following are units of force (F) and which are units of mass (M).
   a. ____ kilogram   c. ____ pound
   b. ____ newton   d. ____ gram

9. What happens to a spring's force if you stretch it more?

10. The value of g is different on Earth and the Moon.
    a. What are the values of g on Earth and the Moon?
    b. How does the strength of gravity affect the mass and weight of objects measured on Earth and the Moon?

11. How are force vectors represented?

Section 4.2

12. Does it require more force to start an object sliding or to keep it sliding? Explain your answer.

13. Explain why ice generally has very little friction when it is in contact with other materials.

14. Explain how friction keeps a nail in place in a block of wood. If you try to pull out the nail, which way does the friction act?

15. Name two types of energy generated by friction and give an example of each.

16. Why is it much easier to slide a cardboard box when it is empty compared to when it is full of heavy books?

17. Explain two ways friction can be reduced.

18. Is friction something we always want to reduce? Explain.

Section 4.3

19. Standing on Earth, gravity exerts a downward force on you.
    a. What other force acts on you?
    b. What is the direction of the other force?
    c. What do you know about the magnitude, or strength, of this other force?

20. If the net force on an object is zero, can the object be moving? Explain.

21. Describe the motion of the race car shown in the figure to the right. Is it speeding up or slowing down?

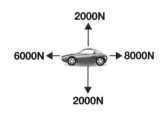

22. What four main forces act on an airplane in flight? If the plane accelerates forward, which two forces must be out of balance? To fly on a level path, which two forces must be in balance?

23. Which of the following diagrams correctly shows the normal force on the block of wood sliding down the incline?

a. 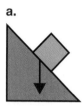　b. 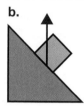　c. 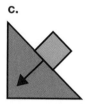　d.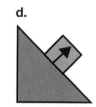

24. Draw a free-body diagram for the forces acting on the parachutist shown. Don't forget about air friction!

Problems

Section 4.1

1. Calculate the weight of a 66-N bowling ball in pounds.

2. A frozen turkey bought in Canada is labeled "5.0 kilograms." This is a measurement of its *mass*. What is its *weight* in newtons?

3. What is the mass of a large dog that weighs 441 newtons?

4. How much does a 40-kg student weigh on Earth in newtons?

5. How much mass does a 50,000-N truck have?

6. An astronaut has a mass of 70 kilograms on Earth. What would her mass be on Mars? What would her weight be on Mars? The value of g on Mars is 3.7 N/kg.

7. Using a scale of 1 cm = 5 N, draw a force vector representing a +20 newton force.

8. A spring is stretched 15 cm by a 45-N force. How far would the spring be stretched if a 60-N force were applied?

9. You and your friend pull on opposite ends of a rope. You each pull with a force of 10 newtons. What is the tension in the rope?

10. Two friends decide to build their strength by having a tug of war each day. They each pull with a force of 200 N.

    a. How much tension is in the rope?
    b. One day, one of the friends is sick and cannot work out. The other friend decides to build strength by tying the rope around a tree and pulling on the rope. How much must the single friend pull in order to get the same workout as he normally does? What is the tension on the rope in this case? Explain.
    c. In both cases above, what is the net force on the rope if neither person is moving, and the tree stays put?

Section 4.2

11. Thomas pushes a 250-N box across a wooden floor using 75 N of force. If a second box of the same weight is stacked on top of the first, how much force would Thomas need to push the two boxes across the same floor?

12. Your backpack weighs 50 N. You pull it across a table at a constant speed by exerting a force of 20 N to the right. Draw a free-body diagram showing all four forces on the backpack. State the strength of each.

13. You exert a 50-N force to the right on a 300-N box, but it does not move. Draw a free-body diagram for the box. Label all the forces and state their strengths.

Section 4.3

14. Find the net force on each box.

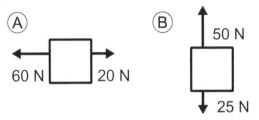

15. A 20-kilogram monkey hangs from a tree limb by both arms. Draw a free-body diagram showing the forces on the monkey. (*Hint*: Twenty kilograms is not a force!)

16. The weight of a book resting on a stationary table is 9 N. How much is the normal force on the book?

17. Is it possible to arrange three forces of 100 N, 200 N, and 300 N so they are in equilibrium? If so, draw a diagram.

18. You weigh a bear by making him stand on four scales as shown. Draw a free-body diagram showing all the forces acting on the bear. If his weight is 1,500 newtons, what is the reading on the fourth scale?

UNIT 3

LAWS OF MOTION AND ENERGY

CHAPTER 5
Newton's Laws
of Motion

CHAPTER 6
Energy and Machines

CHAPTER 7
Gravity and Space

Exploring on Your Own

Aerospace scientists face a number of challenges when they launch spacecraft from Earth to a faraway destination, such as Mars. Some of these challenges include having enough energy to get the spacecraft off the ground and landing at the right location. Use common materials to build your own spacecraft. How can you launch and guide it toward a target? Use a notebook to record your drawings, data from your trial launches, and other observations.

Artist concept of Phoenix Mars Lander courtesy of NASA/JPL-Caltech/University of Arizona

106

Newton's Laws of Motion

Over the last 30 years, astronauts on different space missions have brought toys on board to compare how they work on Earth to how they work in "microgravity." During the missions, crew members take out the toys and play with them. Can you imagine trying to jump rope while floating around in the International Space Station? How about throwing a toy boomerang—do you think it would come back to you? Do an Internet search for "toys in space" to learn more about these interesting experiments. This chapter will help you use the laws of motion to explain the motion of objects on Earth, and help you to predict how toys will work in space.

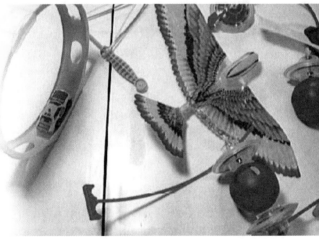

Sir Isaac Newton (1642–1727) discovered answers to many questions about motion. Many historians believe Newton's ideas about motion were the beginning of modern science. Read this chapter and you will know all about motion too!

Key Questions:

1. *Why is a bowling ball harder to move than a golf ball?*

2. *What would happen if Sir Isaac Newton had a skateboard contest with an elephant?*

3. *What happens to the speed of an object as it falls freely?*

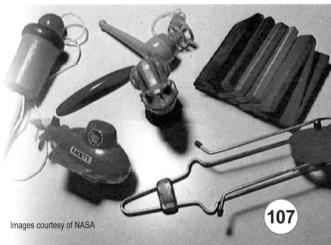

5.1 Newton's First Law

Two of Newton's laws of motion explain the relationship between the forces acting on an object and the object's motion. The third law describes how objects interact with one another. The motion of objects, from soccer balls to skydivers, can be explained using Newton's laws. This section discusses Newton's first law.

Force changes motion

Force and motion   Imagine you are teaching a child to play soccer. You are showing her how to pass the ball to a teammate. What do you do to get the ball to start moving? A force is needed. This force is what changes the ball from being at rest to being in motion. Motion can change only through the action of a force. This statement is the beginning of Newton's first law.

Net force   When the ball is sitting on the ground, there *are* forces acting on it. Earth's gravity pulls the ball downward, and the normal force of the ground pushes upward. These two forces are balanced, so the net force is zero. The ball stays at rest as long as there are no unbalanced forces. When you kick the ball, the force of your foot is not balanced by any other force. This unbalanced force is what changes the motion of the ball (Figure 5.1).

Why objects stop moving   Suppose you kick the ball so it rolls on the ground toward the opposite end of the field. The ball slows down and eventually stops. For a long time, scientists thought the natural state of all things was to be at rest. They believed that force had to keep being applied to keep an object moving. Scientists thought constant motion required a constant force. We now know that this idea is incorrect.

The real explanation   The ball stops because friction acts on it. Suppose the field were perfectly level and had no friction. After being kicked, the ball would keep moving in a straight line at a constant speed forever. The ball would neither slow down nor change direction unless another force acted on it. In a world without friction, the soccer ball would keep going on forever.

Forces are balanced, so the ball stays at rest

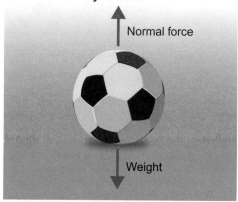

Normal force

Weight

There is an unbalanced force, so the ball starts to move

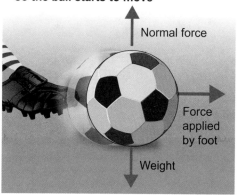

Normal force

Force applied by foot

Weight

Figure 5.1: *An unbalanced force is needed to change the motion of an object.*

The law of inertia

Newton's first law
Newton's first law says objects continue the motion they already have unless they are acted on by a net force greater than zero. When the net force is zero, objects at rest stay at rest and objects that are moving keep moving in the same direction with the same speed.

> *When the net force is zero, objects at rest stay at rest and objects in motion keep moving with the same speed and direction.*

Changing motion
The first law says there can be no change in motion without a net force. An object cannot speed up, slow down, or change direction unless there is a net force acting on it. If forces are truly balanced, a moving object will keep moving forever with the same speed, in the same direction.

Unbalanced forces
Another way to explain whether there is a net force on an object is to use the terms *balanced* and *unbalanced*. Forces are balanced when they add up to zero net force. An object with balanced forces is in equilibrium. An object in equilibrium may either be at rest or may be moving at a constant velocity. Forces are unbalanced when the net force is not exactly zero. Changes in motion come from **unbalanced forces**. A soccer ball rolling on grass is not in equilibrium because friction is an unbalanced force.

Inertia
The first law is often called the "law of inertia" because **inertia** is the property of an object that resists changes in motion. Inertia comes from mass. Objects with more mass have more inertia. To understand inertia, imagine moving a bowling ball and a golf ball that are at rest (Figure 5.2). A golf ball has a mass of 0.05 kilogram, and an average bowling ball has a mass of 5 kilograms. A bowling ball has 100 times the mass of a golf ball, so it has 100 times the inertia. The bowling ball needs more force to start it moving because a bowling ball has more inertia than a golf ball. The greater an object's inertia, the greater the force needed to change its motion.

VOCABULARY

Newton's first law - an object at rest will stay at rest and an object in motion will stay in motion with the same velocity unless acted on by an unbalanced force.

unbalanced forces - result in a net force on an object that can cause changes in motion.

inertia - the property of an object that resists changes in its motion.

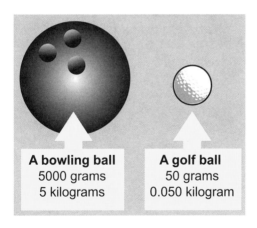

A bowling ball
5000 grams
5 kilograms

A golf ball
50 grams
0.050 kilogram

Figure 5.2: *A bowling ball has more mass than a golf ball. The bowling ball is harder to move because it has more inertia.*

The net force

Multiple forces   When you hit a golf ball, the force from the club is not the only force that acts on the ball (Figure 5.3). The ball's weight, the normal force from the ground, and friction are also acting. Which force determines how the ball moves?

Net force causes motion   You are right if you answered "all forces together." There is almost always more than one force present because gravity acts on all objects. The first law is written in terms of the *net force* because that is what affects motion. Individual forces only matter in that they contribute to the net force.

Adding forces   Recall that force is a vector. When adding up forces, the *directions* of the forces matter. To find the net force, you must include positive and negative signs to account for the directions of the forces.

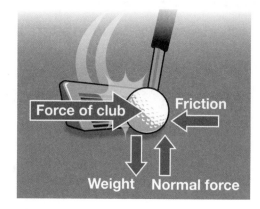

Figure 5.3: *Four forces act on a golf ball. The net force determines how it moves.*

Net force and the first law

A car drives along the highway at constant velocity. Find the car's weight and the friction force if the engine makes a force of 2,000 newtons between the tires and the road, and the normal force on the car is 12,000 N.

1. Looking for: You are asked for the weight and the friction force.

2. Given: You are given the normal force and engine force. The car is moving at a constant velocity.

3. Relationships: Newton's first law states that if the car is moving at a constant velocity, the net force must be zero.

4. Solution: The weight balances the normal force, so the weight is −12,000 N. The engine force balances the friction force, so the friction force is −2,000 N.

Your turn...

a. Identify the forces on the same car if it is stopped at a red light on level ground. **Answer**: The friction force and engine force are zero. The weight and normal force are still each 12,000 N.

b. As you sit on a chair, the chair exerts a normal force of 550 N on you. If you weigh 600 N, what is the normal force of the ground on your feet? **Answer**: 50 N

5.1 Section Review

1. A force is a push or a pull that could change motion. For each of the following situations, identify what creates the force.
   a. A flag flaps back and forth at the top of a flagpole.
   b. A soccer ball is passed from one player to another.
   c. A large piece of hail falls to the ground.
   d. The tide goes from high to low at the shore (you might have to do a little research to get this one if you don't know already).
2. Which has more inertia—a shopping cart full of groceries or an empty shopping cart?

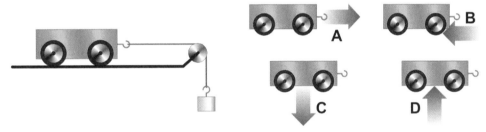

3. Four forces contribute to the net force on a car rolling on a ramp.
   a. Which force is the ramp supporting the car?
   b. Which force accelerates the car along the ramp?
   c. Which force acts against the motion of the car?
4. Imagine whirling a ball on a string over your head. Suppose the knot holding the ball comes loose and the ball is instantly released from the string. What path does the ball take after leaving the string? Use Newton's first law to explain your answer.

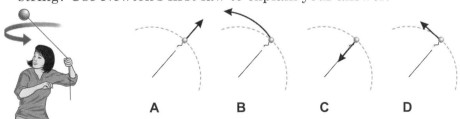

Lightweight vehicles

STEM

Vehicles with less inertia take less force to accelerate. Inertia comes from mass, so in order to reduce inertia you must reduce mass. A car made of paper would have less mass, but it wouldn't be strong enough to use. The mass of a vehicle is a trade-off between strength and inertia. There needs to be enough mass to provide strength, but not so much that a large, gas-wasting engine is required.

(Photo - Courtesy Rutgers University)

1. Research three ways that cars have been designed to have less mass.
2. How was the balance between strength and mass resolved when designing the cars?

5.2 Newton's Second Law

Newton's first law says that a force is needed to change an object's motion. But what kind of change happens? The answer is *acceleration*. According to Newton's second law, the amount of acceleration depends on both the force and the mass.

The three main ideas of the second law

What is the second law about? Newton's first law tells us that motion cannot change without a net force. The second law tells us exactly what kind of change is caused by unbalanced forces. The second law answers questions like: "How much force does it take to change the speed of a 1,000 kg car from 0 to 55 mph?" Anyone who does anything involving motion needs to understand the second law.

The three main ideas There are three main ideas related to the second law.

1. Acceleration is the result of unbalanced forces.

2. A larger force makes a proportionally larger acceleration.

3. Acceleration is inversely proportional to mass.

Unbalanced forces cause acceleration The first law tells us things in motion can continue to move even without any net force. This is true as long as the motion is at a constant speed and in a straight line. The second law says that any unbalanced force results in acceleration. We know that acceleration causes changes in velocity (speed or direction). Putting these two ideas together tells us two things about force and motion: (1) Unbalanced forces cause changes in speed, direction, or both; and (2) any time there is a change in speed or direction, there must be an unbalanced force acting.

Force and motion connect through acceleration The second law is the connection between force, mass, and motion. The connection occurs through *acceleration*, which results in *changes* in speed and/or direction. In fact, the unit of force (newton) is defined by the second law (Figure 5.4).

Newton
One newton (N) is the force it takes to change the speed of a 1 kg mass by 1 m/s in 1 second.

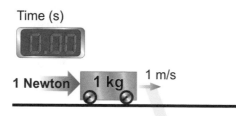

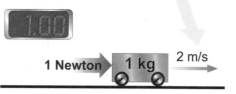

Figure 5.4: *The newton, a unit of force, is defined in terms of the acceleration it can create.*

Acceleration and force

Acceleration is proportional to force

The second law says that acceleration is *proportional* to force. What does that mean? It means that all other things being equal, if the force doubles, the acceleration also doubles. If the force is reduced by half, the acceleration is also reduced by half (Figure 5.5).

Example: A robot mail cart

Here is an example. Two engineers are each asked to design an battery-operated motor for a robot mail cart. The cart is supposed to drive around to people's offices and stop so they can collect their mail. One engineer chooses a motor that produces a force of 50 newtons. The other chooses a motor that produces a force of 100 newtons.

The acceleration of the mail cart

The robot with the smaller motor goes from rest to a top speed of 4 m/s in 4 seconds. The acceleration is 1 m/s^2. The robot with the larger motor accelerates to the same top speed (4 m/s) in 2 seconds. Its acceleration is 2 m/s^2. Both robots have the same top speed. The one with the bigger motor accelerates to its top speed twice as fast because it uses twice as much force. Of course, the one with the bigger motor drains its batteries faster too. There is always a trade-off between performance and battery life.

Acceleration is in the direction of the net force

Another important factor of the second law is that the acceleration is always in the same direction as the net force. A force in the positive direction causes acceleration in the positive direction. A force in the negative direction causes acceleration in the negative direction. A sideways net force causes a sideways acceleration.

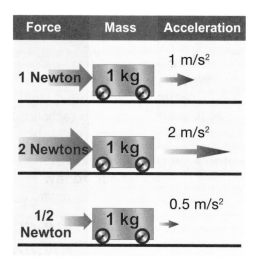

What it means to say
acceleration is proportional to force

Force	Mass	Acceleration
1 Newton	1 kg	1 m/s^2
2 Newtons	1 kg	2 m/s^2
1/2 Newton	1 kg	0.5 m/s^2

Figure 5.5: *"Acceleration is proportional to force" means that if force is increased or decreased, acceleration will be increased or decreased by the same factor.*

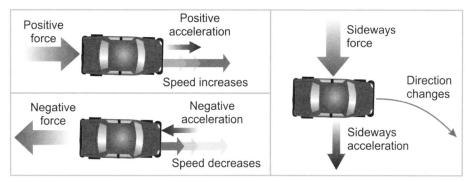

Acceleration and mass

Mass and acceleration

The greater the mass, the smaller the acceleration for a given force (Figure 5.6). That means acceleration is *inversely proportional* to mass. When the forces stay the same, increasing mass decreases the acceleration. For example, an object with twice the mass will have half the acceleration if the same force is applied. An object with half the mass will have twice the acceleration.

Why mass reduces acceleration

Acceleration decreases with mass because mass creates inertia. Remember, inertia is the property of matter that resists changes in motion (acceleration). More mass means more inertia, and therefore more resistance to acceleration.

Newton's second law

Force causes acceleration, and mass resists acceleration. **Newton's second law** relates the net force on an object, the mass of the object, and the object's acceleration.

> *The acceleration caused by a force is proportional to force and inversely proportional to mass.*

The formula for the second law

The relationships between force, mass, and acceleration are combined in the formula for Newton's second law.

NEWTON'S SECOND LAW

$$\text{Acceleration } (m/s^2) \longrightarrow a = \frac{F \longleftarrow \text{Force } (N)}{m \longleftarrow \text{Mass } (kg)}$$

VOCABULARY

Newton's second law - acceleration is force divided by mass.

A **force** acts on a **mass** to cause **acceleration**.

The same **force** acting on **more mass** causes **less acceleration**.

Figure 5.6: *How acceleration is affected by mass.*

Race car design   STEM

Race cars are designed to have strong engines which create large forces between the car and the road. They are also designed to be as light as possible. How does the combination of high forces and low mass affect acceleration? Use Newton's second law to explain.

Applying the second law

Writing the second law You can use Newton's second law to calculate force, mass, or acceleration if two of the three values are known. As you solve problems, keep in mind the concepts shown in Figure 5.7. Larger force leads to larger acceleration. Larger mass leads to smaller acceleration.

Net force and the second law Newton's second law explains the effect of the *net force* on motion. You must consider all the forces that are acting and add them up to find the net force. Then you use the net force to calculate any acceleration. You can also use the second law to work in the other direction, calculating net force from a given mass and acceleration.

To use Newton's second law properly, keep the following important ideas in mind.

1. The *net* force is what causes acceleration.
2. If there is *no* acceleration, the net force *must* be zero.
3. If there *is* acceleration, there *must* also be a net force.
4. The force unit of newtons is based on kilograms, meters, and seconds.

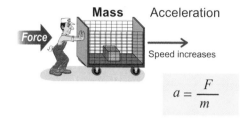

Mass   Acceleration

Force

Speed increases

$$a = \frac{F}{m}$$

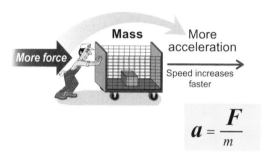

Mass   More acceleration

More force

Speed increases faster

$$a = \frac{F}{m}$$

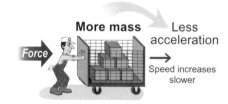

More mass   Less acceleration

Force

Speed increases slower

$$a = \frac{F}{m}$$

Figure 5.7: *More force causes more acceleration, and more mass causes less acceleration.*

Newton's second law

A car has a mass of 1,000 kg. If a net force of 2,000 N is exerted on the car, what is its acceleration?

1. Looking for: You are asked for the car's acceleration.
2. Given: You are given mass (kg) and net force (N).
3. Relationships: acceleration = force ÷ mass
4. Solution: acceleration = (2,000 N) ÷ (1,000 kg) = 2 m/s^2

Your turn...

a. As you coast down a hill on your bicycle, you accelerate at 0.5 m/s^2. If the total mass of your body and the bicycle is 80 kg, with what force is gravity pulling you down the hill? **Answer:** 40 N

5.2 Section Review

1. A 2-kg rabbit starts from rest and is moving at 6 m/s after 3 seconds. What force must the rabbit exert to make this change in speed? (Figure 5.8)

2. Explain how changing force or mass affects the acceleration of an object. Provide one example to support your answer.

3. A tow truck pulls a 1,500-kilogram car with a net force of 4,000 newtons. What is the acceleration of the car?

4. A potato launcher uses a spring that can apply a force of 20 newtons to potatoes. A physics student launched a 100-gram potato, a 150-gram potato, and a 200-gram potato with the launcher. Which potato had the greatest acceleration?

5. An experiment measures the speed of a 250-kilogram motorcycle every 2 seconds (Figure 5.9). The motorcycle moves in a straight line. What is the net force acting on the motorcycle?

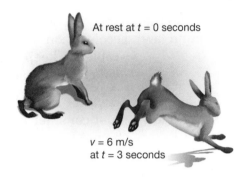

At rest at $t = 0$ seconds

$v = 6$ m/s
at $t = 3$ seconds

Figure 5.8: *Question 1.*

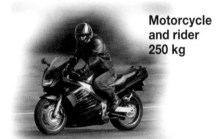

Motorcycle and rider 250 kg

Speed	Time
0 m/s	0 s
5 m/s	2 s
10 m/s	4 s
15 m/s	6 s
20 m/s	8 s

Figure 5.9: *Question 5.*

5.3 Newton's Third Law

Newton's first and second laws apply to the motion of an *individual* object. However, all forces must be applied *by* something. Think about throwing a basketball (Figure 5.10). You feel the ball push back against your hand as you throw it. You know you apply a force to the ball to make it move. Where does the force against your hand come from?

Forces always come in matched pairs

An imaginary skateboard contest Imagine a skateboard contest between Isaac Newton and an elephant. They can only push against each other, not against the ground. The one whose skateboard moves the fastest wins. The elephant knows he is much stronger and pushes off Newton with a huge force thinking he will surely win. But will he?

The winner Newton flies away with a great speed and the puzzled elephant moves backward with a much smaller speed. Newton wins—and will always win this contest against the elephant. No matter how hard the elephant pushes, Newton will always move away faster. Why?

Forces always come in pairs It takes force to make both Newton and the elephant move. Newton wins because *forces always come in pairs*. The elephant pushes against Newton and that *action* force pushes Newton away. The elephant's force against Newton creates a *reaction* force against the elephant. The action and reaction forces are equal in strength. Newton has much less mass so he has much more acceleration.

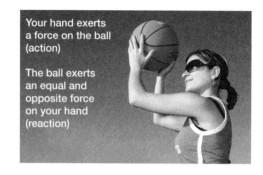

Figure 5.10: *You experience Newton's third law (action-reaction) whenever you apply force to any object, such as a basketball.*

Think of three examples of action-reaction that you experienced before class today. Write each one down and identify the action and reaction forces. Also write down what object each force acted on. (*Hint*: The action and reaction forces never act on the same object.)

The third law: Action and reaction

The first and second laws The first two laws of motion apply to individual objects. The first law says an object will remain at rest or in motion at a constant velocity unless acted upon by a net force. The second law states that acceleration equals the force on an object divided by the mass of the object.

The third law The third law of motion deals with pairs of objects. This is because *all forces come in pairs*. **Newton's third law** states that every action force creates a reaction force that is equal in strength and opposite in direction.

Every action force creates a reaction force that is equal in strength and opposite in direction.

Force pairs There can never be a single force, alone, without its action-reaction partner. Forces *only* come in action-reaction pairs. In the skateboard contest, the force exerted by the elephant (action) moved Newton since it acted on Newton. The reaction force acting back on the elephant was what moved the elephant.

The labels *action* and *reaction* The words *action* and *reaction* are just labels. It does not matter which force is called action and which is called reaction. You simply choose one to call the action and then call the other one the reaction (Figure 5.11).

Why action and reaction forces do not cancel each other out Why don't action and reaction forces cancel each other out? The reason is *action and reaction forces act on different objects*. For example, think again about throwing a ball. When you throw a ball, you apply the action force to the ball, creating the ball's acceleration. The reaction is the ball pushing back against your hand. The action acts on the ball and the reaction acts on your hand. The forces do not cancel each other out because they act on different objects. You can only cancel out forces acting on the same object (Figure 5.12).

VOCABULARY

Newton's third law - for every action force there is a reaction force equal in strength and opposite in direction.

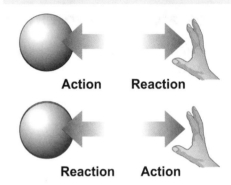

Figure 5.11: *It doesn't matter which force you call the action and which you call the reaction.*

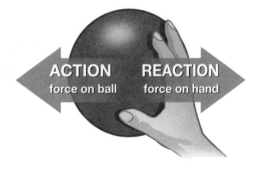

Figure 5.12: *Action and reaction forces do not cancel each other out. One force acts on the ball, and the other force acts on the hand.*

Action and reaction forces

A skateboard example Think carefully about propelling a skateboard with your foot. Your foot presses backward against the ground (Figure 5.13). The force acts *on* the ground. However, *you* move, so a force must act on you, too. Why do you move? What force acts on you? You move because the action force of your foot against the ground creates a reaction force of the ground against your foot. You "feel" the ground because you sense the reaction force pressing on your foot. The reaction force is what makes you move because it acts on *you*.

Draw diagrams When sorting out action and reaction forces, it is helpful to draw diagrams. Draw each object apart from the other. Represent each force as an arrow in the appropriate direction. Here are some guidelines to help you sort out action and reaction forces:

- Both are always there whenever any force appears.
- They always have the exact same strength.
- They always act in opposite directions.
- They always act on different objects.
- Both are real forces and can cause changes in motion.

Action
You pushing on ground

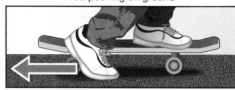

Reaction
Ground pushing on you

Figure 5.13: *You move forward because of the reaction force the ground exerts on your foot.*

Action and reaction

A woman with a weight of 500 N is sitting on a chair. Describe an action-reaction pair of forces.

1. Looking for:	You are asked for a pair of action and reaction forces.
2. Given:	You are given one force in newtons.
3. Relationships:	Action-reaction forces are equal and opposite, and act on different objects.
4. Solution:	The downward force of 500 N exerted by the woman on the chair seat is an action. The chair seat acting on the woman with an upward force of 500 N is a reaction.

Action:
sitting on
a chair

Your turn...

a. A baseball player hits a ball with a bat. Describe an action-reaction pair of forces. **Answer:** The force of the bat on the ball (action) accelerates the ball. The force of the ball on the bat (reaction) slows down the swinging bat.

b. The Earth and the Moon are linked by what action-reaction pair? **Answer:** The Earth attracts the Moon (action) and the Moon attracts the Earth (reaction) in an action-reaction pair. Both action and reaction are due to gravity.

Collisions

The effect of forces   Newton's third law tells us that any time two objects hit each other, they exert equal and opposite forces on each other. However, the *effect* of the force is not always the same. Imagine two hockey players moving at the same speed toward each other, one with twice the mass of the other. The force on each during the collision is the same strength, but they do not have the same change in motion.

Force = 200 N   m = 80 kg   Force = 200 N   m = 40 kg

Figure 5.14: *The car has less inertia, so it accelerates more and may become more damaged than the truck.*

More mass results in less acceleration   The person with more mass has more inertia. More force is needed to change his motion. Because of his greater inertia, the more massive skater will have a smaller change in motion during the collision. The forces on each skater are always exactly equal and opposite. The two skaters have different changes in motion because they have different amounts of inertia, *not because the forces are different.*

Auto collisions   The same is true of vehicles in a collision. When a large truck hits a small car, the forces are equal (Figure 5.14). However, the small car experiences a much greater change in velocity much more rapidly than the big truck.

Safety features   Riding in a vehicle with a large mass does not guarantee passengers will be safe in a collision. Large SUVs are more likely to roll over during accidents. Auto manufacturers conduct crash tests to help them improve the design of cars. Safety features such as seat belts, airbags, and antilock brakes help make cars safer (Figure 5.15).

Figure 5.15: *Safety features help passengers avoid injury during a collision.*

5.3 Section Review

1. Emilio tries to jump to a nearby dock from a canoe that is floating in the water. Instead of landing on the dock, he falls into the water beside the canoe. Use Newton's third law to explain why this happened.

2. Two teams participate in a tug-of-war contest. Describe the action-reaction force pair that will determine who wins the contest. (*Hint*: Action-reaction force pairs act on different objects.)

3. You push backward against the ground to move a skateboard forward. The force you make acts against the ground. What force acts against you to move you forward?

4. Explain why action-reaction forces do not cancel each other out, resulting in zero net force.

5. The engine of a jet airplane pushes fuel backward. That creates a force on the fuel. What pushes the jet forward?

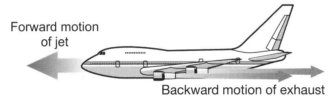

Forward motion of jet

Backward motion of exhaust

6. A child throws a small rubber ball at a heavier, larger basketball that is sitting still. The small ball bounces backward off the basketball. Describe the motion of the basketball after the small ball bounces back. Does it move at all? Does it move faster or slower than the small ball? What direction does it move? How does Newton's third law affect your answer?

SOLVE IT!

Squid Science

Photo courtesy of NOAA

Airplanes are not the only example of jet propulsion. Several animals have adapted jet propulsion in order to get around. A squid takes water into its body chamber and rapidly pushes it out of a backward-facing tube. The water squirts backward and the squid jets forward. What are the action-reaction forces in this example? Draw a diagram to go with your answer.

Most species of squid are small, but *Architeuthis*, the giant squid, is not! In September 2004, Japanese scientists took over 500 photos of a giant squid. The animal was nearly 25 feet long! This was the first ever record of a live giant squid in the wild. Check out http://animals.nationalgeographic.com/animals/invertebrates/giant-squid for more information and photos.

Rockets: Out of This World Travel

What if you wanted to travel to space? What type of vehicle would get you there? You would need to reach incredible speeds to travel huge distances. Speed is also important in overcoming the gravitational pull of planets, moons, and the Sun. Your vehicle would need to be able to travel in a vacuum because space has no air. A rocket would be the best choice, of course!

Rockets and Newton's third law

A rocket is a vehicle with a special type of engine. The basic principle behind how a rocket works is Newton's third law, *for every action, there is an equal and opposite reaction*.

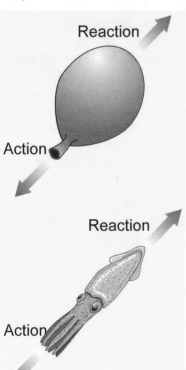

What happens when you blow up a party balloon, then let it go, allowing the air to blow out the open end? The balloon darts around the room, travelling through the air. The *action* is the air moving out. The *reaction* is the movement of the balloon in the opposite direction. Another example is the movement of squid. A squid takes water into its body chamber and rapidly pushes it out of backward-directed tube.

Rocket science

The action/reaction forces demonstrated by the balloon and squid are also at work in a rocket engine. A rocket engine forces material out the nozzle in one direction, causing the rocket to move in the opposite direction.

To break free from Earth's gravity and get into space, a rocket must reach a speed of over 40,250 kilometers per hour (called *escape velocity*). This high speed requires a rocket engine to achieve the greatest possible action force, or *thrust*, in the shortest time. To do this, the engine must burn a large mass of fuel and push the gas out as fast as possible. The speed of the exhaust is very high, often more than 1,000 meters per second. The fuel required to achieve a large amount of thrust weighs over 30 times more than the rocket and its payload (what it carries). Rockets that travel into space are so huge because you need to carry lots of fuel!

Rocket scientists

Robert Goddard (1882–1945), an American scientist, concluded that it was possible to travel to space by applying the kind of thrust demonstrated by the balloon example. Goddard applied his ideas and actually designed and built rockets. He launched the first liquid-fueled rocket in 1926. Perhaps more importantly, Goddard proved rockets can propel objects in a vacuum. His patents and technology innovations would solve the large

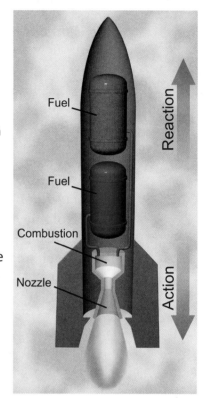

Chapter 5 Connection

problems of rockets in space. There are over 200 patents from Goddard's work.

A little help from gravity

In August 2011, NASA launched Juno, a spacecraft that would orbit the planet Jupiter for about a year. The entire trip covered about 2.8 billion kilometers (1.74 billion miles), which is 18.7 times the distance between Earth and the Sun. Juno was the first mission to Jupiter using solar-powered technology instead of nuclear power.

Robert Goddard, bundled against the cold New England weather of March 16, 1926, holds the launching frame of his most notable invention — the first liquid-fueled rocket.

Juno was launched into space with an Atlas V rocket. Only part of the trip was powered by the energy of the rocket. About 54 minutes after launch, the spacecraft separated from the rocket launcher and began to extend its solar panels. Once the solar panels were deployed and locked, Juno's batteries began to recharge, and it continued its journey under solar power. Juno did not head directly to Jupiter. Its path was planned so it would orbit around the Sun for two years and then make a flyby near Earth to get a slingshot-like boost of speed from Earth's gravity field before turning toward Jupiter. By January 2016, Juno had become the farthest solar-powered spacecraft in the solar system.

The future of rockets

Some new technologies being developed and tested for deep space travel minimize the fuel storage burden, by having their energy sources located behind them. One of these technologies uses the particles from the Sun as a "wind" to accelerate the spacecraft like a sail boat. Another idea uses extremely light gases for fuels to reduce the mass required and increase the distances that can be covered. Still another idea is to find ways to accelerate atomic particles to extremely high speeds, creating thrust more efficiently. Even with these advanced technologies, all rockets rely on the ideas in Newton's laws.

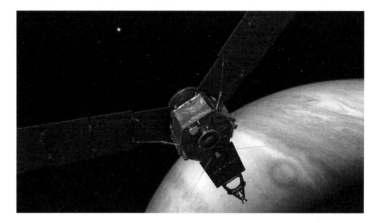

This illustration depicts NASA's Juno spacecraft at Jupiter, with its solar arrays and main antenna pointed toward the distant Sun and Earth.

QUESTIONS

1. How does a rocket achieve a large amount of thrust?
2. Why are rockets for deep space travel so huge?
3. How is a rocket engine different than an automobile engine?
4. What are the major obstacles to bringing humans deeper into space?

Image of Juno courtesy of NASA/JPL-Caltech

Making a Spool Car

Newton's three laws can be used to explain the motion of everyday objects: from a car driving down the highway to the moon orbiting around Earth. The first law says that objects at rest tend to stay at rest and objects in motion tend to stay in motion with constant speed and direction. The second law explains the relationship between force and acceleration ($a = F/m$). According to the third law, an action created by one object results in an equal but opposite reaction on another object. In this activity you will build a car and apply Newton's laws to explain how it works and why it moves as it does.

Materials:

thread spool; assorted rubber bands, approximately 2–3 cm long; metal washer, approximately 2 cm in diameter; piece of masking tape; pencil; paper clip; carpeted floor, rug, or fabric on which to run the car

What you will do

1. Attach a rubber band to the paper clip.

2. Slide the paper clip partially through the center of the spool, leaving the rubber band exposed at one end.

3. Place the washer over the rubber band and slide a pencil through the loop.

4. Push the paper clip through to the other end of the spool.

5. Adjust the paper clip so it lies flat against the spool and holds the rubber band in place. Use a piece of tape to secure it.

6. Turn the pencil several times to twist the rubber band. Place the car on the carpeted floor and release it.

7. Experiment with the car until you can get it to move in a straight line. Adjusting the position of the pencil may be helpful.

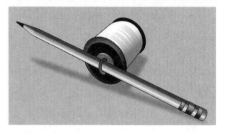

8. Determine the number of turns of the pencil that gives the greatest distance of travel.

9. If time allows, experiment with other rubber bands until you have made a spool car that goes as far and as straight as possible. Race your car against your classmates to determine who has the best car.

10. Try to run your car on a smooth floor and observe what happens.

Applying your knowledge

a. What were you giving to the car when you turned the pencil?

b. Did winding the rubber band a greater number of turns always make the car go farther? Why do you think this is?

c. What was the force that caused the car to move forward?

d. Describe what happened when you ran the car on a smooth floor. Why was there a difference in the motion?

e. Explain how each of Newton's three laws relates to the motion of the car.

Chapter 5 Assessment

Vocabulary

Select the correct term to complete the sentences.

force   unbalanced   inertia

Newton's first law   Newton's second law   Newton's third law

Section 5.1

1. The tendency of an object to resist a change in motion is called ____.

2. An action that is able to change motion is a(n) ____.

3. ____ says that objects continue the motion they already have unless they are acted on by an unbalanced force.

4. If the net force acting on an object is *not* zero, then the forces acting on the object are ____.

Section 5.2

5. The relationship between the force on an object, the mass of the object, and its acceleration is described by ____.

Section 5.3

6. ____ states that every action force creates a reaction force that is equal in strength and opposite in direction.

Concepts

Section 5.1

1. Newton's first law states that no force is required to maintain motion in a straight line at constant speed. If Newton's first law is true, why must you continue to pedal a bicycle on a level surface to keep moving?

2. Two identical-looking, large, round balls are placed in front of you. One is filled with feathers and the other is filled with water. Without picking up the balls, how could you use Newton's first law to distinguish between them?

3. What happens to the inertia of an object if its mass is decreased?

4. What two quantities do you need to include when describing a force?
   a. Speed and direction
   b. Strength and direction
   c. Acceleration and time

Section 5.2

5. Explain the difference between "directly proportional" and "inversely proportional."

6. What does it mean to say that the "net force" determines an object's acceleration?

7. Describe three ways you could cause an acceleration of a moving car.

8. If you are applying the brakes on your bicycle, and you are slowing down, are you accelerating? Why or why not?

9. What is the formula that summarizes Newton's second law?

10. Which of the following is the equivalent unit to a newton?
    a. m/s^2 b. m/s c. $kg \cdot m/s^2$

Section 5.3

11. A brick is sitting on a table. The force of gravity pulls down on the brick. What prevents the brick from accelerating downward and falling through the table?

12. When a bug traveling west hits the windshield of a car traveling east, what can be said about the collision?
    a. The bug feels a stronger force than the car.
    b. The bug and the car feel the same size force.
    c. The car accelerates more than the bug.
    d. The bug does not accelerate due to the force.

Problems

Section 5.1

1. While an object is moving at a constant 20 m/s, a 5-N force pushes the object to the left. At the same time, a 5-N force is pushing the object to the right. What will the object's velocity be after 10 seconds?

2. A bowling ball has a mass of 6 kg. A tennis ball has a mass of 0.06 kg. How much inertia does the bowling ball have compared to the tennis ball?

3. A rider and motorcycle with a combined mass of 250 kg are driving down the road at a constant speed of 55 mph. The motorcycle's engine is producing a force of 1,700 newtons between the tires and the road.

    a. Find the weight of the motorcycle and rider in newtons.
    b. Find the normal force of the road on the motorcycle and rider.
    c. Find the frictional force of the road and air on the motorcycle and rider.

4. What is the net force on the refrigerator shown to the right?

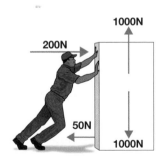

Section 5.2

5. What force is needed to accelerate a 1,000-kg car from a stop to 5 m/s^2?

6. What is the acceleration of a truck with a mass of 2,000 kg when its brakes apply a force of 10,000 N?

7. A 20-N force accelerates a baseball at 140 m/s^2 (briefly!). What is the mass of the baseball?

8. Gina is pushing a 10-kg box with 50 N of force toward the east. Dani is pushing the same box at the same time with 100 N of force toward the west. Assuming there is no friction, what is the acceleration of the box?

9. A cheetah can accelerate at 7 m/s^2, and the average cheetah has a mass of 40 kg. With what average force does the cheetah push against the ground?

10. A car speeds up from 5 m/s to 29 m/s over 4 seconds.

    a. What is the car's acceleration?
    b. If the car had started at 29 m/s and ended at 5 m/s after 4 seconds, what would its acceleration be? How is this different from the answer above?

Section 5.3

11. Identify at least three action-reaction pairs in the picture of the firefighter below.

12. Jane has a mass of 40 kg. She pushes on a 50-kg rock with a force of 100 N. What force does the rock exert on Jane?

13. A 3,000-kg car collides with a 5,000-kg truck. The acceleration of the car due to the force of the collision is 2 m/s^2. What is the acceleration of the truck due to the force of the collision?

Chapter 6

Energy and Machines

Look around you. Do you see any changes taking place? Is a light bulb giving off heat and light? Is the Sun shining? Are your eyes moving across the page while you read this introduction? When an object falls toward Earth, when you play a sport or a musical instrument, when your alarm clock wakes you up in the morning, and when a bird flies through the air, there are changes taking place that could not occur without the effects of energy.

Energy is everywhere! Energy is responsible for explaining how the world works. As you read this chapter, think about the examples you'll find (including weight lifting, bicycling, and eating) and see if you can identify the forms of energy that are responsible for the changes that take place in each system. Can you identify the different forms of energy in the picture?

Key Questions:

1. What is energy?

2. What does it mean to conserve energy?

3. What is "work" to a physicist?

6.1 Energy and the Conservation of Energy

Without energy, nothing could ever change. Pure energy itself cannot be smelled, tasted, touched, seen, or heard. However, energy does appear in many forms, such as motion and heat. Energy can travel in different ways, such as in light and sound waves and in electricity. The workings of the entire universe (including all of our technology) depend on energy flowing and changing back and forth from one form to another.

What is energy?

A definition of energy *Energy* is a quantity that measures the ability to change. Anything with energy can change itself or cause change in other objects or systems. Energy can cause changes in temperature, speed, position, momentum, pressure, or other physical variables. Energy can also cause change in materials, such as burning wood changing into ashes and smoke.

Energy measures the ability to change in a physical system.

Examples
- A gust of wind has energy because it can move objects in its path.
- A piece of wood in a fireplace has energy because it can produce heat and light.
- You have energy because you can change the motion of your body.
- Batteries have energy; they can be used in a radio to make sound.
- Gasoline has energy; it can be burned in an engine to move a car.
- A ball at the top of a hill has energy because it can roll down the hill and move objects in its path.

Units of energy The unit of measurement for energy is the **joule** (J). One joule is the energy needed to push with a force of 1 newton over a distance of 1 meter. The joule is an abbreviation for one newton multiplied by 1 meter. If you push on your calculator with a force of 1 newton while it moves a distance of 1 meter across a table, 1 joule of your energy is converted into the energy of the calculator's motion.

VOCABULARY

joule - a unit of energy. One joule is enough energy to push with a force of 1 newton for a distance of 1 meter.

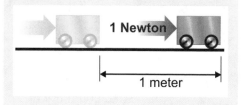
1 Newton

1 meter

Energy from food

We get energy from eating food. The *calorie* is a unit of energy often used for food. One food calorie equals 4,187 joules.

Systems and variables

Defining a system
The universe is huge and complex. The only way to make sense of it is to think about only a small part at a time. If you want to understand a car rolling down a ramp, you don't need to concern yourself with the Sun, or the Milky Way galaxy, or even the room next door. When you want to understand something, you focus your attention on a small group called a **system**. A system is a group of objects, effects, and variables that are related. You set up the system to include the things you wish to investigate and exclude the things that don't matter.

Variables
When you are trying to find out how a system works, you look for relationships between the important variables of the system. For example, imagine you are doing an experiment with a car rolling down a ramp. The car and ramp are the system. The car's speed is one important variable. Time, position, mass, and the angle of the ramp are other variables.

VOCABULARY

system - a group of objects, effects, and variables that are related.

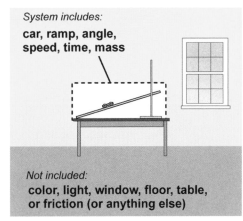

System includes:

car, ramp, angle, speed, time, mass

Not included:
color, light, window, floor, table, or friction (or anything else)

Figure 6.1: *Choose variables that are important to your investigation.*

Some important variables in this system

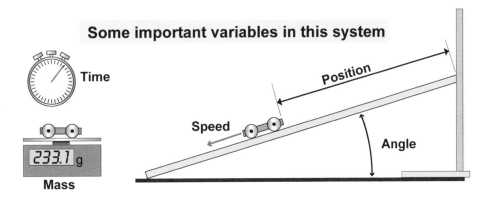

Time

233.1 g

Mass

Position

Speed

Angle

What to include
The ideal choice of a system includes all the objects, effects, and variables that affect what you are trying to understand (Figure 6.1). To understand the motion of a car on a ramp you might include the car, the ramp, and the mass, angle, and speed. The fewer the variables, the easier it is to find important relationships. You can include more variables, like friction from the wheels, after you understand how the more important variables fit together (Figure 6.2).

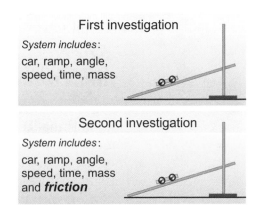

First investigation

System includes:
car, ramp, angle, speed, time, mass

Second investigation

System includes:
car, ramp, angle, speed, time, mass
and ***friction***

Figure 6.2: *You may change the system later to include new objects, effects, or variables.*

The law of conservation of energy

Kinds of energy Energy appears in many forms, such as heat, motion, height, pressure, electricity, and chemical bonds between atoms.

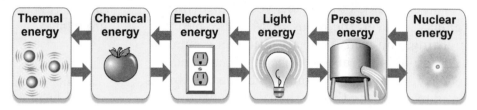

Energy transformations Systems change as energy flows from one part of the system to another. Parts of the system may speed up, slow down, get warmer or colder, or change in other measurable ways. Each change transfers energy or *transforms* energy from one form to another. Friction transforms energy of motion to energy of heat. A bow and arrow transform energy in a stretched bow into energy of motion of an arrow (Figure 6.3).

Law of conservation of energy Energy can never be created or destroyed, just converted from one form into another. The idea that energy converts from one form into another without a change in the total amount is called the **law of conservation of energy**. The law of conservation of energy is one of the most important laws in physics. It applies to all forms of energy.

Energy can never be created or destroyed, just converted from one form into another.

Energy has to come from somewhere The law of conservation of energy tells us energy cannot be created from nothing. If energy increases somewhere, it must *decrease* somewhere else. The key to understanding how systems change is to trace the flow of energy. Once we know how energy flows and transforms, we have a good understanding of how a system works. When we use energy to drive a car, that energy comes from chemical energy stored in gasoline. As we use the energy, the amount left in the form of gasoline decreases.

Figure 6.3: *A stretched bowstring on a bent bow has energy, so it is able to create change in itself and in the arrow.*

Following an energy transformation

An experiment in energy You may do an experiment in class that follows a rolling marble up and down a hilly track. The marble starts slow then speeds up as it rolls down the first hill. The marble slows down almost to a stop as it rolls up and over the second hill. The marble speeds up again as it rolls down the second hill. How do we explain the changes in the speed of the marble? The easiest way is to think about energy.

Potential energy The marble and the track are a system. This system has two major kinds of energy called *potential energy* and *kinetic energy*. **Potential energy** is energy due to *position*. Potential energy depends on mass, height, and the acceleration due to gravity. When you lift the marble off the ground it gets potential energy because of its height. The higher you lift it, the more potential energy it has.

Kinetic energy **Kinetic energy** is energy of motion that depends on an object's mass and velocity. The faster the marble moves, the more kinetic energy it has; it has zero kinetic energy at the start because it is not moving. The marble has the most kinetic energy when its speed is greatest.

Using the law of conservation of energy Assume the system starts with the marble at the top of the first hill (Figure 6.4). *Conservation of energy says the total energy stays the same as the marble moves up and down.* As the marble moves down, it loses potential energy. Where does the energy go? It changes into kinetic energy which is why the marble speeds up. To get up the hill the marble needs potential energy. It can only get it by reducing its kinetic energy. That is why the marble slows down as it goes up. Its kinetic energy is being changed into potential energy. The potential energy changes back into kinetic energy again as the marble rolls down the last hill.

VOCABULARY

potential energy - energy of position.

kinetic energy - energy of motion.

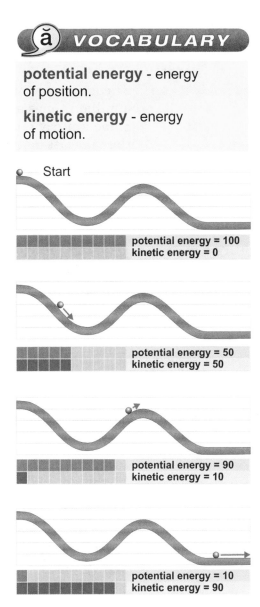

Figure 6.4: *The main energy transformations that occur as the marble moves up and down the track.*

Energy in your life

Common units of energy A joule is a tiny amount of energy compared to what you use every day. One joule is just enough energy to lift a pint of ice cream 21 centimeters off the table. That same pint of ice cream releases 3 million times as much energy when it is digested by your body! Some units of energy that are more appropriate for everyday use are the kilowatt hour, food calorie, and British thermal unit (Figure 6.5).

Daily energy use The table below gives some average values for the energy used by humans in daily activities.

Table 6.1: Daily energy use in different energy units

Activity	Kwh	Joules	Gallons of gas
Climb a flight of stairs	0.017	60,000	0.0005
Use an electric light for 1 hour	0.1	360,000	0.003
Cook an average meal	1	3,600,000	0.03
Cut the grass	18	65,000,000	0.5
Drive 30 miles to the mall and back in a small, efficient car	36	130,000,000	1
Drive 30 miles to the mall and back in a large SUV	72	260,000,000	2

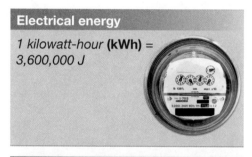

Electrical energy

1 kilowatt-hour **(kWh)** = *3,600,000 J*

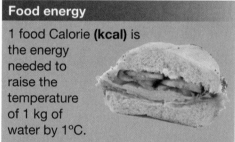

Food energy

1 food Calorie **(kcal)** is the energy needed to raise the temperature of 1 kg of water by 1°C.

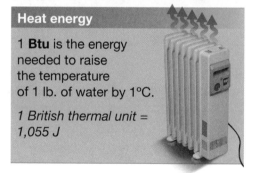

Heat energy

1 **Btu** is the energy needed to raise the temperature of 1 lb. of water by 1°C.

1 British thermal unit = *1,055 J*

Figure 6.5: *Energy units you might use in daily life.*

"Using" and "conserving" energy in the everyday sense

"Conserving" energy

STEM

Almost everyone has heard that is good to "conserve energy" and not waste it. This is good advice because energy from gasoline or electricity costs money and uses resources. But what does it mean to "use energy" in the everyday sense? If energy can never be created or destroyed, how can it be "used up"? Why do smart people worry about "running out" of energy?

"Using" energy

When you "use" energy by turning on a light, you are really converting energy from one form (electricity) to other forms (light and heat). What gets "used up" is the amount of energy *in the form of electricity*. Electricity is a valuable form of energy because it is easy to move over long distances (through wires). In the "physics" sense, the energy is not "used up," but converted into other forms. The total amount of energy stays constant.

Power plants

Electric power plants don't *make* electrical energy. Energy cannot be created. What power plants do is convert other forms of energy (chemical, solar, nuclear) into electrical energy. When someone asks you to turn out the lights to conserve energy, they are asking you to use less electrical energy. If people used less electrical energy, power plants would burn less oil, gas, or other fuels in "producing" the electrical energy they sell.

"Running out" of energy

Many people are concerned about "running out" of energy. What they worry about is running out of certain *forms* of energy that are easy to use, such as oil and gas. At the beginning of the industrial age, the planet Earth had a certain amount of oil and gas. It took millions of years to accumulate and once it is used up, there will be no more. When you use gas in a car, the chemical energy in the gasoline mostly becomes heat energy. It is impractical to put the energy back into the form of gasoline, so we say the energy has been "used up" even though the energy itself is still there, only in a different form. Other forms of energy, such as flowing water, wind, and solar energy are not as limited. Many scientists hope our society will make a transition to these forms of energy over the next 100 years.

Switch to fluorescent bulbs

75 W Incandescent bulb

Same amount of light!

20 W Compact fluorescent bulb

There are about 300 million people in the United States. If an average house has four light bulbs per person, it adds up to 1.2 billion light bulbs. One kwh of electrical energy will light a bulb for 10 hours. Adding up four bulbs per person totals 120 million kwh every hour just for light bulbs!

An average electric power plant puts out 1 million kwh of electrical energy per hour. That means 120 power plants are burning up resources each hour just to run light bulbs! Regular (incandescent) light bulbs convert only 10 percent of electrical energy to light. Fluorescent bulbs make the same amount of light with one quarter the electrical energy. If everyone switched from incandescent bulbs to fluorescent bulbs we would save 75 percent of the electricity currently used for lighting!

6.1 Section Review

1. Write a paragraph about a system inside your home or school building. Describe what the system does as a whole. Describe at least three parts of the system. Describe how each part contributes to the function of the whole system.

2. Scientists would like to understand many things that are large and complex, like the ecology of Earth. Scientists divide complex things into smaller groups called *systems* because
   a. it is easier to understand a small group than a large, complex thing.
   b. there is not enough money to study the entire complex thing.

3. Write the law of conservation of energy in your own words. How does it apply to eating and exercising?

4. A marble rolls down a hilly track as shown in Figure 6.6. At what place on the track will the marble have the greatest speed (A, B, C, or D)? Why do you think this is so?

5. Arrange the four energy units from largest to smallest
   a. joule (J)
   b. kilowatt hour (kwh)
   c. British thermal unit (Btu)
   d. food calorie (kcal)

6. Imagine you are the teacher of a science class. A student brings in a newspaper article that claims the world will run out of energy by the year 2050 because all the oil will be pumped out of the planet. The student is confused because she has learned in your class that energy can never be created or destroyed. How would you explain to her what "running out of energy" means in the article?

7. List two ways that you can conserve each of the following forms of energy.
   a. electrical energy
   b. gasoline

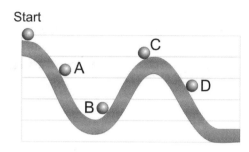

Start

Figure 6.6: *Question 4.*

CHALLENGE

Research what is going on in your community regarding energy conservation. Write about a project designed to save energy that is being planned or is already implemented. How much energy has been or might be saved?

CHALLENGE

Every month your family pays an electric bill for energy you have used. Research the cost of electricity in your area. How much does it cost for 1 million joules? This is the amount of energy used by a single electric light bulb in 3 hours.

6.2 Work and Power

Energy is a measure of an object's ability to do work. Suppose you lift your book over your head. The book gets potential energy which comes from your action. Now suppose you lift your book fast, then lift it again slowly. The energy is the same because the height is the same. But it feels different to transfer the energy fast or slow. The difference between moving energy fast or slow is described by *power*. Power is the rate at which energy flows or at which work is done. This section is about power and its relation to work and energy.

ⓐ VOCABULARY

work - a form of energy that comes from force applied over distance. A force of 1 newton does 1 joule of work when the force causes 1 meter of motion in the direction of the force.

The scientific meaning of *work*

Work means different things

The word *work* is used in many different ways.

- You should always check over your *work* before handing in a test.
- Your parents go to *work*.
- The toaster doesn't *work*.
- You *work* with other students on a group project.

What *work* means in physics

In science, **work** has a different, and very specific meaning. Work is a kind of energy you either use or get when a force is applied over a distance. Work is energy and is measured in joules, just like other kinds of energy.

Work is a form of energy that comes from force applied over distance.

Work is measured in joules

You do 1 joule of work if you push with a force of 1 newton for a distance of 1 meter (Figure 6.7). You may remember this is exactly the definition given for the joule, the unit of energy. Energy is defined in terms of the amount of work that can be done. If you have a lot of energy, you can do a lot of work, meaning you can push with a large force for a great distance. Science makes the everyday meaning of work much more precise. By making work equal to force multiplied by distance we can calculate exactly how much work is done in any given situation.

Figure 6.7: *A force of 1 newton applied for 1 meter does 1 joule of work on the block.*

Work and energy

Work and potential energy   Doing work always means transferring energy. The energy may be transferred to the object you apply the force to, or it may go somewhere else. You can increase the potential energy of a rubber band by exerting a force that stretches it. The work you do stretching the rubber band is stored as energy in the rubber band. The rubber band can then use the energy to do work on a paper airplane, giving it kinetic energy (Figure 6.8).

Work may not increase the energy of an object   You can do work on a block by sliding it across a level table. In this example, though, the work you do does not increase the energy of the block. Because the block will not slide back all by itself, it does not gain the ability to do work *itself*, therefore it gains no energy. The work you do to slide the block is done to overcome friction. The block does gain a tiny bit of energy because its temperature rises slightly from the friction. However, that energy comes from the force of friction, not from your applied force.

Not all force does work

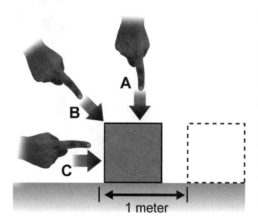

1 meter

Sometimes force is applied to an object, but no work is done. If you push down on a block sitting on a table and it doesn't move, you have not done any work (force A) *in the scientific sense*. You used your muscles but your force did not cause the block to move and therefore no work was done. Work is only done when forces cause motion.

Force at an angle to distance   There are times when only *some* of a force does work. Force B is applied at an angle to the direction of motion of a block. Only a portion of the force is in the direction the block moves, so only that portion of the force does work. The most effective force is force C. All of force C acts in the same direction the block moves.

Work done stretching a rubber band increases its potential energy.

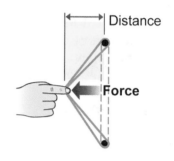

Distance

Force

The rubber band can then do work on the plane, giving it kinetic energy.

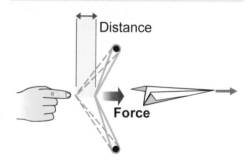

Distance

Force

Figure 6.8: *You can do work to increase an object's potential energy. Then the potential energy can be converted to kinetic energy.*

Calculating work in joules

Work equals force multiplied by distance To calculate work, you multiply the force by the distance the object moves in the direction of the force. If you lift a block with a weight of 1 newton for a distance of 1 meter, you do 1 joule of work. One joule of energy is transferred from your body to the block, changing the block's energy.

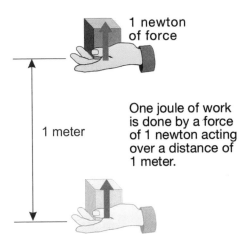

1 newton of force

1 meter

One joule of work is done by a force of 1 newton acting over a distance of 1 meter.

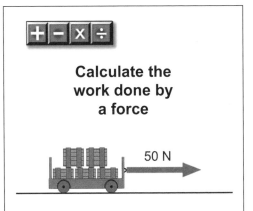

Calculate the work done by a force

50 N

How much work is done by a person who pulls a cart with a force of 50 newtons if the cart moves 20 meters in the direction of the force?

1. You are asked for work.
2. You are given force and distance.
3. Work = force × distance.
4. The work done is: 50 N × 20 m = 100 joules.

Your turn...

a. How far does a 100-newton force have to move to do 1,000 joules of work?
   Answer: 10 meters
b. An electric hoist does 500 joules of work lifting a crate 2 meters. How much force does the hoist use?
   Answer: 250 N

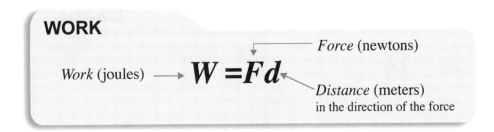

WORK

Work (joules) ⟶ $W = Fd$

Force (newtons)

Distance (meters) in the direction of the force

Work is done on objects When thinking about work you should always be clear about which force is doing the work on which object. Work is done *by* forces. Work is done *on* objects. If you lift a block 1 meter with a force of 1 newton, you have done 1 joule of work *on the block.*

Energy is needed to do work An object that has energy is able to do work; without energy, it is impossible to do work. In fact, one way to think about energy is as *stored work.* Anything that has energy can use that energy to do work. A falling block has kinetic energy that can be used to do work. If the block hits a ball, it will do work on the ball and change the ball's motion. Some of the block's energy is transferred to the ball during the collision.

Power

What is power? Suppose Michael and Jim each lift a barbell weighing 100 newtons from the ground to a height of 2 meters (Figure 6.9). Michael lifts quickly and Jim lifts slowly. Michael and Jim do the same amount of work. However, Michael's *power* is greater because he gets the work done in less time. **Power** is the rate at which work is done.

Units of power The unit for power is the unit of work (joules) divided by the unit of time (seconds). One **watt** is equal to 1 joule per second. The watt was named after James Watt, the Scottish engineer who invented the steam engine. Another unit of power is the **horsepower**. Watt expressed the power of his engines as the number of horses an engine could replace. One horsepower is equal to 746 watts.

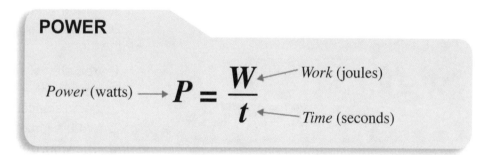

POWER

$$\text{Power (watts)} \longrightarrow P = \frac{W}{t} \begin{array}{l} \longleftarrow \text{Work (joules)} \\ \longleftarrow \text{Time (seconds)} \end{array}$$

Calculating work Michael and Jim do the same work since they lift the same weight the same distance. Use the relationship *work = force × distance*. The force is the weight of the barbell (100 N). The work is 100 N × 2 m = 200 J. Each of them does 200 joules of work.

Calculating power Michael's power is his work (200 joules) divided by his time (1 second). Michael has a power of 200 watts. Jim's power is 200 joules divided by 10 seconds. Jim's power is 20 watts. Jim takes 10 times as long to lift the barbell, so his power is one-tenth as much. The maximum power output of an average person is a few hundred watts.

VOCABULARY

power - the rate of doing work or moving energy. Power is equal to energy (or work) divided by time.

watt - a power of 1 joule per second.

horsepower - a unit of power equal to 746 watts.

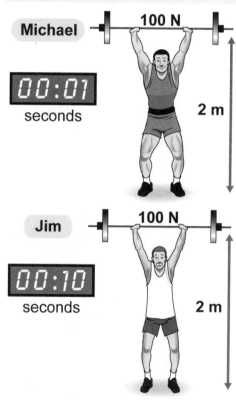

Figure 6.9: *Michael and Jim do the same amount of work but do not have the same power.*

6.2 Section Review

1. A man pushes a television crate across the floor with a force of 200 newtons. How much work does he do if the crate moves 20 meters in the same direction as the force?

2. How much work can be done with 10 joules of energy?

3. A certain battery contains 20 joules of energy. The battery is connected to a perfect motor which uses 100 percent of the energy to make force.

   a. For how much distance can a 2-newton force push?

   b. How large a force can be sustained for 5 meters?

4. A bottle rocket is a toy that is made from an empty soda bottle. A bicycle pump is used to pump air into the bottle (Figure 6.10). The rocket shoots upward when it is released from the launcher, allowing the high-pressure air to come out.

   a. Work is done as the pump is pushed, forcing air into the bottle. What happens to this work? Does it just disappear?

   b. Suppose a person does 2,000 joules of work using the pump. What is the maximum kinetic energy the rocket can have after it is launched?

   c. Do you think the rocket could actually have this much kinetic energy? Explain why or why not.

5. An average car engine can produce about 100 horsepower. How many 100-watt light bulbs does it take to use the same amount of power?

6. A cup of ice cream contains about 200 food calories. How much power can be produced if the energy in a cup of ice cream is expended over a period of 10 minutes (600 seconds)? Each food calorie is equal to 4,184 joules.

7. A gallon of gasoline contains about 36 kilowatt hours of energy. A gallon of gas cost $2.50. A kilowatt hour of electricity costs 8¢. Which form of energy is less expensive?

8. Work is force × distance. What is power × time?

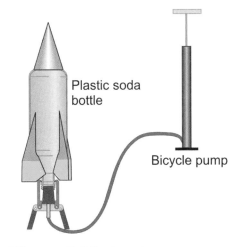

Plastic soda bottle

Bicycle pump

Figure 6.10: *Question 4.*

6.3 Simple Machines

How do you move something that is too heavy to carry? How do you pry open a tight lid? How do you transfer pedaling motion to the wheels on a bicycle? The answer to these questions has to do with the use of simple machines. In this section, you will learn how simple machines multiply forces to accomplish many tasks.

Using machines

What technology allows us to do

Machines allow us to do incredible things. Moving huge steel beams, digging tunnels that connect two islands, and building 100-story skyscrapers are examples. What makes these things possible? Have we developed super powers since the days of our ancestors?

What is a machine?

In a way, we *have* developed super powers. Our powers come from the clever human invention of machines. A **machine** is a device, like a bicycle, with moving parts that work together to accomplish a task (Figure 6.11). All the parts of a bicycle work together to transform forces from your muscles into motion. A bicycle allows you to travel at faster speeds and for greater distances than you could on foot.

Work output is forward motion

Work input is force applied to pedals

The concepts of input and output

Machines are designed to do something. To understand how a machine works, think about **input** and **output**. The *input* includes everything you do to make the machine work, like pushing on the bicycle pedals. The *output* is what the machine does for you, like going fast or climbing a steep hill. For the machines in this chapter, the input and output may be force, power, or energy.

VOCABULARY

machine - a device with moving parts that work together to accomplish a task.

input - forces, energy, or power supplied to make a machine work.

output - the forces, energy, or power provided by the machine.

Parts of a Bicycle

Gears Pedals
Wheels

Figure 6.11: *A bicycle contains machines working together.*

Simple machines

The beginning of technology
The development of cars, airplanes, and other modern machines began with the invention of **simple machines**. A simple machine (such as a lever) is an unpowered mechanical device that accomplishes a task with only one movement. A lever allows you to move a rock that weighs 10 times (or more) what you weigh (Figure 6.12). Some important types of simple machines are shown below.

VOCABULARY

simple machine - an unpowered mechanical device that accomplishes a task with only one movement.

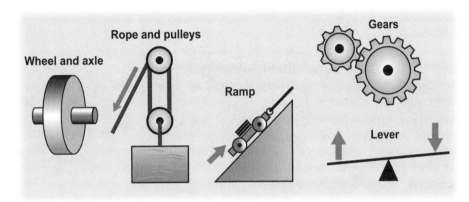

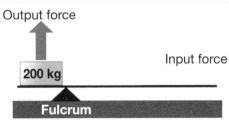

Figure 6.12: *A small input force can create a large output force if a lever is arranged correctly.*

Input force and output force
Simple machines work with forces. The *input force* is the force you apply to the machine. The *output force* is the force the machine applies to what you are trying to move. Figure 6.12 shows how a lever is arranged to create a large output force from a small input force.

Ropes and pulleys
A rope and pulley system is a simple machine made by connecting a rope to one or more pulleys. You apply the input force to the rope and the output force is applied to the load you are lifting. One person could easily lift an elephant with a properly-designed system of ropes and pulleys (Figure 6.13).

Machines within machines
Most of the machines we use today are made up of combinations of different types of simple machines. For example, the bicycle uses wheels and axles, levers (the pedals and kickstand), and gears. If you look closely at a complex machine such as a tow truck or a tower crane, you will find simple machines working together.

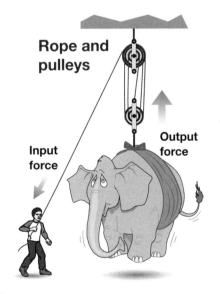

Figure 6.13: *A simple machine made with a rope and pulleys allows one person to lift tremendous loads.*

Work and machines

Input and output work A simple machine does work because it applies a force over a distance. If you are using the machine, you also do work, because you apply force to the machine to make it move. By definition, a simple machine has no source of energy except the immediate forces you apply. That means the only way to get output work *from* a simple machine is to do input work *on* the machine. In fact, the output work done by a simple machine can never exceed the input work done on the machine.

The output work of a simple machine is always less than, or equal to, the input work.

Perfect machines In a *perfect* machine the output work exactly equals the input work. Of course, there are no perfect machines. Friction always converts some of the input work to heat and wear, so the output work is always *less* than the input work. However, for a well-designed machine, friction can be minimal and we can often assume input and output work are approximately equal.

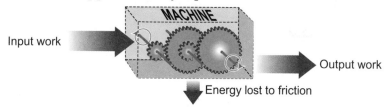

An example Figure 6.14 shows a perfect machine that lifts a 10-newton weight a distance of 0.5 meters. The machine does output work of 5 joules (10 N × 0.5 m). How much input work must be supplied?

This simple machine has been designed to multiply force. Notice that the input force is only 5 newtons! That means the input distance must be 1 meter because 5 N × 1 m = 5 J. You must do 5 joules of input work get 5 joules of output work. Since the input force is half, you have to apply the input force for twice the distance.

The cost of multiplying force The output work of a machine can never be greater than the input work. This is a rule that is *true for all machines*. When you design a machine that multiplies force, you pay by having to apply the force over a greater distance.

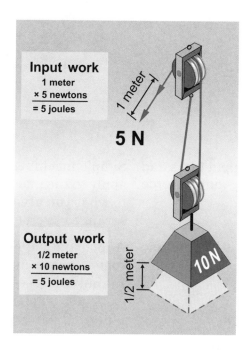

Figure 6.14: *In a perfect machine the output work equals the input work, even though the forces are different.*

Real machines and efficiency

Efficiency The efficiency of a machine is the ratio of work output to work input. Efficiency is usually expressed in percent. A perfect machine has an **efficiency** of 100 percent. That means the output work exactly equals the input work. No energy is diverted by friction or other factors.

Perfect machines are impossible Because some friction is always present, *perfect machines are impossible!* The bicycle is one of the most efficient machines ever made. A good bicycle can convert 95 percent of the input work of your muscles into output work (motion).

Calculating efficiency You calculate efficiency by dividing the output work by the input work. A machine that is 75 percent efficient can produce three joules of output work for every four joules of input work (Figure 6.15). That means that 1 joule out of every 4 (25 percent) is lost to friction.

Real machines

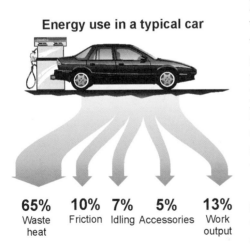

Energy use in a typical car

65%	10%	7%	5%	13%
Waste heat	Friction	Idling	Accessories	Work output

In real machines, the output work is less than the input work because of friction. When analyzing a machine, it helps to think like the diagram at the left. The input work is divided between output work and "losses" due to friction. You can see that cars are not very efficient at using the energy in gasoline. Only 13 percent of the energy in a gallon of gas is transformed into output work. Engineers are constantly working to improve the efficiency of cars.

Improving efficiency An important way to increase the efficiency of a machine is to reduce friction. Ball bearings and oil reduce rolling friction. Slippery materials like you would find in nonstick cookware reduce sliding friction. Designing a car with a streamlined shape reduces air friction. All these techniques increase efficiency.

efficiency - the ratio of output work divided by input work. Efficiency is often expressed as a percent with a perfect machine having 100 percent efficiency.

A machine with 75% efficiency

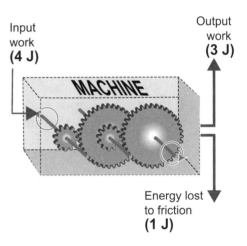

Input work
(4 J)

Output work
(3 J)

MACHINE

Energy lost to friction
(1 J)

Figure 6.15: *If the input work is 4 joules, and the output work is 3 joules, then the efficiency is 75 percent.*

Mechanical advantage and levers

Example of a lever You can make a lever by balancing a board on a log (Figure 6.16). Pushing down on one end of the board lifts a load on the other end of the board. The downward force you apply is the input force. The upward force the board exerts on the rock is the output force.

Parts of the lever All levers include a stiff structure that rotates around a fixed point called the *fulcrum*. The side of the lever where the input force is applied is called the *input arm*. The *output arm* is the end of the lever that applies the output force. Levers are useful because you can arrange the fulcrum and the input and output arms to make the output force much larger than the input force.

Mechanical advantage **Mechanical advantage** is the ratio of output force divided by input force. If a machine has a mechanical advantage of 2, then the output force is 2 times the input force. When the fulcrum is in the center, the input and output forces are the same. The mechanical advantage is 1.

Multiplying force The input and output forces are different if the fulcrum is not in the center. The side of the lever with the longer arm has the smaller force. If the input arm is 3 times longer than the output arm, the output force is 3 times greater than the input force. This lever has a mechanical advantage of 3.

Mechanical advantage of a lever Levers are found in many common machines. Pliers, a wheelbarrow, and even your arm work as levers. Levers are classified as one of three types, or classes, defined by the location of the input and output forces relative to the fulcrum (Figure 6.17).

mechanical advantage - the ratio of output force divided by input force.

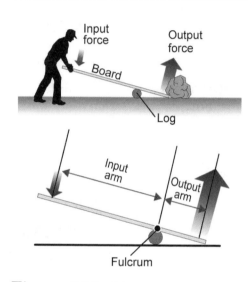

Figure 6.16: *A board and log can make a lever used to lift a rock.*

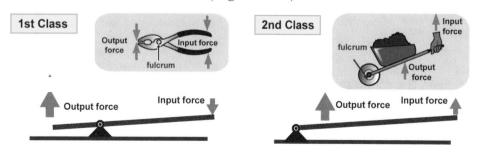

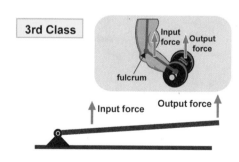

Figure 6.17: *The classes of levers.*

Ropes and pulleys

Tension in ropes and strings Ropes and strings carry *tension* forces along their length. The tension is the same at every point in a rope. If the rope is not moving, its tension is equal to the force pulling on each end (below). Ropes or strings do *not* carry pushing forces.

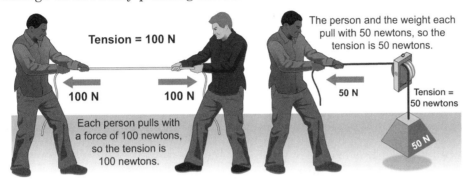

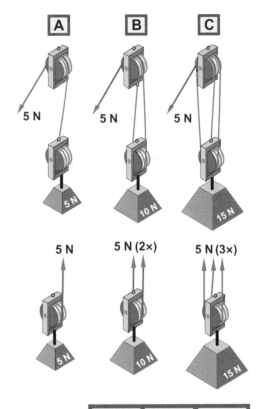

The forces in a pulley system Figure 6.18 shows three different configurations of ropes and pulleys. Imagine pulling with an input force of 5 newtons. In case A the load feels a force equal to your input force. In case B there are 2 strands of rope supporting the load, so the load feels 2 times your input force. In case C there are 3 strands, so the output force is 3 times your input force.

Mechanical advantage The mechanical advantage of a pulley system depends on the number of strands of rope directly supporting the load. In case C, three strands directly support the load, so the output force is three times the input force. The mechanical advantage is 3. To make a rope and pulley system with a greater mechanical advantage, you can increase the number of strands directly supporting the load by using more pulleys.

Work To raise the load 1 meter in case C, the input end of the rope must be pulled for 3 meters. This is because *each* of the 3 supporting strands must shorten by 1 meter. The mechanical advantage is 3, but the input force must be applied for 3 times the distance as the output force. This is another example of the rule stating that output and input work are equal for a perfect machine.

	A	B	C
Input force	5 N	5 N	5 N
Output force	5 N	10 N	15 N
Mechanical advantage	1	2	3

Figure 6.18: *A rope and pulley system can be arranged to have different mechanical advantages.*

Gears, ramps, and screws

Rotating motion Machines that rotate often use gears (Figure 6.19). Machines such as small drills require small forces at high speeds. Other machines, such as the paddle wheel on the back of a steamboat, require large forces at low speed. Gears allow rotating speeds to change while power stays constant.

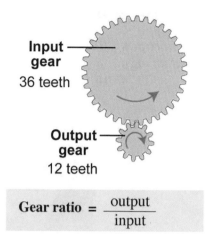

Input gear
36 teeth

Output gear
12 teeth

$$\text{Gear ratio} = \frac{\text{output}}{\text{input}}$$

How gears work The rule for how two gears turn depends on the numbers of teeth on each. Gear teeth don't slip. Moving 36 teeth on one gear means that 36 teeth also move on any connected gear. Consider a 36-tooth gear connected to a 12-tooth gear. The 12-tooth gear must turn three times ($3 \times 12 = 36$) for every turn of the 36-tooth gear (Figure 6.19).

Figure 6.19: *The 12-tooth gear makes three turns for each turn of the 36-tooth gear.*

Ramps

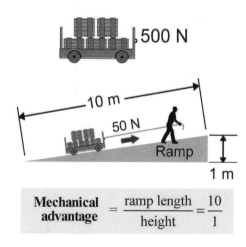

500 N

10 m

50 N

Ramp

1 m

$$\text{Mechanical advantage} = \frac{\text{ramp length}}{\text{height}} = \frac{10}{1}$$

A ramp allows you to raise a heavy cart with less force than you would need to lift it straight up. Ramps reduce the input force by increasing the distance over which the input force acts. For example, suppose a 10-meter ramp is used to lift a car 1 meter. The input distance is 10 times the output distance. If the ramp were frictionless, the input force would therefore be 1/10th the output force.

Screws A screw is a simple machine that turns rotating motion into linear motion (Figure 6.20). A screw works just like a ramp that curves as it gets higher. The "ramp" on a screw is called a thread. Imagine unwrapping one turn of a thread to make a straight ramp. Each turn of the screw advances the nut the same distance it would have gone sliding up the ramp. The *lead* of a screw is the distance it advances in one turn. A screw with a lead of 1.2 millimeters advances 1.2 millimeters for each turn.

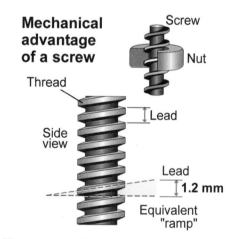

Mechanical advantage of a screw

Screw

Nut

Thread

Side view

Lead

Lead
1.2 mm

Equivalent "ramp"

Figure 6.20: *A screw is a rotating ramp.*

6.3 Section Review

1. Name two simple machines that are found on a bicycle.
2. Explain the difference between input work and output work for a machine.
3. Is a gas-powered lawn mower a simple machine? Explain why or why not.
4. The human body is often called a machine because of the way the bones and muscles work together. Is the body a "simple" machine in the sense that we defined in the last section? Explain.
5. What is the efficiency of the bicycle in Figure 6.21?
6. An inventor claims to have created a new unpowered machine. He says the machine can push with an output force of 100 newtons for 1 meter if you apply an input force of 50 newtons for 0.5 meter. Could this machine work? Explain why or why not.
7. Why is the efficiency of a real machine always less than 100 percent?
8. The efficiency of a certain machine is 25 percent. How much input work must be supplied to get 100 joules of output work?
9. A clever inventor arranges ropes and pulleys to lift a heavy log. The log weighs 2,000 newtons. If she pulls 10 meters of rope to lift the log 2 meters, what force does she apply to the rope? You may assume a perfect machine (no friction).
10. Calculate the mechanical advantage of the crowbar shown in Figure 6.22.
11. A large gear with 24 teeth is connected to a small gear with 12 teeth. If the large gear turns twice, how many times must the small gear turn?
12. What is the mechanical advantage of a 15-meter ramp that rises 3 meters?

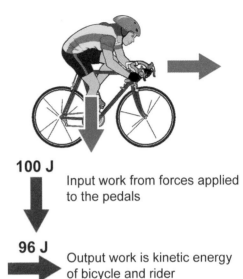

100 J Input work from forces applied to the pedals

96 J Output work is kinetic energy of bicycle and rider

4 J Work done against friction

Figure 6.21: *Question 5.*

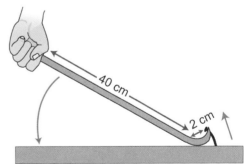

Figure 6.22: *Question 10.*

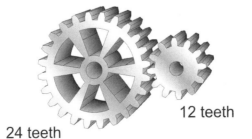

24 teeth

12 teeth

A Mighty Energizing Wind

There is a new kind of farm that is unlike any other. It doesn't produce food, it produces energy from wind. These farms can help solve the energy crisis by generating electricity from the powerful forces in wind.

Not that long ago, most farms in the United States had a windmill. It was used to pump water from a well. These days, an electric motor pumps the water, and the old windmill is gone or just admired as an antique.

New windmills, however, are going strong. Tower-mounted wind turbines that are far larger and more efficient have replaced the old models. When these big turbines are grouped, they form a wind farm. They are being built on land that is still used for farming. With support from industry and the government, wind farms are sprouting across the country. Researchers are finding ways to improve windmill efficiency and solve the issue of low wind speed.

A wind turbine is almost the opposite of a fan. A fan uses electricity to make wind; the turbine uses wind to make electricity. Wind turns the turbine's blades, which spins a shaft that connects to a generator, which produces electricity. The old farm windmills had several blades on a small metal or even wooden tower. Today's wind turbines have two or three blades mounted on towers that may be hundreds of feet tall.

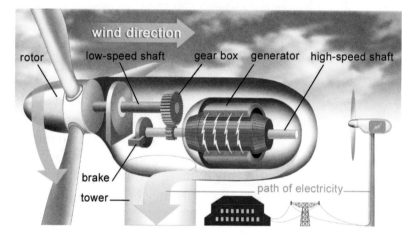

The promise of wind's power

According to the U.S. Department of Energy, wind power costs 4 to 6¢ per kilowatt-hour. Coal-fired power costs 4.8 to 5.5¢, and natural gas can cost as little as 4¢, so wind power is competitive, and it has advantages.

- A clean fuel source that does not pollute the air like coal- or gas-burning power plants
- Does not need to be imported
- Abundant resource—it will never run out
- Requires no mining or drilling
- One of the lowest-priced renewable energy technologies available

Wind power can also benefit the economies of rural areas. The power companies pay rent to landowners. Since the turbines occupy only a fraction of the land on a wind farm, the landowner can farm around the towers.

Obstacles, naturally

The biggest problem with wind power is obvious: Wind comes and goes. It cannot be counted on to blow when electricity is needed. It does not blow at a steady rate.

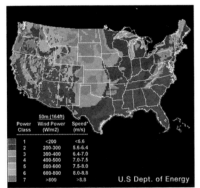

Also, the best sites for wind farms are often in remote locations, in mountains or deserts, far from cities where the most electricity is needed. The map of the United States shows wind energy potential. Find your state to see how windy it is compared with other states.

According to the Department of Energy, 6 percent of the nation's land mass has wind energy resources. This area has the potential to supply more than one and a half times the electricity being consumed today. Yet obstacles stand in the way of harvesting this natural resource.

- Wind farms are not always welcome in communities, for a variety of reasons.
- As the turbines spin, rotor blades produce a certain amount of noise.
- Some people dislike the industrial look of the wind-farm towers.
- Concern for the fact that some birds and bats are killed when they fly into the rotors.

Searching for solutions

There needs to be more research and better methods of harvesting in areas with less wind speed. Wind industry scientists and engineers, in partnership with the Department of Energy, are designing, analyzing, and testing equipment and methods in order to improve performance.

Progress in research requires test after test. Before a new product, such as an improved wind turbine, is placed on the market, a single model is made and tested repeatedly.

Not all wind farms are on land. Offshore wind energy projects such as the Block Island wind farm off the coast of Rhode Island are being looked at more closely. Research is underway on floating turbines to be tested in US coastal waters and the lower Great Lakes. Such sites would be one way to solve the drawback of distance from large cities that need electricity.

QUESTIONS

1. How does a wind turbine operate?
2. Compare and contrast wind energy with fossil fuel.
3. What are the disadvantages to wind power?
4. Why is it important to research and study wind energy?

Pop Goes the Balloon!

Rube Goldberg was a Pulitzer Prize winning cartoonist, sculptor, and author. He is well known for creating fun illustrations that show how many simple steps can work together to accomplish something. The illustration below is similar to a Rube Goldberg cartoon. For this activity, you will design and build a multi-step device that will pop a balloon.

How To Take A Picture of Yourself
1. Pull rope 2. Cage lifts to release bowling ball 3. Ball falls on see-saw
4. Monkey gets tossed up, grabs stick which pulls a string tied to watering can
5. Watering can tips over and drips on sleeping parrot
6. Parrot wakes up and eats breadcrumbs sprinkled on camera
7. Parrot presses the flash button – your picture is taken!

Materials (per group):

one box top from a copy/printer paper box; scissors; tape; string; several small balloons; assorted household/classroom objects such as thread spools, straws, thumb tacks, paper clips, rubber bands, cardboard, toothpicks, etc.

What you will do

1. Your group must design and build a device that will pop a balloon.

2. Plan a design for a three-step device that will pop the balloon. You can only touch the device to start the first step.

3. Assemble the device from the available materials. Be creative!

4. Once you get a working model, draw and label a sketch that shows how your machine works.

5. Demonstrate your machine for other groups.

The device must follow these guidelines:

· Fits inside the box top.

· Uses at least three steps to accomplish the task.

· You can operate the device at step 1, and then the device does the rest of the work to pop the balloon.

· If you use more than one type of simple machine in your device, you will receive extra credit.

Applying your knowledge

a. How many times did you change your design until you got a model that worked? Explain the process your group went through to get a working model.

b. What was the most challenging part of this project?

c. How many different simple machines did you use to pop the balloon? Describe and explain.

d. What energy conversions took place from step one to the end? Label these on your diagram.

Chapter 6 Assessment

Vocabulary

Select the correct term to complete the sentences.

energy	efficiency	law of energy conservation
input	joule	horsepower
simple machines	machine	kinetic energy
work	potential energy	mechanical advantage
watt	power	

Section 6.1

1. Energy of position is called ____.

2. Energy of motion is called ____.

3. The unit of energy needed to exert a force of 1 newton over a distance of 1 meter is a(n) ____.

4. The ability to cause change is referred to as ____.

5. "Energy can never be created or destroyed, just converted from one form to another" describes ____.

Section 6.2

6. A form of energy that comes from force applied over a distance is known as ____.

7. The unit of power equal to 1 joule of work per second of time is the ____.

8. The rate of doing work or moving energy is ____.

9. A unit of power equal to 746 watts is the ____.

Section 6.3

10. A device with moving parts that work together to accomplish a task is a(n) ____.

11. The ratio of work output to work input is called ____.

12. The ratio of the output force divided by the input force is called ____.

Concepts

Section 6.1

1. Name five objects or substances that contain energy.

2. Name five examples of changes caused by energy.

3. Why do scientists organize nature into systems?

4. Explain how force and energy are related.

5. Energy takes many forms. Compare potential energy to kinetic energy and give two examples of each.

6. Since energy is never lost, what is meant when someone says they are "saving energy"?

7. Do power plants create electrical energy?

8. A ball is thrown up in the air. Explain what happens to its potential and kinetic energies and it moves up and then back down.

9. When energy transformations occur in a system, what happens to the total amount of energy in the system?

Section 6.2

10. For each situation, explain whether work (*W*) is done or not (*N*) done:
    a. ____ standing still while holding a box of heavy books
    b. ____ hitting baseball with a bat
    c. ____ picking up a suitcase
    d. ____ pushing hard against a stone wall for an hour
    e. ____ falling toward Earth while sky diving

11. Explain why energy and work are measured using the same units.

12. Write the formula relating force (F), work (W), and distance (d).

13. Mikhail lifts a 500-N weight 2 meters in 2 seconds. Tobias lifts the same 500-N weight 2 meters in 4 seconds.

    a. Which boy does more work?

    b. Which boy uses greater power?

Section 6.3

14. Name five locations on a car where simple machines are used and name the simple machines.

15. Under what conditions is a machine considered "perfect"?

16. Why can't the output work for a machine be greater than the input work? Explain.

17. What determines the mechanical advantage of a pulley system?

Problems

Section 6.1

1. A 5-kg can of paint is sitting on the ground next to a 2-meter high step ladder. How much work would you have to do to move the can of paint to the top of the ladder?

2. A skateboard and rider at the top of a 3-meter high pipe have 1,620 joules of potential energy.

    a. When the rider reaches the bottom of the friction-free pipe, how much kinetic energy will the rider and skateboard have?

    b. When the potential energy is reduced to 620 joules, how much kinetic energy will the rider and skateboard have?

3. How far can 6 joules of energy move a box if a 2-N force is needed to slide the box?

Section 6.2

4. Sara's mother has a flat tire on her car while driving to school. They use a jack to change the tire. It exerts a force of 5,000 N to lift the car 0.25 meters. How much work is done by the jack?

5. How far does Isabella lift a 50-N box if she does 40 joules of work in lifting the box from a floor to a shelf?

6. A machine is used to lift an object a distance of 2 meters. If the power of the machine is increased, what happens to the time it takes for the object to be lifted 2 meters?

7. During construction, a crane lifts a 2,000-N weight to the top of a 50-meter tall building. How much power must the crane have to perform this task in 5 seconds?

8. What is the minimum time needed to lift a 2,000-N weight 10 meters using a motor with a maximum power rating of 8,000 watts?

Section 6.3

9. Jaime lifts a 1,000-N carton using a lever. If he applies a force of 200 N to lift the carton, what is the mechanical advantage of the lever?

10. What is the mechanical advantage of a 20-meter ramp that rises 5 meters?

11. A gear with 20 teeth is connected to a gear with 15 teeth. If the larger gear turns three times, how many turns will the smaller gear make?

12. A 60-watt light bulb uses 60 joules of electrical energy every second. However, only 6 joules of electrical energy is converted into light energy each second.

    a. What is the efficiency of the light bulb?

    b. What do you think happens to the "lost" energy?

Chapter 7

Gravity and Space

In the past 100 years, humans have been able to look beyond Earth with large telescopes. They have found more stars than anyone imagined—millions of new galaxies of stars. Within the past 10 years, people have found planets around some stars. Could there be other intelligent life like ours out there? Some think it's very likely, others are not so sure.

Earth is a planet that is just right for living things. What makes it so special? How do the Earth, Moon, and Sun fit together to make such a comfortable planet? People have long wondered if other planets in our solar system have life. Mars and Europa (a moon of Jupiter) are good candidates for supporting living organisms. Space probes have explored only a tiny fraction of the surface of Mars looking for signs of life. The small amount of evidence collected gives no definite answers.

Key Questions:

1. What is the solar system and how does gravity affect it?

2. How do the other planets in the solar system compare with Earth? Could they support life?

3. What are stars?

4. How big is the universe?

7.1 Gravity

To a physicist, gravity is a weak force. It takes something the size of a whole planet to make gravity strong enough to feel. To regular people, however, gravity is a comfortingly strong force. Earth's gravity holds you firmly to its surface despite the fact that our planet is rotating with a speed of nearly 700 miles per hour at the equator.

Gravity comes from mass

Gravitational force, mass, and distance

Gravity creates an attractive force between *all* objects that have mass. There is even a gravitational force between you and this book (Figure 7.1)! You don't notice gravity between ordinary objects because it takes a huge amount of mass to create a force big enough to feel. You feel the force of gravity between you and Earth because our planet's mass is so incredibly large.

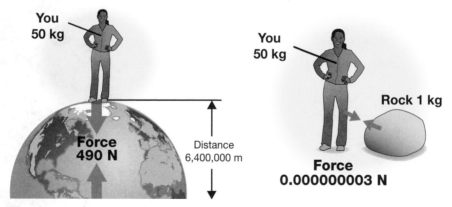

Direction of the gravitational force

The force of gravity between two objects always lies along the line connecting their centers. As objects move, the direction of the force changes to stay pointed along the line between their centers. For example, the force between Earth and your body points from your center to the center of Earth. The direction of the planet's gravitational force is what we use to define "down." If you tell a person on the North Pole and one on the South Pole to point down, they will be pointing in opposite directions (Figure 7.2).

Comparing gravitational forces between ordinary objects and between objects and planets

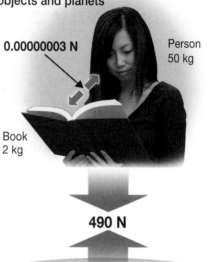

Figure 7.1: *The gravitational force between you and Earth is much stronger than between you and your book.*

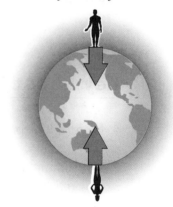

Figure 7.2: *Earth's gravity pulls toward the center of the planet. That's why "down" is opposite on the North and South Poles.*

The force of gravity

Mass and gravity Gravity is a force that attracts every mass to every other mass. **Newton's law of universal gravitation** says the strength of the force depends on mass and distance. The greater the mass, the greater the force. If one object doubles in mass, then the gravitational force doubles. If both objects double in mass, then the force doubles twice, becoming four times as strong (Figure 7.3).

Distance and gravity Distance also affects the force of gravity acting between objects. The closer objects are, the greater the force between them. The force of gravity gets weaker as objects get farther apart. Doubling the distance divides the force by four (2^2). If you are twice as far from an object, you feel one-fourth the gravitational force. Tripling the distance divides the force by nine ($9 = 3^2$). If you are three times as far away, the force is one-ninth as strong.

Weightlessness The astronauts in the space shuttle are not far enough away to escape Earth's gravity. How do they float around with no apparent weight? The answer is that they are actually *falling* around the Earth in their orbit. Think about being in an elevator. An elevator accelerating upward makes you feel *heavier*. The floor pushes against your feet to accelerate your body upward. A scale in the elevator would read your weight *plus* the additional force applied to accelerate you. The opposite happens when the elevator is falling. The scale "falls away" beneath your feet with the same acceleration as you fall. The scale would read zero because there would be no force between it and your feet. This is why astronauts in free fall are *weightless*.

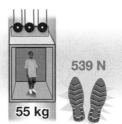
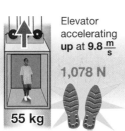
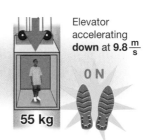

Elevator **at rest** or moving with **constant speed** — 539 N — 55 kg

Elevator accelerating **up at 9.8** $\frac{m}{s}$ — 1,078 N — 55 kg

Elevator accelerating **down at 9.8** $\frac{m}{s}$ — 0 N — 55 kg

ă VOCABULARY

Newton's law of universal gravitation - a mathematical rule that tells us how the strength of the force of gravity depends on mass and distance.

Mass and the force of gravity

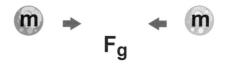

F_g

$2F_g$

$4F_g$

Figure 7.3: *Doubling one mass doubles the force of gravity. Doubling both masses quadruples the force of gravity.*

Orbital motion

Gravitational force and orbits

Together with gravity, Newton's second law explains the motion of planets, moons, and satellites. Remember from Chapter 4 that sideways acceleration bends a velocity vector to make curved motion. According to the second law, sideways accelerations are caused by sideways forces. Consider an object moving near a planet. The force of gravity bends the object's path as it passes by. If the object is not moving fast enough, gravity bends its motion all the way into a circle (or ellipse). The object goes into *orbit* around the planet. An **orbit** is the circular (or elliptical) path an object takes around a gravity source, such as a planet or star.

VOCABULARY

orbit - the repeating circular (or elliptical) path an object takes around a gravity source, such as a planet or star.

Why the Moon doesn't fall to Earth

The Moon moves in a 384,000 km orbit around Earth (Figure 7.4). Why doesn't Earth's gravity just pull the Moon into Earth? To answer that question, imagine kicking a ball off the ground at an angle. If you kick it at a slow speed, it curves and falls back to the ground. The faster you kick the ball, the farther it goes before hitting the ground. If you could kick it fast enough, the curve of the ball's path would match the curvature of Earth and the ball would go into orbit instead of falling back to Earth.

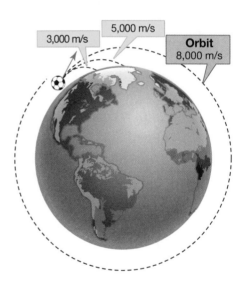

The Moon falls around Earth

The same idea applies to the motion of the Moon. The Moon's speed and inertia carry it forward as it *falls around Earth.* As it falls, Earth curves away beneath it. If the gravitational force between the Moon and Earth were gone, the Moon's inertia would cause it to move in a straight line at a constant speed. The Moon would fly off into space! The gravitational force between the Moon and Earth causes a sideways acceleration that keeps the Moon in orbit.

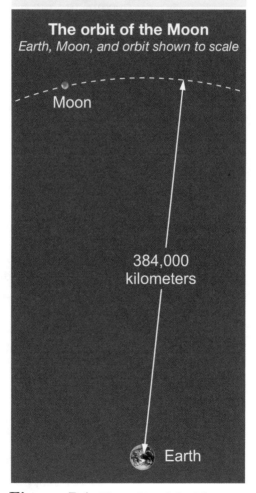

The orbit of the Moon
Earth, Moon, and orbit shown to scale

Moon

384,000 kilometers

Earth

Figure 7.4: *The orbit of the Moon shown to scale.*

Earth and the Sun

Gravity from the Sun

Compared to Earth, the Sun is huge. The Sun has 330,000 times the mass of Earth and is 110 times larger in diameter (Figure 7.5). Unlike Earth, the Sun is a hot ball of gas without a solid surface. However, at its gaseous "surface," the Sun's gravity is 28 times as strong as Earth's gravity. A person weighing 100 pounds on Earth would weigh 2,800 pounds on the Sun!

The Sun's gravity on Earth

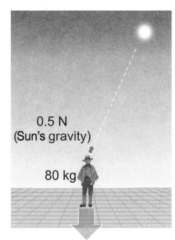

0.5 N
(Sun's gravity)

80 kg

784 N (**Earth's** gravity)

The force of gravity gets weaker with distance but never "ends." Earth orbits at an average distance of about 150 million kilometers from the Sun. At this distance, the Sun's gravity has a strength of 0.006 N/kg. That means an average, 80-kg person is *attracted to the Sun* with a force of about half a newton (about 2 ounces). Fortunately, Earth's gravity gives the same person a weight of 784 newtons. The person's weight pulls then toward the center of Earth with a force that is 1,650 times stronger than the force from the Sun. That's why the Sun isn't pulling people up into the sky during the day!

Earth's orbit

Even at 150 million kilometers, however, the Sun's gravity is enough to bend Earth's motion into a nearly circular orbit. Earth completes one orbit around the Sun every 365.25 days. During this yearly journey, Earth travels almost 600 million miles through space. The "solid ground" you are standing on is actually moving through space at an incredible speed. How fast is Earth going? There are 8,766 hours in a year (365.25 × 24). Dividing the distance Earth moves in one year by 8,766 hours gives a speed of 66,800 miles per hour (Figure 7.6)! Even standing still, you are really moving quite fast. You don't notice because Earth's orbital motion is at *constant speed*. There is no acceleration in the direction of Earth's motion. Acceleration is what results in forces you can feel.

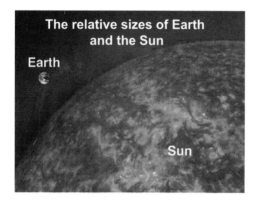

The relative sizes of Earth and the Sun

Earth

Sun

Figure 7.5: *The Sun is much larger and more massive than Earth.*

66,800 mph!

Figure 7.6: *Earth moves through space at 66,800 miles per hour.*

SOLVE IT!

Earth spins on its axis once every 24 hours. The distance around Earth at the equator is about 40,000 kilometers. What speed (in km/h) does the planet's rotation give a person standing on the equator?

The Earth and Moon

The Moon The Moon is much smaller than Earth, with 81 times less mass than Earth. The Moon's diameter is 3,476 kilometers compared to Earth's diameter of 12,756 kilometers (Figure 7.7). Because the Moon has much less mass, its surface gravity is about 1/6 as strong as the gravity on Earth. A barren and hostile place, the Moon has no atmosphere because its gravity is so low.

Gravitational locking The Moon rotates much more slowly than Earth. Over millions of years, Earth's gravity has locked the moon's rotation to its orbit around Earth. One lunar "day" takes 27.3 Earth days, exactly the same time it takes the Moon to complete one orbit around Earth. That is why the same side of the Moon always faces Earth.

Moon **Earth**

Figure 7.7: *The relative sizes of the Earth and Moon.*

The Moon's orbit and the lunar cycle

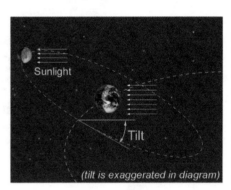

Sunlight

Tilt

(tilt is exaggerated in diagram)

The orbit of the Moon is tilted about 5 degrees from the orbit of Earth. This means the Moon is not in Earth's shadow except for rare *eclipses*. The Sun-facing side of the Moon is bright almost all the time. This is a puzzle because the Moon has "phases" where part of it appears to be in shadow. How do we explain the phases of the Moon?

Why the Moon has "phases" The diagram in Figure 7.8 shows the Moon's orbit from above. Imagine standing on the Earth looking up at the Moon. At position A, the Moon is on the far side of the Earth from the Sun. The side facing Earth is brightly lit and you see a full Moon.

At position B, half the Moon is dark *due to its own shadow*. Looking up in the night sky you see a half Moon. The bright half is the side facing the Sun. The dark half is the side facing away from the Sun.

At position C, the brightly lit side of the Moon is facing the Sun. The shadowed side is facing the Earth. You see a dark Moon (the new Moon) because you are looking at the Moon's shadowed side!

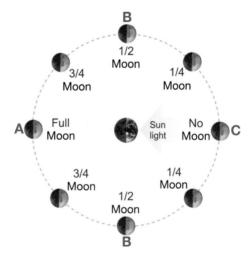

B

1/2 Moon

3/4 Moon   1/4 Moon

A Full Moon   Sun light   No Moon C

3/4 Moon   1/4 Moon

1/2 Moon

B

Figure 7.8: *How the Moon's own shadow creates the phases that we see.*

Tides

Tides are caused by the Moon's gravity

The Moon's gravity has an important effect on Earth. As Earth rotates beneath the Moon, every kilogram of mass feels a "Moonward" force of 0.00003 N from the Moon's gravity. Earth is made of strong rock and can easily resist this small force. However, water flows easily and even this small force causes the ocean to rise several meters (Figure 7.9)! This daily rise in ocean level is called the **tide**. Tides are caused by the gravitational pull of the Moon acting on the water in the oceans.

The mystery of the "second" tide

The Moon passes overhead once every 24 hours. You would expect the tide to rise once every 24 hours in response. But the tide actually rises *twice* every 24 hours! The ocean on the side of Earth directly *opposite* the Moon also rises. What causes this "second," or far-side tide (Figure 7.10)?

The center of mass

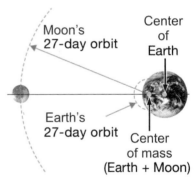

The answer is that the Moon does not really orbit the Earth as if the Earth were fixed in place. Instead, the Earth and Moon orbit around a common *center of mass*. Imagine balancing the Earth and Moon on a giant see-saw. There is a point at which the see-saw balances even though the Earth is much heavier than the Moon. That point is the center of mass of the Earth–Moon system. It is inside the Earth, about 75 percent of the way to the surface, but not at the center. Both Earth and Moon revolve around this point every 27.3 days.

Explaining the "second" tide

When you turn a corner sharply in a car, your body slides to the outside of the curve, away from the center. This happens because your body wants to move in a straight line in the direction it was going *before* the turn. This is the explanation for the "other" tide on the side of Earth that does not face the Moon. As the Earth rotates around the center of mass, the ocean on the opposite side from the Moon is "flung outward" a little by its own inertia (Figure 7.10).

tide - a cycle of rising and falling sea levels that repeats every 12 hours.

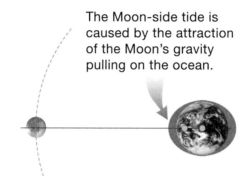

The Moon-side tide is caused by the attraction of the Moon's gravity pulling on the ocean.

Figure 7.9: *The cause of the Moon-side tide.*

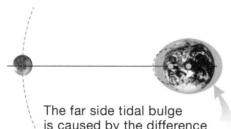

The far side tidal bulge is caused by the difference in the Moon's gravity on solid Earth and the water of the oceans.

Figure 7.10: *The cause of the far-side tide.* Note: *The tides in the diagram are much larger than actual tides. Also, both tides actually "lag" behind the overhead passing of the Moon due to friction between the ocean water, land, and the sea floor.*

7.1 **Section Review**

1. What factors does *weight* depend on?
2. Why don't people on the opposite side of Earth fall off?

Earth's gravity

Orbit

3. Earth exerts a gravitational force on the Moon. Why doesn't the force of gravity pull the Moon into the Earth?
4. Gravitational force gets weaker as _____ increases and gets stronger as the _____ of the objects increases.
5. Gravity exists between all objects with mass. Why is it that you don't you notice the force of gravity between you and all of the objects around you?
6. Is a satellite orbiting Earth free from Earth's gravity? Why or why not?
7. The three diagrams below show the motion of an object passing near a planet. Which one has a speed that is between the other two? How did you know?

A   B   C

8. The Sun's gravity is strong enough to hold the entire Earth in orbit. Why doesn't the Sun's gravity pull us off the planet?
9. Does the Moon fall partly into Earth's shadow when it is not "full"?
10. How many times does the tide rise in a 24-hour period?

MY JOURNAL

What do people believe?

People have many different explanations for what they see. The phases of the Moon are something that everyone sees. Ask some people outside your class what they think causes the phases of the Moon. Be careful not to give them your ideas, but listen to theirs. Write down their explanations as carefully as you can. Can you see how these people might have come to their conclusions?

Satellites

STEM

There are many ways that manmade satellites affect your daily life. Think of three things that you did in the last week that were affected by satellites. Research which satellites were used. When were they launched?

7.2 The Solar System

Ancient people noticed that five bright objects seemed to wander among the stars at night. They called these objects *planets*, from the Greek word meaning "wandering star." The planets were named Mercury, Venus, Mars, Jupiter, and Saturn. In 140 CE, the Greek astronomer Ptolemy theorized that all other planets and the Moon circled the Earth. For the next 1,400 years people believed his ideas until science proved him wrong!

How the solar system was discovered

Planets shine by reflecting sunlight

Today we know that **planets** are not stars. Stars give off their own light. We see the planets *because they reflect light from the Sun*. For example, Venus appears as a crescent like the Moon, becoming dark at times. This is because Venus does not give off its own light. When Earth is on the same side of the Sun as Venus, we see Venus's shadowed side (Figure 7.11).

The Sun, planets, and other objects

The **solar system** includes the Sun, eight major planets, and their moons. A large number of smaller objects are also part of the solar system, including dwarf planets, asteroids, comets, and meteors.

VOCABULARY

planet - a massive, round body held together by its own gravity that revolves around a star in its own orbit.

solar system - the Sun, planets, moons, and other objects that are gravitationally bound to the Sun.

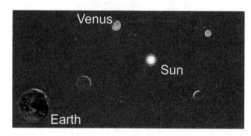

Figure 7.11: *The phases of Venus.*

The solar system is roughly divided into inner and outer planets. The diagram shows the orbits to scale but the planets are not drawn to scale.

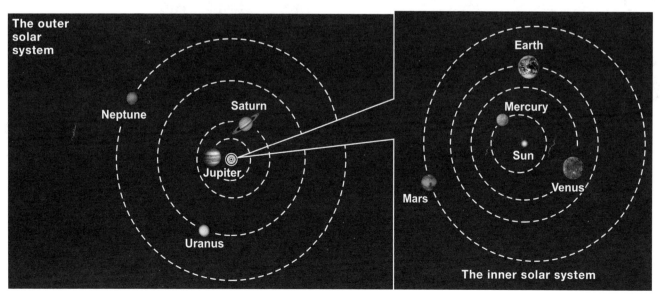

Comparing size and distance in the solar system

Relative sizes   The Sun is by far the largest object in our solar system. The next largest objects are the planets Jupiter, Saturn, Uranus, and Neptune. As you can see from the scale diagram below, the planets Mercury, Venus, Earth, Mars, and the dwarf planet Pluto appear as small dots compared with the size of the Sun.

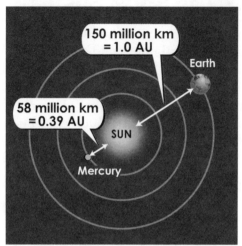

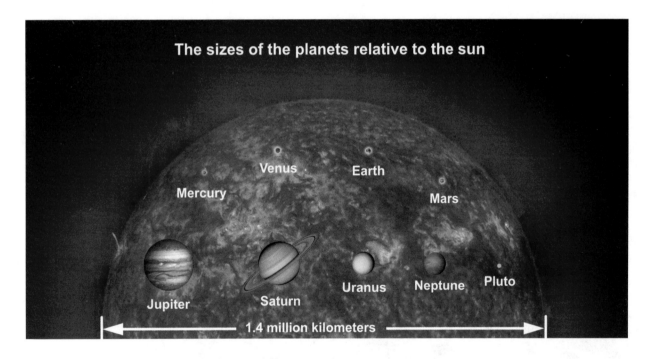

Figure 7.12: *One astronomical unit (AU) is equal to 150 million kilometers. If Earth is 1.0 AU from the Sun, then Mercury, with a distance of 58 million kilometers, is 0.39 AU from the Sun.*

Pluto, originally considered the ninth planet, was reclassified in 2006 by the International Astronomical Union as a dwarf planet. By 2016, six dwarf planets had been identified. It is estimated there may be hundreds more in the solar system.

astronomical unit - a distance equal to 150 million kilometers, or the distance from Earth to the Sun.

Distance   Astronomers often use the distance from Earth to the Sun to measure the solar system. One **astronomical unit** (AU) is equal to 150 million kilometers. This is the average distance from Earth to the Sun. Mercury is 58 million kilometers from the Sun. To convert this distance to astronomical units, divide it by 150 million kilometers (or 58 by 150). Mercury is 0.39 AU from the Sun (Figure 7.12).

An overview of the planets

Classifying the planets
The planets fall into two groups. The **terrestrial planets** are rocky and include Mercury, Venus, Earth, and Mars. These planets are mostly made of rock and metal. They have relatively high densities, slow rotations, solid surfaces, and few moons. The **gas planets** include Jupiter, Saturn, Uranus, and Neptune. They are made mostly of hydrogen and helium. These planets have relatively low densities, rapid rotations, thick atmospheres, and many moons. The dwarf planet Pluto is neither terrestrial nor gas, but in a class of its own. Table 7.1 compares the planets.

ⓐ VOCABULARY

terrestrial planets - Mercury, Venus, Earth, and Mars.

gas planets - Jupiter, Saturn, Uranus, and Neptune.

Table 7.1: Comparing properties of the planets

Property	Mercury	Venus	Earth	Mars	Jupiter	Saturn	Uranus	Neptune	Pluto (dwarf)
Diameter (*km*)	4,878	12,102	12,756	6,794	142,796	120,660	51,200	49,500	2,200
Mass (*kg*)	3.3×10^{23}	4.9×10^{24}	6.0×10^{24}	6.4×10^{23}	1.9×10^{27}	5.7×10^{26}	8.7×10^{25}	1.0×10^{26}	1.3×10^{22}
Density (*g/cm³*)	5.44	5.25	5.52	3.91	1.31	0.69	1.21	1.67	1.75
Average distance from Sun (*million km*)	58	108	150	228	778	1,430	2,870	4,500	5,910
Moons (#)	0	0	1	2	67	62	27	14	1
Strength of gravity (*N/kg*)	3.7	8.9	9.8	3.7	23.1	9.0	8.7	11.0	0.6
Surface temperature (*°C*)	−170 to +400	+450 to +480	−88 to +48	−89 to −31	−108	−139	−197	−201	−223
Rotation period (*Earth days*)	59	243	1	1.03	0.41	0.43	0.72	0.67	6.4
Revolution period (*Earth years*)	0.24	0.62	1	1.9	12	29	84	165	249
Orbital speed (*km/s*)	47.89	35.04	29.80	24.14	13.06	9.64	6.80	5.43	4.74

Asteroids, comets, and meteors

Asteroids

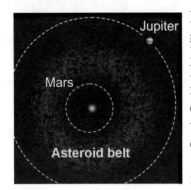

Between Mars and Jupiter there is a huge gap that cuts the solar system in two. Between 320 million and 495 million kilometers from the Sun, the *asteroid belt* is filled with thousands of small, rocky bodies called *asteroids*. An **asteroid** is an object that orbits the Sun but is too small to be considered a planet. So far, more than 10,000 asteroids have been discovered and more are found each year.

Comets

We believe **comets** are mostly ice and dust. The comets big enough to see with a telescope are about the size of a mountain on Earth. Comets revolve around the Sun in highly elliptical orbits. As a comet approaches the Sun, ice turns into gas and dust and forms a *tail*. A comet's tail can stretch for millions of kilometers into space and faces away from the Sun as the comet continues its orbit (Figure 7.13).

Meteors

Imagine a tennis ball traveling at about 30,000 miles per hour. That's about the size and speed of most **meteors**. These chunks of dust or rock travel through space. Some of them end up hitting Earth's atmosphere. When this happens, meteors rub against air particles and create friction, heating up to more than 2,000°C. The intense heat vaporizes most meteors, creating a streak of light known as a "shooting star." On average, a meteor can be seen in the night sky about every 10 minutes.

Meteorites

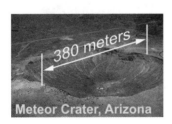

If a meteor is large enough to get through Earth's atmosphere and hit the ground, it becomes a **meteorite**. Most meteorites weigh only a few pounds or less. Meteor Crater in Winslow, Arizona, is believed to have been caused by a giant, 50-meter-diameter meteorite about 50,000 years ago.

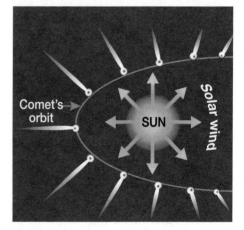

Figure 7.13: *A comet's tail faces away from the Sun and can stretch for millions of kilometers in space.*

The planets

The great unknown

The eight major planets of our solar system combined have 250 times the surface area of Earth. This vast territory includes environments baked by heat and radiation (Mercury) and frozen far colder than ice (Neptune). Venus, the most Earth-like planet in size, has a surface atmosphere of hot dense sulfuric acid that would be instantly fatal to any form of life on Earth. Our own blue world is unique in having the right balance of temperature and environment to sustain life—or is it? Might there be unusual kinds of life unknown to us on the other planets? With a combined surface area 1,700 times the size of North America, the planets are an unexplored frontier full of discoveries waiting to be made.

Figure 7.14: *Mercury was named for the messenger of the Roman gods because of its quick motion in the sky. (Image from radar maps, NASA.)*

Mercury

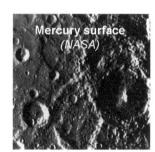

Mercury surface (NASA)

Mercury (Figure 7.14), the closest planet to the Sun, is the second smallest (after Pluto) in both size and mass. Mercury appears to move quickly across the night sky because its period of revolution is the shortest of all of the planets. Only 40 percent larger than Earth's Moon, Mercury is a rocky, cratered world, more like the Moon than like Earth. Like the Moon, Mercury has almost no atmosphere (except for traces of sodium). Mercury has no moons.

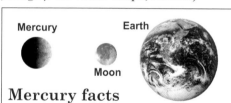

Mercury facts

Type: rocky
Moons: none
Distance from Sun: 0.39 AU
Diameter: 0.38 × Earth
Surface gravity: 38% of Earth
Surface temp.: −170 to 400°C
Atmosphere: none
Length of day: 59 Earth days
Length of year: 88 Earth days

Surface environment

Of all the planets, Mercury has the most extreme variations in temperature. The side of Mercury that faces the Sun is very hot, about 400°C, while the other side is very cold, about −170°C. This is partly because Mercury's rotation is locked in a 3:2 ratio with its orbit. The planet completes three "Mercury days" every two "Mercury years." This also translates into one day on Mercury being about 59 Earth days long, and one year on Mercury being not much longer, about 88 Earth days.

Venus

Venus is similar to Earth as a planet

Venus (Figure 7.15) appears as the brightest planet in the evening sky and is the third brightest observable object (after the Sun and Moon). Venus was named after the Roman goddess of love because of its beautiful, shiny appearance. Of the planets, Venus is closest to Earth in terms of size, surface gravity, and rocky composition. Venus is slightly smaller than Earth and, like Earth, has volcanoes and an active geology. But the similarity ends there. The dense, hot, acid atmosphere on the surface of Venus is not Earth-like at all.

Venus's surface is unpleasant

Venus has a thick atmosphere which is mostly (96 percent) carbon dioxide at a pressure 90 times that of Earth. Carbon dioxide traps heat; the greenhouse effect makes Venus the hottest planet

Surface of Venus - Venera 13 - Soviet Academy of Sciences/U.S.S.R.

in the solar system. The surface temperature is more than 500°C, hot enough to melt lead and zinc. Clouds on Venus are not water, but toxic sulfuric acid (H_2SO_4) fumes from active volcanoes. The first successful landing on Venus was the Soviet probe Venera 7 in 1970. This tough lander sent the first images of Venus's rocky surface. Venera 7 lasted only 23 minutes before the acid and heat destroyed it. More recently, Venus was studied by the US Magellan (1989–1994) and Messenger (2004) missions, and by the European Venus Express orbiter (2005).

Venus day and year

Venus is one of three planets that rotate "backward," that is, east to west. Its rotation is the slowest of all of the planets; Venus makes a little less than one rotation for each revolution around the Sun. This means that a day on Venus is 243 Earth days, while a year is shorter than that, just 225 Earth days. Venus is currently being studied by Japan's Akatsuki probe.

Figure 7.15: *This radar map was colored to match Venus's surface colors, normally hidden by clouds. (Photo courtesy of NASA.)*

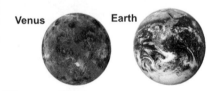

Venus   Earth

Venus facts

Type: rocky

Moons: none

Distance from Sun: 0.72 AU

Diameter: 0.95 × Earth

Surface gravity: 91% of Earth

Avg. surface temp.: 460°C

Atmosphere: dense, 96% CO_2

Length of day: 243 Earth days

Length of year: 225 Earth days

Earth and Moon

Earth Earth (Figure 7.16) is a small, rocky planet with an atmosphere that is mostly nitrogen (78 percent N_2) and oxygen (21 percent O_2). Earth is one of only two bodies in the solar system known to have liquid water (the other is Europa, a moon of Jupiter). Earth has an active geology, including volcanoes and crustal movement. Earth's atmosphere, along with its vast oceans and moderate temperature range, supports an incredible variety of life. *As far as we know,* Earth is the only planet in the solar system to support life. Although space probes have begun searching, the ultimate answer to whether there is life on other planets may have to wait until humans can go in person.

The Moon Earth's single rocky Moon is about one-quarter the diameter of Earth. At a distance of 385,000 kilometers, the Moon is about 30 Earth-diameters away from the planet, completing one orbit every 29 days.

The seasons Earth's orbit is within 2 percent of a perfect circle. The seasons are caused by the 23-degree tilt of Earth's axis of rotation relative to its orbit. When Earth is on one side of the Sun, the northern hemisphere receives a greater intensity of sunlight because the Sun passes nearly straight overhead once per day, making it summer. Six months later, on the opposite side of Earth's orbit, the northern hemisphere tilts away from the Sun. This spreads the sunlight over a larger surface area. The lower intensity of sunlight each day causes winter.

Moon   **Earth**

Figure 7.16: *Earth is the only planet not named after a Roman god. Its name comes from Old English* oerthe, *meaning "land" or "country." (Photo courtesy of NASA.)*

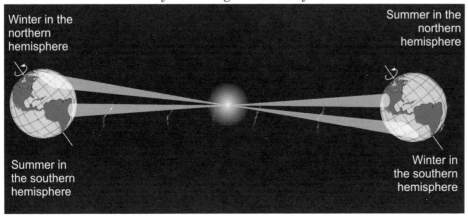

Winter in the northern hemisphere

Summer in the northern hemisphere

Summer in the southern hemisphere

Winter in the southern hemisphere

Earth facts

Type: rocky

Moons: one

Distance from Sun: 1 AU

Diameter: 12,800 km

Surface gravity: 9.8 N/kg

Avg. surface temp.: 10°C

Atmosphere: dense, N_2, O_2

Length of day: 24 hours

Length of year: 365.25 days

Mars

Mars The fourth planet out from the Sun, Mars (Figure 7.17) appears as a reddish point of light in the night sky. Mars is a relatively small, rocky planet with a mass only 11 percent the mass of Earth. Mars has two tiny, irregular-shaped moons named Deimos and Phobos. Both are much smaller than Earth's Moon and are more like asteroids.

The surface of Mars The surface of Mars has deserts, huge valleys, craters, and volcanic mountains even larger than those on Earth. However, Mars's "air" is mostly carbon dioxide and is less than 1 percent as thick as Earth's atmosphere. Like Earth, Mars has polar ice caps, but they are made of a combination of water and frozen carbon dioxide. Because of the thin atmosphere and the planet's distance from the Sun, temperatures are below 0°C most of the time. Because it is tilted like Earth, Mars also has seasons. A day on Mars (24.6 hours) is similar in length to an Earth day. But Mars's larger orbit makes a Martian year (687 days) almost twice as long as an Earth year.

Martian surface
Viking 2 (NASA)

Mars was different in the past Mars is cold and dry today. However, there is strong evidence that Mars was much wetter and had a thicker atmosphere in the past. Aerial photos of the Martian surface show erosion and patterns of riverbeds similar to those formed by flowing water on Earth. Even today, there is evidence of water beneath the Martian surface. Several robot space probes have landed on Mars searching for life but the results have been inconclusive. Since Mars is Earth's nearest match in climate, the US Orion mission is being planned to send astronauts to Mars by 2030.

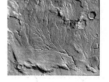

Figure 7.17: *Mars was named after the Roman god of war. (Photo courtesy of ESA.)*

Mars   Earth

Mars facts

Type: rocky
Moons: 2
Distance from Sun: 1.5 AU
Diameter: 0.53 × Earth
Surface gravity: 38% of Earth
Avg. surface temp.: −50°C
Atmosphere: thin, CO_2
Length of day: 24.6 hours
Length of year: 687 Earth days

Jupiter

Jupiter The fifth planet out from the Sun, Jupiter (Figure 7.18) is by far the largest. Jupiter's mass is greater than the combined mass of all of the other planets. Jupiter also spins the fastest, rotating about once every 10 hours. Jupiter is very different from the rocky, inner planets like Earth. Jupiter's average density is only 1.3 g/cm^3 compared with Earth's density of 5.1 g/cm^3. Jupiter is a gas planet composed mostly of hydrogen and helium, similar to the Sun. In fact, if Jupiter were larger it would be a star, like the Sun.

Jupiter's environment Jupiter does not have a solid surface. In fact, Jupiter is more liquid than gaseous or solid—more than half of its volume is an ocean of liquid hydrogen. Its atmosphere is about 88 percent hydrogen, 11 percent helium, and 1 percent methane, ammonia, and other gases. The atmospheric pressure below Jupiter's thick clouds is more than 1 million times that of Earth. A huge storm called the Great Red Spot has been observed in Jupiter's atmosphere for more than 300 years.

Figure 7.18: *Jupiter was king of the Roman gods. The planet's brightness inspired its name. (Photo courtesy of NASA.)*

Jupiters 4 largest moons
Photos courtesy of NASA

Io   Europa   Ganymede   Callisto   Size of Earth's moon

Jupiter's fascinating moons With 67 known moons, Jupiter is like a mini solar system. In 1995, when the US Galileo probe took these photographs, the four largest moons became some of the most fascinating objects in the solar system. Io, Europa, Ganymede, and Callisto are like small planets. Because it is heated by gravitational forces from Jupiter itself, Io looks like a boiling pizza and is covered with smoking sulfur volcanoes. Europa has a surface layer of ice as much as 20 kilometers thick. Beneath the ice is a vast ocean of liquid water that may even be warm enough to support life. Ganymede, the largest moon in the solar system, has a magnetic field like Earth. No other moons have this feature. Even pock-marked Callisto has many mysteries.

Earth   Jupiter

Jupiter facts

Type: gas giant
Moons: 67 plus faint rings
Distance from Sun: 5.2 AU
Diameter: 11.2 × Earth
Surface gravity: 253% of Earth
Avg. atmos. temp.: −108°C
Atmosphere: 90% H, 10% He
Length of day: 10 Earth hours
Length of year: 11.9 Earth years

Saturn

Saturn Saturn (Figure 7.19), at almost 10 times the size of Earth, is the second largest planet. Similar to Jupiter's, Saturn's atmosphere is mostly hydrogen and helium. Saturn also spins quickly, with a day on Saturn lasting about 11 Earth hours. As with Jupiter, Saturn's rapid rotation is one contributor to huge planetary storms in its atmosphere. Because of its distance from the Sun, a year on Saturn is about 29 Earth years.

Saturn's rings

The most striking feature of Saturn is its system of rings, which are visible from Earth with a telescope. Saturn's rings are made up of billions of particles of rock and ice ranging from microscopic to the size of a house. Although they are hundreds of thousands of kilometers wide, the rings are less than 100 meters thick. (Photo courtesy of NASA.)

Courtesy NASA/JPL-Caltech

Figure 7.19: *Because of its slow orbit around the Sun, Saturn was named after the Roman god of agriculture and time.*

Saturn has many moons Saturn, again like Jupiter, has many natural satellites. There are 8 larger moons and many smaller ones. Some of the smaller moons act as "shepherds," keeping the particles in Saturn's rings confined through a complex waltz of gravity.

Titan is the largest moon

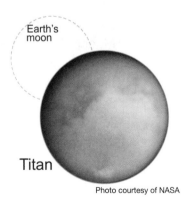

Earth's moon

Titan

Photo courtesy of NASA

Titan is Saturn's largest moon, and like Jupiter's large moons, it is like a small planet. It has an atmosphere of nitrogen and a surface pressure comparable to Earth's. Astronomers have found spectroscopic evidence of organic molecules in Titan's atmosphere, raising the possibility of life there. Titan is very cold, with an average temperature of −183°C. We know little about its surface because of its dense cloud cover.

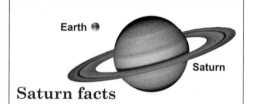

Earth

Saturn

Saturn facts

Type: gas giant
Moons: 62 plus rings
Distance from Sun: 9.5 AU
Diameter: 9.4 × Earth
Surface gravity: 1.06% of Earth
Avg. atmos. temp.: −139°C
Atmosphere: 96% H, 3% He
Length of day: 10.7 Earth hours
Length of year: 29.5 Earth years

Uranus and Neptune

Uranus and Neptune are similar

Both Uranus and Neptune are huge, cold gas planets very much like Jupiter and Saturn. Both are about four times the diameter of Earth, considerably smaller than Jupiter or Saturn. Like the other gas giants, these planets' atmospheres are mostly hydrogen and helium, similar to the Sun. Scientists believe all the planets condensed out of the same cloud of interstellar material as the Sun. The smaller inner planets could not hold onto their lighter gases (hydrogen and helium) and their exposed cores became the rocky planets. Under their deep atmospheres, the gas giants also have rocky cores.

Uranus

The seventh planet from the Sun, Uranus can barely be seen without a good telescope. It was not discovered until 1781. It rotates "backward" and has an axis that is tilted 98 degrees to the plane of its orbit. A day on Uranus is only 18 Earth hours, but a year takes 84 Earth years. Uranus has at least 27 moons, all of them relatively small. Titania, the largest, has only 4 percent of the mass of Earth's Moon.

Photo courtesy of NASA

Neptune

Neptune is the farthest planet from the Sun. It was discovered in 1846, and its discovery almost doubled the diameter of the known solar system. Neptune's orbit is nearly a perfect circle; only Venus has a more circular orbit. Neptune has a series of faint rings invisible from Earth. They were first discovered in photographs taken by space probes such as Voyager. Neptune has 14 known moons. Six of these were found in photographs taken by Voyager 2 in 1989. Of its moons, only Triton is bigger than a few hundred kilometers.

Photo courtesy of NASA

Uranus | Neptune
Earth

Uranus facts

Type: gas giant
Moons: 27 plus rings
Distance from Sun: 19.1 AU
Diameter: 4 × Earth
Surface gravity: 90% of Earth
Avg. atmos. temp.: −197°C
Atmosphere: 82% H, 15% He
Length of day: 17 Earth hours
Length of year: 84 Earth years

Neptune facts

Type: gas giant
Moons: 14 plus rings
Distance from Sun: 30 AU
Diameter: 3.9 × Earth
Surface gravity: 114% of Earth
Avg. atmos. temp.: −201°C
Atmosphere: 96% H, 3% He
Length of day: 16 Earth hours
Length of year: 165 Earth years

Triton, Pluto, and the far outer system

Triton and Pluto are similar

Triton is Neptune's largest moon. Pluto is a dwarf planet, and most of the time the farthest from the Sun. Triton and Pluto are similar objects in both composition and size. In fact, Pluto is slightly smaller than Triton and only a fraction larger than Earth's Moon. Some astronomers believe Pluto may actually be an "escaped" moon of Neptune.

Triton

Triton was not discovered until 1846 and not seriously investigated until the Voyager 2 space probe in 1989. Triton is about three-quarters the diameter of Earth's Moon, but its mass is much lower. Triton's low density of 2.2 g/cm^3 points to a mix of rock and ice. Of the moons in the solar system, only Triton revolves around its planet (Neptune) in a direction opposite from its planet's direction of rotation. (Photo courtesy of NASA.)

Pluto

Discovered in 1930, Pluto (Figure 7.20) was named for the Roman god of the underworld. The first dwarf planet discovered, Pluto rotates slowly—one turn every six days—and backward. Its orbit is quite off-center from the Sun (elliptical). Pluto crosses Neptune's orbit for 20 of the 249 years it takes to orbit around the Sun. Since their orbits are not in the same plane, Neptune and Pluto will never collide. Little is known about Pluto because it is so far away.

Are there more?

Outside the orbit of Pluto is a region called the Kuiper Belt. The Kuiper Belt stretches to 1,000 AU and is believed to contain many asteroid-size and a few Pluto-size objects. As of this writing, two Pluto-size bodies have been found, nicknamed Sedna and Xena. To avoid confusion, astronomers no longer count Pluto as a planet. Instead, Pluto is grouped along with Sedna, Xena, and similar distant bodies in the Kuiper Belt Objects (or KBOs).

Figure 7.20: *Very little is known about Pluto since it is so far from Earth. No space probe has yet visited this cold, icy dwarf planet. This image from the Hubble Space Telescope shows Pluto and its single "moon", Charon. (Photo courtesy of NASA.)*

Pluto   Earth

Pluto facts

Type: rock and ice
Moons: 1
Distance from Sun: 39.2 AU
Diameter: 0.31 × Earth
Surface gravity: 2% of Earth
Avg. atmos. temp.: −223°C
Atmosphere: almost none
Length of day: 153 Earth hours
Length of year: 248 Earth years

7.2 Section Review

1. Do we see planets because, like the Sun, they are sources of light?
2. What is an astronomical unit?
3. Which planet has the most extreme temperature variations?
4. Which planet looks brightest in the sky?
5. Mercury is most similar to
   a. Earth's Moon.
   b. Pluto.
   c. Venus.
   d. Mars.
6. Which planet is closest to Earth in size, gravitational strength, and composition?
7. What happened to the space probe that first landed on Venus?
8. What is the cause of Earth's seasons?
9. Why do scientists believe the surface of Mars may have contained liquid water in the past?
10. What important feature do Europa and Earth have in common?
11. What makes up Saturn's rings?
12. Is Saturn the only planet with rings?
13. The gas giant planets have atmospheres made of hydrogen and helium. What evidence does this give scientists about the formation of the planets?
14. Why is Neptune sometimes farther from the Sun than Pluto?
15. Which three planets rotate backward?
16. What is the difference between a meteor and a meteorite?
17. What is the asteroid belt and where is it located?
18. Compared with Earth's diameter, Saturn's diameter is roughly
    a) the same.   b) 5 times larger.
    c) 10 times larger.   d) 50 times larger.

CHALLENGE

Use the data provided about the planets to make a graph of surface temperature vs. distance from the Sun for the nine planets. Graph the distance on the *x*-axis and the temperature on the *y*-axis. Use these values for the surface temperature of the four inner planets:

Mercury 167°C; Venus 465°C, Earth 15°C, Mars –65°C.

What does your graph show you about the relationship between temperature and distance from the Sun?

Do the planets perfectly follow this relationship?

What other factors might affect the surface temperature of the planets?

7.3 The Sun and the Stars

What are stars? Where did they come from? How long do they last? During most of the day, we see only one star, the Sun, which is 150 million kilometers away. On a clear night, about 6,000 stars can be seen without a telescope. Ancient astronomers believed that the Sun and the stars were different from each other. Today we know that the Sun is just one star like all the others in the night sky. The others appear to be so dim because they are incredibly far away. The closest star to Earth is Alpha Centauri: 4.3 light years (41 trillion kilometers) away. That is 7,000 times farther away than Pluto.

Why stars shine

Nuclear fusion A **star** is basically an enormous, hot ball of gas held together by gravity. Gravity squeezes the matter at the core of stars so tightly that atoms are ripped apart. At high density and pressure, **nuclear fusion** occurs, releasing tremendous amounts of energy. The nuclear fusion that powers the Sun combines four hydrogen atoms to make helium (Figure 7.21). The minimum temperature required for fusion to occur is 7 million °C. The Sun's core reaches a temperature of 15 million °C.

The dense core of a star The extreme pressure and temperature needed for fusion occur only in a small core at the center of a star. The density at the Sun's core is about 158.0 g/cm^3. This is about 18 times the density of solid copper. In order to reach this high density, a star must have a mass much larger than a planet. For example, the Sun has a mass about 330,000 times larger than the mass of Earth.

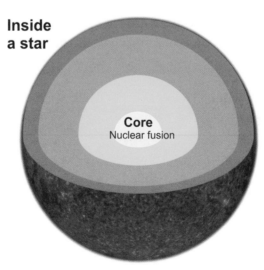

Inside a star

Core
Nuclear fusion

The fusion reactions in the sun combine hydrogen to make helium

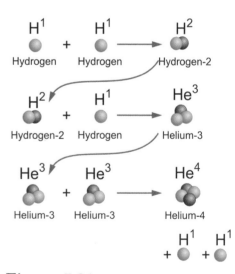

Figure 7.21: *One of several nuclear fusion reactions that release energy in the Sun by combining hydrogen into helium.*

The Sun

The Sun has three regions   Because the Sun is made of gas, its surface is hard to define. The apparent surface that we can see from a distance is called the *photosphere,* which means "sphere of light." Just above it is the *chromosphere.* This is a very hot layer of plasma, a high-energy state of matter. The *corona* is the outermost layer of the Sun's atmosphere, extending millions of kilometers beyond the Sun. Both the corona and chromosphere can be seen during a total eclipse of the Sun, as shown in Figure 7.22.

Sunspots   You should *never* look directly at the Sun. A safe method for viewing the Sun is to use a telescope to project its image onto a white surface. When the Sun is observed in this way, small, dark areas can be seen on its surface. These areas, called *sunspots,* may look small, but they can be as large as Earth. Sunspots are areas of gas that are cooler than the gases around them. Because they don't give off as much light as the hotter areas, they appear as dark spots on the photosphere (Figure 7.23).

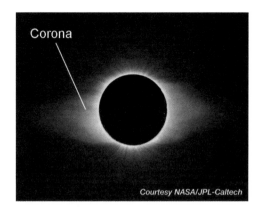

Courtesy NASA/JPL-Caltech

Figure 7.22: *The Sun's corona and chromosphere can be seen during a total eclipse.*

Anatomy of the Sun

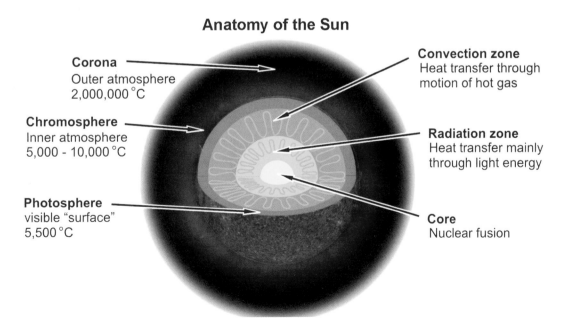

Corona
Outer atmosphere
2,000,000 °C

Chromosphere
Inner atmosphere
5,000 - 10,000 °C

Photosphere
visible "surface"
5,500 °C

Convection zone
Heat transfer through motion of hot gas

Radiation zone
Heat transfer mainly through light energy

Core
Nuclear fusion

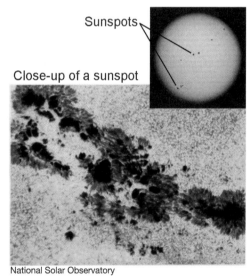

Sunspots

Close-up of a sunspot

National Solar Observatory

Figure 7.23: *Sunspots appear as dark spots on the photosphere.*

Types of stars

How are stars classified?
Stars come in a range of sizes and temperatures. Our Sun is almost an average star in many ways. Some stars are larger and hotter. Other stars are smaller and cooler. Astronomers classify stars according to *size, temperature, color,* and *brightness.*

Sizes of stars
Stars come in a range of masses. The largest stars have a mass of about 60 times the mass of the Sun. The smallest stars are about one-twelfth the mass of the Sun. This is about the smallest mass that makes enough gravitational pressure to start fusion reactions in the core. The Sun is a medium-sized star (Figure 7.24), as is Alpha Centauri, the nearest star to the Sun.

Giant stars

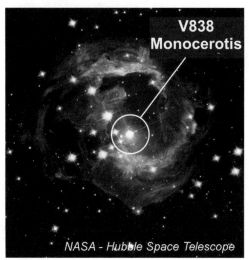

V838 Monocerotis

NASA - Hubble Space Telescope

Stars vary in size as well as mass. There are two types of giant stars. Blue giant stars are hot and much more massive than the Sun. Rigel in the constellation of Orion is a blue giant star. Red giants are of similar mass to the Sun and much cooler. The red giants are huge because they began as sunlike stars but have expanded out past the equivalent of Earth's orbit. As they expanded they cooled down. The photograph shows V838 Monocerotis, a red giant star. Light from this star is illuminating the nebula around it.

Dwarf stars
Stars that are smaller than the Sun come in two main categories, *dwarfs* and *neutron stars.* Dwarf stars are about the size of the smaller planets. Sirius B, the largest known dwarf star, is slightly smaller than Earth. Neutron stars are even smaller. Their diameter is only 20 to 30 kilometers, about the size of a big city.

White dwarf star

Sun-like star

Giant star

Figure 7.24: *Comparing different sizes of stars.*

CHALLENGE

Do stars shine forever? If not, then how are they "born"? How do they "die"? How long do astronomers expect our Sun to last?

Distances to the nearest stars

What is a light year? Because distances in space are huge, astronomers use units much larger than kilometers or meters. You may have heard of *light years* (ly). Light years are a common way to measure distance outside the solar system. One **light year** is the *distance* that light travels through space in one year. A light year is a unit of distance, *not time* (Figure 7.25).

Calculating a light year In space, light travels at the amazing speed of 300,000 kilometers per second. How far does light go in a year? Recall from Chapter 2 that *distance = speed × time.* We calculate the distance light travels in one year by multiplying the speed of light by the number of seconds in one year's time. Here's how to solve the problem:

$$1 \text{ lightyear (ly)} = \text{speed of light} \times \text{time}$$

$$= (300{,}000 \text{ km/s}) \times \left(1 \text{ y} \times \frac{365 \text{ d}}{1 \text{ y}} \times \frac{24 \text{ h}}{1 \text{ d}} \times \frac{3600 \text{ s}}{1 \text{ h}} \right)$$

$$= (300{,}000 \text{ km/s}) \times (31{,}536{,}000 \text{ s})$$

$$= 9{,}460{,}000{,}000{,}000 \text{ km} \quad \text{or} \quad 9.46 \times 10^{12} \text{ km}$$

A light year is the distance light travels in one year through space.

Why we need units as large as light years The stars are light years distant from Earth. By comparison, even Pluto is only 5.4 *light hours* away from the Sun. The nearest stars are 4.3 light years away, 7,000 times farther away than Pluto. Our best rockets travel at 30 kilometers per second. That speed would take you from Los Angeles to San Francisco in *25 seconds*. Even at this enormous speed it would take *40,000 years* to reach the nearest star. If humans are ever to venture beyond the solar system, we clearly need to develop faster ways to travel.

VOCABULARY

light year - the distance light travels through space in one year—9.46×10^{12} km.

Crab Nebula

Image courtesy of NASA

Object	Distance from Earth (light years)
Sirius (brightest star in the sky)	8.8
Betelgeuse (appears as a red star in the sky)	700
Crab Nebula (remnant of an exploded star)	4,000

Figure 7.25: *Distance from Earth (in light years) of some well-known objects in the universe.*

Temperature and color

Temperatures of stars   If you look closely at the stars on a clear night, you might see a slight reddish or bluish tint to some of them. This is because stars' surface temperatures are different. Red stars are cooler than white stars (Figure 7.26), and blue stars are the hottest. The table below lists some stars, their colors, and their surface temperatures.

Table 7.2: Stars, their colors, and their surface temperatures

Star	Color	Temperature range (°C)
Betelgeuse	red	2,000 to 3,500
Arcturus	orange	3,500 to 5,000
Sun	yellow	5,000 to 6,000
Polaris	yellow-white	6,000 to 7,500
Sirius	white	7,500 to 11,000
Rigel	blue-white	11,000 to 25,000
Zeta Orionis	blue	25,000 to 50,000

Figure 7.26: *Sirius, the Dog Star in the constellation of Canis Majoris, is a good example of a white star.*

Color and energy   The color of light is related to its energy. Red light has the lowest energy of the colors we can see. Blue and violet light have the most energy. Yellow, green, and orange are in between. White light is a mixture of all colors at equal brightness.

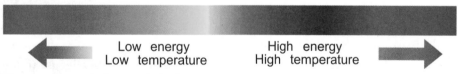

Low energy
Low temperature

High energy
High temperature

Color and temperature   When matter is heated, it first glows red at about 600°C. As the temperature increases, the color changes to orange, yellow, and finally white. The graph in Figure 7.27 shows the colors of light given off at different temperatures. The curve for 2,000°C crosses red and yellow, but drops off before getting to blue. That means a surface at 2,000°C gives off mostly red and some yellow. At 10,000°C a star gives off an even mix from red to blue so it appears white. At 20,000°C the emitted light is white with a bluish color.

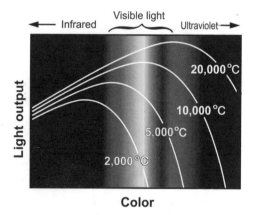

Figure 7.27: *The range of light given off by a star depends on its temperature. Stars at 2,000°C give off mostly red and some yellow light. At 10,000°C a star gives off an even mix from red to blue, so the light appears white.*

Galaxies

The size of the universe

Early civilizations believed that Earth was the center of the universe. In the 16th century, people became aware that Earth is a small planet orbiting a medium-size star. It was only in the 20th century that we became aware that the Sun is one of billions of stars in the Milky Way galaxy, and that there are billions of other galaxies in the universe. In the past 50 years, astronomers have found evidence that the universe is expanding and that it originated 10 billion to 20 billion years ago. In this section, you will learn about galaxies and theories about how the universe began.

The discovery of other galaxies

A **galaxy** is a huge group of stars, dust, gas, and other objects bound together by gravitational forces. The Sun, along with an estimated 200 billion other stars, belongs to the **Milky Way galaxy**. The Milky Way is a typical *spiral galaxy* (Figure 7.28). From above, it would look like a giant pinwheel, with arms radiating out from the center. Although some stars are in *globular clusters* above and below the main disk, the majority are arranged in a disk that is more than 100,000 light years across and only 3,000 light years thick.

Milky Way (side view)

Disc — Galactic core — Globular clusters — Sun — 26,000 light years

Our Sun is 26,000 light years from the center

The disk of the Milky Way is a flattened, rotating system that contains young to middle-aged stars, along with gas and dust (Figure 7.29). The Sun sits about 26,000 light years from the center of the disk and revolves around the center of the galaxy about once every 250 million years. When you look up at the night sky, you are looking through that disk of the galaxy. On a crystal clear night, you can see a faint band of light stretching across the sky. This is the combined light of billions of stars in the galaxy, so numerous that their light merges.

VOCABULARY

galaxy - a group of stars, dust, gas, and other objects held together by gravitational forces.

Milky Way galaxy - the spiral galaxy to which our solar system belongs.

NASA - Hubble Space Telescope

Figure 7.28: *The Whirlpool galaxy is a typical spiral, like the Milky Way.*

NASA - Hubble Space Telescope

Figure 7.29: *How the Milky Way appears in the night sky. We are looking in from the edge of the disk.*

Distances between galaxies

Galaxies are a million times farther away than stars
The distances between stars are 10,000 times greater than the distances between planets. *The distances between galaxies are a million times greater than the distances between stars.* For example, the distance from Earth to the nearest star is 4.3 light years, but from Earth to the Whirlpool galaxy is over 30 million light years.

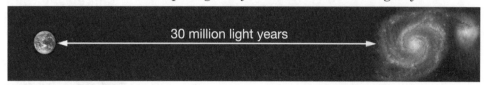

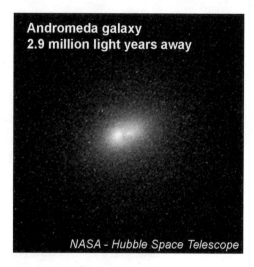

Figure 7.30: *The Andromeda galaxy is an elliptical galaxy in our local group.*

The local group of galaxies
The Milky Way belongs to a group of about 30 galaxies called the local group. This group includes the Large Magellanic Cloud (179,000 light years away) and the Small Magellanic Cloud (210,000 light years away). These Magellanic Clouds are small, irregular galaxies of less than 100,000 stars. The local group also includes Andromeda, an elliptical galaxy 2.9 million light years away (Figure 7.30).

Galactic collisions
Galaxies move through space singly and in groups. Galaxies even collide with each other in slow dances of stars that take millions of years to complete (Figure 7.31)

Determining the distance to nearby galaxies
Figuring out the distance between galaxies is one of the more difficult tasks in astronomy. A faint (low brightness) object in the night sky could be a dim object that is relatively nearby or a bright object that is far, far away. The most reliable method for estimating the distance to a galaxy is to find a star whose luminosity is known. If the luminosity is known, the inverse square law can be used to find the distance from the observed brightness.

Figure 7.31: *Two galaxies that are near to colliding.*

Distant galaxies
This method works for the closest galaxies. However, the vast majority of galaxies are too far away to see single stars even with the best telescopes. Beyond 150 million light years, astronomers compare size and type with closer galaxies to estimate the luminosity of the farther ones. This method is not as accurate and, consequently, the distances to far galaxies are known only to within a factor of two.

7.3 **Section Review**

1. What is the basic process through which the Sun releases energy?
2. Describe the three regions of the Sun.
3. What are sunspots?
4. How big are the biggest known stars compared to the Sun?
   a. about the same size
   b. about 5–6 times larger
   c. about 50–60 times larger
   d. about 500–600 times larger
5. What is a light year?
6. Is the distance to the nearest star outside our solar system on the order of tens, hundreds, or thousands of times longer than the distance between planets of our solar system?
7. Regulus, the brightest star in the constellation Leo, is approximately 77 light years from Earth. Which year did Regulus give off the light you see when looking at the star today?
8. What can you tell about a star by looking at its color?
9. In which galaxy do we live?
10. Is the number of stars in our home galaxy on the order of hundreds, thousands, millions, or billions?
11. The distances between galaxies are in the range of
    a. 100 kilometers.
    b. 100 light years.
    c. 1 million light years.
    d. 1 billion light years.
12. How do astronomers estimate the distance between galaxies?

SOLVE IT!

A light year is the distance light travels in one year. Other units can be defined according to the distance light travels in a certain amount of time. For example, a light second is the distance light travels in one second.

Calculate the number of meters each of the following units represents.

1. Light second
2. Light minute
3. Light nanosecond (a nanosecond is one-billionth of a second)

CHALLENGE

The planet Earth orbits the Sun, an average star. People have wondered for a long time if other stars have planets. What if a planet became so large it turned into a star itself? Research the following questions:

1) Do other stars have planets?

2) Can one star orbit another star just like Earth orbits the Sun?

Extraterrestrial Volcanoes

Mount St. Helens is an active volcano in the western United States that catastrophically erupted in 1980. The amazing explosion blew the top and side off the mountain! A volcanic eruption can quickly change the landscape of an area right before our eyes. There are several active and potentially active volcanoes in the states of California, Oregon, Washington, and Hawaii.

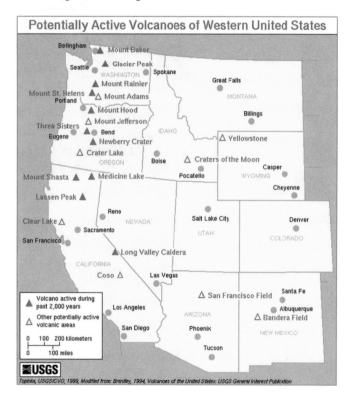

Potentially Active Volcanoes of Western United States

▲ Volcano active during past 2,000 years

△ Other potentially active volcanic areas

0 100 200 kilometers
0 100 miles

≋USGS

Topinka, USGS/CVO, 1999, Modified from: Brantley, 1994, Volcanoes of the United States; USGS General Interest Publication

Did you ever wonder if volcanoes exist on other planets? Planetary volcanologists study volcanoes throughout our solar system. Dr. Rosaly Lopes studies volcanoes on Earth as well as other planets at NASA's Jet Propulsion Laboratory in Pasadena, California.

Volcanology

Volcanology is the study of volcanoes. This fascinating field combines geology, physics, chemistry, and mathematics. Here on Earth, scientists study and monitor volcanoes in hopes of successfully predicting volcanic eruptions. Volcano monitoring can be done locally, observed remotely by aircraft, or by satellites orbiting Earth. Scientists like Dr. Lopes measure ground movement, emission of gases, and changes in temperature.

Scientists from all over the world report their findings of volcanic patterns and behavior monthly. The Smithsonian Institution in the United States publishes them in the *Bulletin of the Global Volcanism Network*.

Dr. Rosaly Lopes standing on the Pu'u O'o eruption of Kīlauea volcano on Hawaii's Big Island

Galileo mission

There are active volcanoes on Earth, but did you know that a *moon of Jupiter* is considered the most volcanically active place in the solar system? A NASA space mission made this exciting discovery.

In 1989, the Galileo mission was launched aboard the space shuttle Atlantis. The Galileo mission goal was to study the four moons of Jupiter, discovered in 1610 by the Italian scientist Galileo Galilei. Io, Europa, Ganymede, and Callisto were studied until the mission's end in 2003.

Pizza moon

In December 1995, the Galileo spacecraft entered into orbit around Jupiter. A series of "flybys" and "close encounters" were the main goals of the mission. The purpose of the flybys and close encounters were to collect pictures and scientific information. The spacecraft beamed the pictures and data back to Earth for scientists to study. Dr. Rosaly Lopes was a member of the Galileo flight project. As an expert on planetary volcanism, she worked from 1996 to 2001 on the NIMS (Near-Infrared Mapping Spectrometer) team. She helped to plan and analyze data from Io. She and her team were responsible for the discovery of *71* volcanoes on Jupiter's volcanic moon, Io.

Today, Io is considered to be the most volcanically-active place in the solar system. Some of the first images of Io were beamed back to Earth from the spacecraft Voyager in 1979. The surface is an array of colors that include red, yellow, white, black, and green. The moon's coloring led to the nickname "Pizza Moon."

Tricky flybys

Dr. Lopes realized that flying too close to Io could be dangerous because of Jupiter's magnetic field and intense radiation. The first planned flyby took place in 1995, but no images were recorded due to equipment failure. Additional flybys were planned and each time volcanic eruptions were observed. Dr. Lopes realized that the plumes of smoke and deposits were responsible for the changing appearance of Io's surface. The brilliant red and yellow coloring of the surface is evidence of sulfur and sulfur dioxide. As the temperature of sulfur changes, so do the colors of the moon. Red is an indication of an active or recently active volcano on Io.

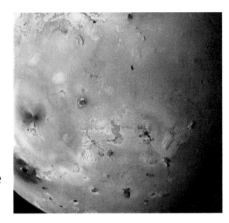

The Galileo spacecraft was so successful that NASA extended the mission three times. After 14 years and 4,631,778,000 kilometers, the spacecraft was intentionally destroyed on September 21, 2003. It will forever change our view of the solar system as scientists continue to explore alien territory.

QUESTIONS

1. How do scientists study volcanic activity on Earth?
2. What was the purpose of the Galileo mission?
3. Why was the appearance of Io's surface constantly changing?
4. Why was it risky for the Galileo spacecraft to fly close to Io?

Galileo and Io images courtesy of NASA

Sunspots

Sunspots are large, dark regions that appear on the surface of the Sun. They appear dark because they are cooler than the areas around them. Sunspots are caused by the Sun's magnetic field. They slowly grow over a few days and then decay over a few days. The largest sunspots may last a few weeks. In the early 1600s, astronomers used the movement of sunspots across the surface of the Sun to figure out that the Sun's rotational period was about 27 days. In this activity, you will determine the diameter of the Sun and the number of sunspots on the Sun.

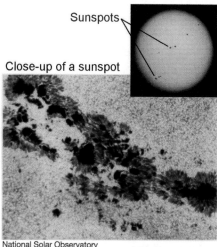

Sunspots

Close-up of a sunspot

National Solar Observatory

Materials:

cardboard; piece of aluminum foil (3 cm × 3 cm); tape' a pin or sharp point to puncture a hole in the aluminum foil; ruler; white paper; solar telescope (sunspotter)

Measure the diameter of the sun

1. First, make a pinhole viewer: Cut a square (2 cm × 2 cm) in the center of the cardboard. Take the aluminum foil and tape it over the opening. Using the pin, puncture a small hole in the center of the aluminum foil.

2. Hold the pinhole viewer so the light of the Sun passes through the hole onto a piece of paper held behind the viewer. Hold the viewer and paper as far apart as you can.

3. Measure the diameter of the Sun's image on the paper.

4. Measure the distance between the pinhole viewer and the image on the paper. Now, calculate the sun's diameter!

Distance from Earth to the Sun: 149,600,000 km

Measured diameter of the Sun: _____ cm

Measured distance from viewer to paper: _____ cm

$$\left(\begin{array}{c} \text{Diameter} \\ \text{of} \\ \text{Sun} \end{array} = \left(\frac{\text{Diameter of image of Sun}}{\text{Distance from viewer to paper}} \right) \times \begin{array}{c} \text{Distance} \\ \text{from} \\ \text{Earth to Sun} \end{array} \right)$$

Measure the size and number of sunspots

5. Using a solar telescope (sunspotter), project the image of the Sun onto a flat surface, then trace the sun's perimeter and any sunspots on a white piece of paper.

Applying your knowledge

a. Using the diameter of the Sun that you calculated, figure out the size of one of the sunspots viewed through the sunspotter. Tell which sunspot you used and how you found your answer.

b. Do you see any patterns associated with sunspot activity on the graph below?

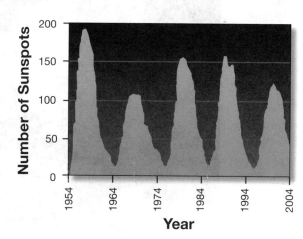

c. The real diameter of the sun is 1.35 million km. By what percent did your estimated diameter of the sun differ from the actual diameter?

Chapter 7 Activity

Chapter 7 Assessment

Vocabulary

Select the correct term to complete the sentences.

asteroid	astronomical unit	Newton's law of
comets	galaxy	universal gravitation
Milky Way galaxy	gas planets	nuclear fusion
solar system	light year	orbit
star	meteor	planet
tide	meteorite	terrestrial planets

Section 7.1

1. The mathematical law relating the force of gravity between two bodies, their masses, and the distance between their centers is known as ____.

2. The daily rise and fall of the ocean level is called the ____.

3. The name for the nearly circular path an object travels around a gravity source such as a star or planet is a(n) ____.

Section 7.2

4. The system containing the Sun, eight major planets, and their moons is called the ____.

5. The average distance from Earth to the Sun, used as a measuring unit, is called a(n) ____.

6. A massive body that revolves around a star in its own orbit is a(n) ____.

7. The four planets composed mostly of rocks and metal are, as a group, called the ____.

8. The four planets composed mostly of hydrogen and helium are, as a group, called the ____.

9. Meteors large enough to fall through the atmosphere without being destroyed by the heat of friction are ____.

10. An object that orbits the Sun, but is too small to be called a planet is a(n) ____.

11. Dust or chunks of rock that enter the atmosphere to become "shooting stars" are also known as ____.

12. Mountain-size chunks of ice and rock that develop "tails" as they approach the Sun in their orbit are known as ____.

Section 7.3

13. The source of energy for the Sun and other stars is ____.

14. The distance light travels in one year is the unit of distance called the ____.

15. A huge group of stars, dust, gas, and other objects bound together by gravitational forces is known as a(n) ____.

16. A hot ball of gas, such as the Sun, held together by gravity is a(n) ____.

17. The spiral galaxy to which our solar system belongs is the ____.

Concepts

Section 7.1

1. Name the factors that determine the strength of the gravitational force between two masses.

2. If you were to double your distance from the center of Earth how would this affect your weight?

3. The balance between the force of _____ and _____ keep the Moon and all other satellites in orbit around Earth.

4. If Earth suddenly disappeared, what would happen to the Moon?

5. Astronauts are often described as being weightless as they "float" in the international space station while orbiting Earth. Explain why they are not.

6. Which cycle is the length of a year based on?
   a. Earth's revolution around the Sun
   b. the Moon's revolution around Earth
   c. Earth's rotation around its axis

7. Describe or draw the relative positions of the Sun, the Moon, and Earth during the phase of the Moon called New Moon.

8. How are tides created on Earth?

9. What is gravitational locking? How does it explain the fact that we can only see one side of the Moon from Earth?

10. Explain why the Moon would need a faster orbital speed to stay in orbit around Earth if it were moved closer to Earth's surface.

Section 7.2

11. For each of the following, tell whether it reflects light or is a source of light.
    a. the Sun
    b. the Moon
    c. Earth
    d. Mars
    e. Stars

12. Name the four gas planets.

13. Name the four terrestrial planets.

14. What causes meteors to glow as "shooting stars"?

15. Are the gas planets made up of only gas?

16. Why does the Sun feel warmer during summer and colder during winter in the northern hemisphere?

17. Mercury is closer to the Sun than Venus, but Venus has higher surface temperatures. Explain why.

18. How do Saturn's rings stay in place?

19. Which planet has a day that is longer than its year?

20. What is important about Jupiter's moon, Io?

21. Which planets, beside Earth, have an atmosphere?

22. Fill in the table below with the name of the major planet that matches each description.

Planet Description	Major Planet Name
smallest diameter	
most dense	
least dense	
farthest from the Sun	
closest to the Sun	
largest gravitational force	
smallest gravitational force	
longest "day"	
shortest "day"	
longest "year"	
shortest "year"	
highest surface temperature	
lowest surface temperature	
has the most moons	

Section 7.3

23. In which part of the Sun does nuclear fusion take place?

24. List three conditions that must exist for nuclear fusion to occur.

25. Which "layer" of the Sun do we see?

26. What characteristics are used to classify stars?

27. Describe the shape and size of our galaxy, the Milky Way.

28. Describe the color changes that occur in matter as it is heated.

29. What is the color and temperature range of a star with the lowest surface temperature?

30. What is the color and temperature range of a star with the highest surface temperature?

Problems

Section 7.1

1. Describe the direction of the force of gravity exerted by Earth on an elephant standing on Earth's surface.

2. Far in the future, an astronaut visits the moon of a distant planet. On this moon, she weighs 100 N. If she leaves the moon to visit the planet, which is eight times the mass and twice the diameter of its moon, what would she weigh?

3. Neptune's mass is about 17 times greater than Earth's mass. Would your weight be 17 times greater if you visited Neptune?

4. Newton's law of universal gravitation explains the strength of the gravitational attraction between Earth and the Moon.
   a. If the mass of Earth suddenly doubles, what would happen to the gravitational force between Earth and the Moon?
   b. If the mass of Earth and the mass of the Moon were both doubled, what would happen to the gravitational attraction between them?
   c. If the distance from Earth to the Moon were doubled, what would happen to the gravitational attraction between them?

5. When Sasha places a 50-kg box on a bathroom scale in a stationary elevator, the scale reads 490 N. If the elevator begins to accelerate upward at 9.8 m/s^2, what will be the reading on the scale?

6. Jupiter's period of rotation is 0.41 of the period of rotation for Earth. How many hours does it take for Jupiter to rotate once on its axis?

Section 7.2

7. Earth's average distance from the Sun is 150 million kilometers. The average distance from Mars to the Sun is 228 million kilometers. What are these distances in astronomical units (AU)?

8. The Andromeda galaxy is 2.3 million light years away from Earth. What does this equal in kilometers?

9. A supernova was observed in 1987. If the star that collapsed into this supernova was 169,000 light years away, how long ago did this explosion occur?

Section 7.3

10. Rank the following systems according to size, from largest to smallest.
    a. Milky Way galaxy
    b. the Solar System
    c. Earth
    d. our Sun
    e. the universe

11. Rank the following distances from largest to smallest.
    a. distance between our Sun and the star Sirius
    b. distance between Earth and Neptune
    c. distance between the Milky Way galaxy and the Andromeda galaxy
    d. distance between Earth and the Moon

UNIT 4

ELECTRICITY, SOUND, AND LIGHT

CHAPTER 8
Electricity and Magnetism

CHAPTER 9
Waves and Sound

CHAPTER 10
Light and Color

Exploring on Your Own

Wind turbines and solar panels are examples of technologies being used to harvest energy from renewable sources. What is microharvesting? How are engineers using energy captured from sources, such as light and vibration, to power smaller devices? What are the benefits of this technology?

Chapter 8

Electricity and Magnetism

What would your life be like without electricity? Do you know how electrical circuits work? Do you know what the words voltage and current mean? Imagine an exercise bike connected to a light bulb. Energy from your pedaling lights the bulb. How fast would you have to pedal to generate enough electrical energy to light the bulb? You would be surprised at how hard you would have to work! Instead, you have all that energy available at the flick of a switch. This chapter will give you the opportunity to explore electricity, electrical circuits, and the nature of electrical energy.

Magnetism is closely related to electricity. Electric currents cause magnetism. The opposite is also true—moving magnets are used to generate electricity. Magnetism is also how a compass works. A compass needle points north because planet Earth has huge electrical currents flowing in its hot, molten iron core. Read this chapter to learn more!

Key Questions:

1. What is electricity?

2. How do magnets work?

3. How is electricity generated?

8.1 Electricity

Mass is one of the more obvious properties of matter. However, matter has other properties that are often hidden. Electricity and magnetism are two of matter's hidden properties. All matter has electrical (and magnetic) properties because the atoms that make up matter are held together by electromagnetic forces. Electromagnetic forces also bond atoms together into molecules and hold molecules together in solids and liquids.

Electric and magnetic forces

Attraction and repulsion What happens when two magnets get near each other? Like gravity, magnets exert forces on each other, even when they are some distance apart. Unlike gravity, the force between magnets can either attract or repel. Magnetic forces can attract or repel because there are *two kinds of magnetic poles*, called **north** and **south**. Gravity is always attractive because there is only one kind of mass.

Opposite poles attract and similar poles repel Whether magnetic forces attract or repel depends on which poles are closest. Opposite poles attract each other. A north pole attracts a south pole and a south pole attracts a north pole. Similar poles repel each other. A north pole repels another north pole and a south pole repels another south pole (Figure 8.1).

Opposite charges attract and similar charges repel Electric charge is another property of matter. Like magnetism, electric charge comes in two types. We call them **positive** and **negative**. Like magnetic poles, opposite charges attract each other. A positive charge attracts a negative charge and vice versa. Two similar charges repel each other. Positive charges repel other positive charges and negative charges repel other negative charges.

Magnetic forces

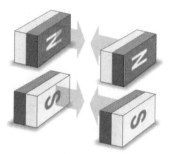

Opposite poles attract each other

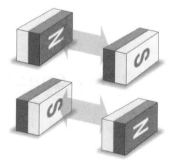

Similar poles repel each other

Figure 8.1: *The two ways magnets can interact with each other.*

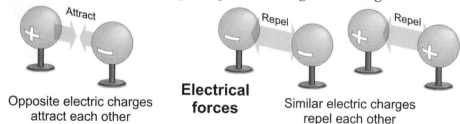

Opposite electric charges attract each other

Electrical forces

Similar electric charges repel each other

Electric charge

Two types of charge

Both electricity and magnetism are caused by electric charge. **Electric charge**, like mass, is a fundamental property of virtually all matter. Unlike mass, electric charge is usually well hidden inside atoms. Charge is hidden because atoms are made with equal amounts of positive and negative charges. Inside the atom, the attraction between positive and negative charges holds the atom together. Outside the atom, the electrical forces cancel each other out (Figure 8.2). The forces from positive charges are canceled by the forces from negative charges, the same way that +1 and −1 add up to 0. Because ordinary matter has zero *net* (total) charge, most matter acts as if there is no electric charge at all.

Static electricity and lightning

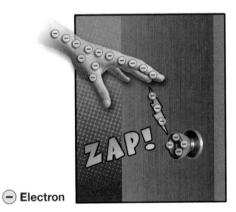

⊖ **Electron**

However, electric charge doesn't *always* cancel out. Sometimes there is a little more of either positive or negative. Then the effects of electric charge can be felt. If you have ever received a shock while touching a doorknob on a dry day, you have felt electric charge yourself. A tiny imbalance in either positive or negative charge is the cause of **static electricity**.

Electric current

You get a shock from static electricity because charge of one type strongly attracts charge of the other type. When you walk across a carpet on a dry day, your body picks up excess negative charge. When you touch a doorknob, some of your excess negative charge moves to the doorknob. Because the doorknob is metal, the charge flows quickly. The moving charge makes a brief, intense **electric current** between you and the doorknob. Electric current is caused by moving electric charge. The shock you feel is the electric current moving negative charge through your skin to the doorknob. Electric current is also one of the most useful ways in which the electrical properties of matter show themselves.

Outside the atom, electrical forces mostly cancel out.

Inside the atom, positive charge in the nucleus attracts negative charge outside the nucleus

Figure 8.2: *Electromagnetic forces hold atoms together on the inside but (mostly) cancel each other out outside of the atom.*

Electric current

Electric current is moving electric charge
The electricity you use every day is *electric current* in wires, motors, light bulbs, and other inventions. Electric current is what makes an electric motor turn or an electric stove heat up. Electric current is almost always invisible and comes from the motion of electric charges that are much smaller than atoms. In fact, the moving charges in a wire are so small they move around and between the atoms in solid copper metal. These charges are called *electrons* and we will talk more about them in Chapter 13.

Electric current and water current
Electric current is similar in some ways to a current of water. Like electric current, water current can carry energy and do work. For example, a waterwheel turns when a current of water exerts a force on it (Figure 8.3). A waterwheel can be connected to a machine such as a loom for making cloth, or to a millstone for grinding wheat into flour. Before electricity was available, waterwheels were used to supply energy to many machines. Today, the same tasks are done using energy from electric current. Look around you right now and you will probably see wires carrying electric current into buildings.

Electric current is measured in amps
Electric current is measured in **amperes** (A), or amps, for short. The unit was named in honor of Andre-Marie Ampere, a French physicist who studied electricity and magnetism. A small, battery-powered flashlight uses about 1/2 amp of electric current (Figure 8.4).

Electricity can be powerful and dangerous
Electric current can carry great deal of energy. For example, an electric motor the size of a basketball can do as much work as five big horses or 20 strong people. Electric current also can be dangerous. Touching a live electric wire can result in serious injury. The more you know about electricity, the easier it is to use it safely.

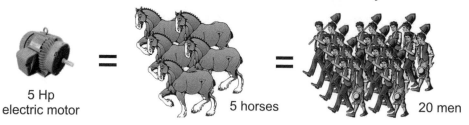

5 Hp electric motor = 5 horses = 20 men

VOCABULARY

ampere - the unit of electric current.

Figure 8.3: *A waterwheel uses the force of flowing water to run machines.*

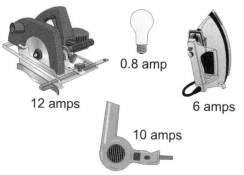

12 amps   0.8 amp   6 amps

10 amps

Figure 8.4: *The amount of electric current used by some common devices.*

Voltage

What does a battery do?

If you touch a piece of wire to a light bulb, nothing will happen. Add a battery to the same piece of wire, and the bulb lights up. What does the battery do that makes the bulb light? If you leave the light on for too long, the battery "dies" and the bulb goes out. What is the difference between a "charged" battery and a "dead" battery?

Electric potential energy

The difference is *energy*. It takes energy to make light, and the battery provides that energy to the circuit. Within the battery, chemical energy is transformed into *electric potential energy*. "Potential" means the energy is stored and *could* be released. Voltage is the potential energy available to move a *single charge* between two points in a circuit. Voltage is always measured *between* two points in a circuit and has units of **volts** (V). A battery stores potential energy, but that energy cannot be released until wires are connected to its terminals. Once the potential electrical energy of the battery is released, current is allowed to flow. Think about a battery lighting a bulb in a circuit in two steps. First, the voltage difference between the battery terminals causes electric current to flow. Second, the current carries energy and makes the bulb turn on.

Current flows from high voltage to low voltage

Current flows from higher voltage to lower voltage. It is a *difference* in voltage that makes electrical current flow just as a difference in height makes water current flow (Figure 8.5). A "charged" battery uses its energy to keep a voltage difference of 1.5 volts between its positive terminal and the negative terminal. A "dead" battery has used up its energy and the voltage difference drops close to zero. No current flows when there is zero voltage difference, which is why a dead battery won't light a bulb.

Current (amps) flows and does work.
A voltage difference causes current to flow.

Current and voltage

We make electrical energy useful by creating a voltage difference then using the voltage to push electric current. Current is what actually flows and does work. A difference in voltage provides the energy that causes current to flow. Current and voltage are two essential ideas of electricity, and they are different! Voltage is the amount of potential energy carried by each charge, energy that *could become* active. Flowing electric current *is* active energy carried by each charge, energy that is moving and doing work.

VOCABULARY

volt - the unit of electric potential.

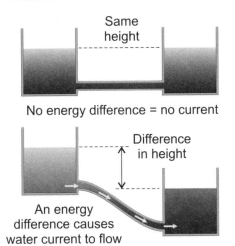

Same height

No energy difference = no current

Difference in height

An energy difference causes water current to flow

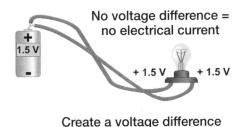

No voltage difference = no electrical current

+ 1.5 V   + 1.5 V

Create a voltage difference and electrical current flows

+ 1.5 V   0 V

Figure 8.5: *Why electrical current flows in a circuit.*

Batteries

How do batteries work? A battery uses stored chemical energy to create a voltage difference. Electrical current carries the energy to electrical devices such as a light bulb. The bulb *transforms* electrical energy carried by current into light and heat. The current returns to the battery, where it gets more energy. Since electric current in wires is invisible, think of a "current" of marchers, each carrying a bucket of energy (see diagram below). The battery refills the buckets with fresh energy and the bulb uses the energy to make light and heat

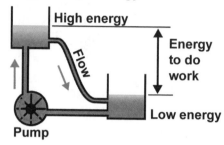

A pump is like a battery because it brings water from a position of low energy to high energy.

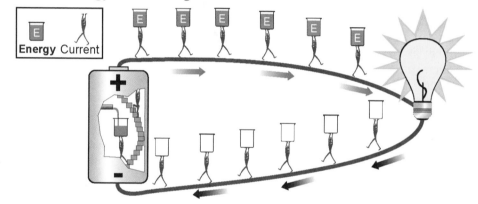

Figure 8.6: *A battery acts like a pump to give energy to flowing electrical current.*

Batteries are like pumps A water pump makes another good analogy for a battery (Figure 8.6). The pump raises the water, increasing its potential energy. As the water flows down, its potential energy is converted into kinetic energy. In a battery, chemical reactions release energy by creating a voltage difference. Current carries the energy to electrical devices.

Current flows from positive to negative Examine any battery and you will always find a positive and a negative end. Electric current flows from positive to negative. The positive end on a AA, C, or D battery has a raised bump, and the negative end is flat.

Battery voltage Since batteries create voltage differences, they can be "stacked up" to make higher voltages (Figure 8.7). The first battery raises the voltage from 0 to 1.5 V. The second one goes from 1.5 V to 3V and the third from 3 V to 4.5 V. Each battery adds an additional 1.5 V.

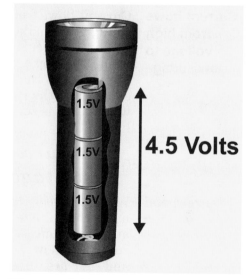

Figure 8.7: *Three 1.5-volt batteries can be stacked to make a total voltage of 4.5 volts in a flashlight.*

8.1 Section Review

1. Describe one way that the force of gravity and magnetic force are similar. Describe one way they are different.
2. Describe the forces between the positive and negative electric charges in the diagram below.

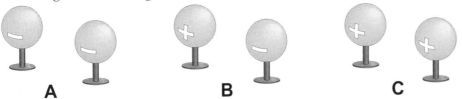

3. Explain how there can be electrical charge inside matter even if the matter shows no electrical forces.
4. List one way electric current is similar to water current and one way it is different.
5. Explain the difference between an object that has "static electricity" and one that does not.
6. List the units for measuring current and voltage.
7. Describe the difference between current and voltage. Can there be current without voltage? Can there be voltage without current?
8. Electrical current flows
   a. through all wires all of the time.
   b. from higher voltage to lower voltage.
   c. whenever matter contains electric charge.
9. What is the voltage difference between the points A and B in the diagram below? Assume each battery is fully charged.

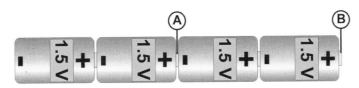

Electrical current is not energy itself. Instead, electrical current is a very efficient way to move energy from one place to another. Energy released from burning gas in a power plant can be moved thousands of miles to businesses and homes where the energy is used. The true value of electricity in technology is as a way to distribute and store energy.

CHALLENGE

Different electrical devices around you use different voltages. Some voltages are relatively safe and others are not. Research 10 electrical devices around your home or classroom to see what voltage they use. What is the highest voltage you found? What is the lowest voltage?

8.2 Electric Circuits and Electrical Power

Every electrical device uses current to carry energy and voltage to push the current. How are electrical devices designed? What types of parts are used in an electrical device? Why are some devices more powerful than others, like an electric saw compared to an electric toothbrush? This section is an introduction to the technology of electricity.

Electric circuits

Electricity travels in circuits An **electric circuit** is a complete path through which electric current travels. A good example of a circuit is the one found in an electric toaster. The circuit has a switch that turns on when the lever on the side of the toaster is pushed down. With the switch on, electric current enters through one side of the plug from the socket in the wall, and goes through the toaster and out the other side of the plug. Bread is toasted by heaters that convert electrical energy to heat.

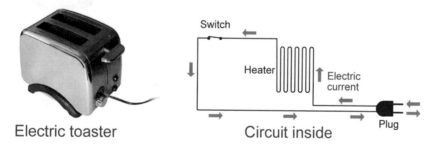

Electric toaster   Circuit inside

Wires are like pipes for electricity Wires act like pipes for electric current, similar to how pipes carry water (Figure 8.8). Water flows into a house through the supply pipe and out through the return (drain) pipe. Electrical current flows in the supply wire and out the return wire. One big difference between wires and water pipes is that you cannot get electricity to leave a wire the way water leaves a pipe. If you cut a water pipe, the water flows out. If you cut a wire, the electric current stops immediately.

VOCABULARY

electric circuit - a complete path through which electric current can flow.

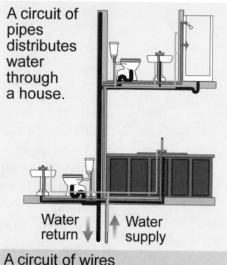

A circuit of pipes distributes water through a house.

Water return   Water supply

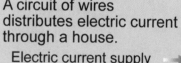

A circuit of wires distributes electric current through a house.

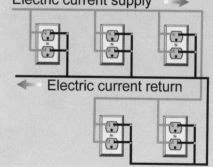

Figure 8.8: *Comparing "circuits" for water and electricity.*

Current in a circuit

Open and closed circuits
Current only flows when there is a complete and unbroken path, called a *closed circuit,* from one end of a battery to the other (Figure 8.9). A light bulb will light only when it is part of a closed circuit. The opposite of a closed circuit is an *open circuit*. A circuit with a break in it is called an open circuit.

Switches
Switches are used to turn electricity on and off. Flipping a switch to the "off" position creates an open circuit by making a break in the wire. The break stops the current because electricity cannot normally travel through air. Flipping a switch to the "on" position closes the break and allows the current to flow again, to supply energy to the bulb or other electrical device.

Current flow is always balanced

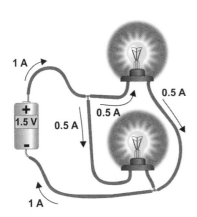

On average, the amount of electric current flowing into any part of a circuit must be the same as the amount flowing back out. Otherwise, charge would "build up" as more charge flowed in than out. This doesn't usually happen because the huge electrical forces between charges immediately attract opposite charges, cancelling any "build-up" before it can occur. It takes special devices (called *capacitors*) to build up even tiny amounts of electric charge.

Why current doesn't "leak out" of a circuit
Current does not "leak out" of an open circuit because electric forces are very, very strong. As an example, imagine you could completely separate the positive and negative charges from inside the atoms in the point of a pencil. At a distance of 1 meter, the attractive force between them would be 50 thousand billion newtons. This is the weight of *three thousand million* cars, just from the charge in a pencil point (Figure 8.10)! The huge forces between charges are the reason current stops flowing the moment a circuit is broken.

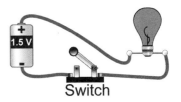

Open circuit

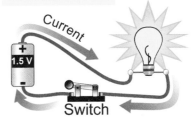

Closed circuit

Figure 8.9: *There is current in a closed circuit but not in an open circuit.*

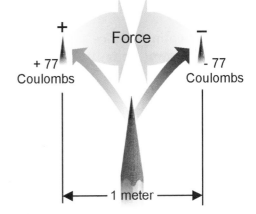

50,000,000,000,000 N

+ 77 Coulombs

− 77 Coulombs

1 meter

Figure 8.10: *At a distance of one meter, the attractive forces between positive and negative charges would be 50 thousand billion Newtons.*

Electrical power

Electrical power is measured in watts

Electrical power is measured in watts, just like mechanical power (Chapter 6). Remember, power is energy per second, or energy flow. One watt is one joule per second. If you look at the top of a light bulb there is a label telling you how many watts it uses. A 100-watt electric light bulb uses 100 joules of energy *every second* (Figure 8.11).

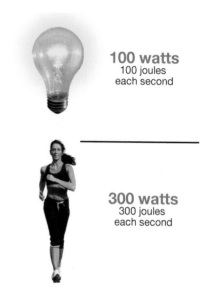

100 watts
100 joules
each second

Electrical power depends on both voltage and current

One amp of current carries one watt of electric power for each volt. The higher the voltage, the more power is carried by each amp of electric current. One amp from a 1.5-volt battery carries 1.5 watts of power. One amp from a 120-volt wall socket carries 120 watts of power.

300 watts
300 joules
each second

Voltage is power (watts) per amp of current.

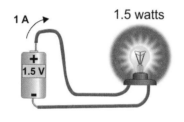

1 A
1.5 V
1.5 watts

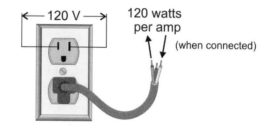

120 V
120 watts
per amp
(when connected)

Figure 8.11: *A 100-watt electric light bulb uses 100 joules of electrical energy every second.*

Calculating power

Since one volt is one watt per amp, to calculate power in an electric circuit you multiply the voltage and current together. For example, suppose a 9-volt battery causes 0.5 amps to flow in a circuit. How much power does the battery provide? Well, 9 V × 0.5 A = 4.5 W. The battery supplies 4.5 watts of power.

Why electrical outlets use higher voltage

Devices that use higher power are often designed to use higher voltages. Higher voltage means the power can be carried with a smaller amount of current. For example, suppose you wanted to run a saw that needs 1,500 watts. Each amp from a 1.5 volt battery carries 1.5 watts. You would need 1,000 amps of current to get 1,500 watts. This is 10 times more current than an average house uses! At 120 volts, the same power is carried by a current of only 12.5 amps. That is why your outlets are at 120 volts instead of 1.5 volts.

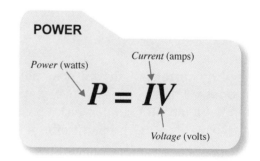

POWER

Power (watts)   *Current* (amps)

$$P = IV$$

Voltage (volts)

Resistance

How much current flows? You can apply the same voltage to different circuits and different amounts of current will flow. For example, when you plug a 60-watt desk lamp into a 120-volt outlet, it draws a current of 0.5 amps. If a hair dryer is plugged into the same outlet the current is 10 amps. How does each device use the right amount of current?

Current and resistance **Resistance** (R) controls how much current flows for a given voltage. When resistance is low, current flows easily. A small voltage can cause a large current to flow. When resistance is high, it takes more voltage to make current flow. The relationship between current and resistance is like water flowing from the open end of a bottle (Figure 8.12). If the opening is large, the resistance is low and lots of water flows (high current). If the opening is small, the resistance is greater and less water flows (low current).

The ohm

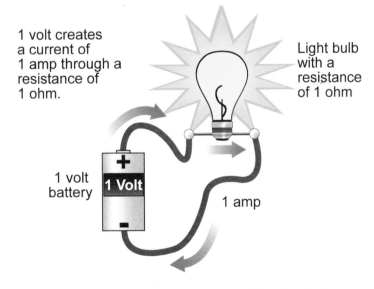

1 volt creates a current of 1 amp through a resistance of 1 ohm.

Light bulb with a resistance of 1 ohm

1 volt battery

1 Volt

1 amp

Electrical resistance is measured in **ohms**. The Greek letter *omega* (Ω) is used to represent resistance in ohms. When you see Ω in a sentence, think or read "ohms." For a given voltage, the greater the resistance, the less current flows. If a circuit has a resistance of 1 ohm, then a voltage of 1 volt causes a current of 1 amp to flow.

High resistance to water flow

Low resistance to water flow

Water

Water

Figure 8.12: *The current is less when the resistance is greater.*

Ohm's law

Ohm's law The current in a circuit depends on voltage and resistance (Figure 8.13). Voltage and current are *directly* related. Doubling the voltage doubles the current. Resistance and current are *inversely* related. Doubling the resistance cuts the current in half. These two relationships form Ohm's law. The law relates current, voltage, and resistance with one formula. If you know two of the three quantities, you can use Ohm's law to find the third.

How much current flows when a 6Ω bulb is connected to 3V from batteries?

$$current = \frac{voltage}{resistance}$$

$$= \frac{3\,V}{6\,\Omega}$$

$$= 0.5\,A$$

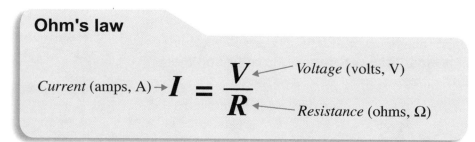

Ohm's law

$$Current\ (amps,\ A) \rightarrow I = \frac{V}{R}$$

Voltage (volts, V)

Resistance (ohms, Ω)

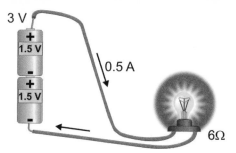

Figure 8.13: *Some examples of Ohm's law in action.*

Using Ohm's law

A toaster oven has a resistance of 12 ohms and is plugged into a 120-volt outlet. How much current does it draw?

1. Looking for: You are asked for the current in amperes.

2. Given: You are given the resistance in ohms and voltage in volts.

3. Relationships: Ohm's law: $I = \dfrac{V}{R}$

4. Solution: Plug in the values for V and R: $I = \dfrac{120\,V}{12\,\Omega} = 10\,A$

a. A laptop computer runs on a 24-volt battery. If the resistance of the circuit inside is 16 ohms, how much current does it use? **Answer:** 1.5 A

b. A motor in a toy car needs 2 amps of current to work properly. If the car runs on four 1.5-volt batteries, what is the motor's resistance? **Answer:** 3 ohms

---

The resistance of common objects

Resistance of common devices

Every electrical device is designed so its resistance causes the right amount of current to flow when connected to the proper voltage. For example, a 60-watt light bulb has a resistance of 240 ohms. When connected to 120 volts from a wall socket, the current is 0.5 amps and the bulb lights (Figure 8.14). If you connect the same light bulb to a 1.5-volt battery it will not light because not enough current flows. According to Ohm's law, only 0.00625 amps flow through 240 ohms when 1.5 volts are applied. This is not enough current to make light.

The resistance of skin

You can get a fatal shock by touching some electrical wires, so why is it safe to touch a 9-volt battery? The reason is Ohm's law. Remember, current is what flows and carries power. The resistance of dry skin is 100,000 ohms or more. According to Ohm's law, 9 V ÷ 100,000 Ω is only 0.00009 amps. This is not enough current to be harmful, but 120 volts from a wall socket is dangerous because it can push 0.0012 amps (120 V ÷ 100,000 Ω) through your skin, 13 times as much as the battery.

Water lowers skin resistance

Wet skin has much lower resistance than dry skin. Lower resistance allows more current to pass through your body at any voltage. The combination of water and 120-volt electricity is especially dangerous because the high voltage and lower resistance allow large (possibly fatal) currents to flow.

Conductors

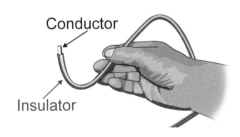

A **conductor** is a material with low electrical resistance. Most metals, like copper, are good conductors. That is why the current-carrying part of a wire is copper or aluminum. **Insulators** are materials with high resistance. The outer part of a wire is an insulator, such as rubber or plastic. The insulator protects your skin by blocking the current. The outside of electrical cords and many electrical devices are insulators for safety. Wires with broken insulation (exposing bare metal) can be very dangerous.

VOCABULARY

conductor - a material with a low electrical resistance. Metals such as copper and aluminum are good conductors.

insulator - a material with a high electrical resistance. Plastic and rubber are good insulators.

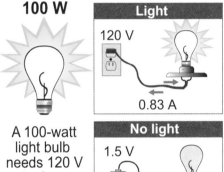

A 100-watt light bulb needs 120 V to draw enough current to light up.

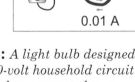

Figure 8.14: *A light bulb designed for use in a 120-volt household circuit does not light when connected to a 1.5-volt battery.*

8.2 Section Review

1. An electrical circuit is
   a. a network of pipes that carry water.
   b. a path for electric current to flow.
   c. a source of voltage that can push current.
   d. what flows and carries electrical power.
2. What is a difference between water in pipes and current in wires?
   a. Water flows but electrical current does not.
   b. Water leaks out of open pipes but current does not leak out of open wires.
   c. Low resistance allows more water to flow and high resistance allows less to flow.
3. How much electrical power is carried by 2 amps of current from a 1.5-volt battery?

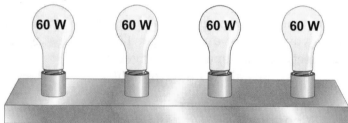

4. How much current must flow to carry 240 watts at 120 volts? This is the amount of electrical power used by the bathroom light fixture with four 60 W bulbs shown above.
5. Which carries more power: 100 amps at 12 volts or 10 amps at 120 volts? (*Hint*: Is one more, or are they equal?)
6. What happens to the current if a circuit's resistance increases? What if the voltage increases instead?
7. List the units used to measure resistance, voltage, and current. Give the abbreviation for each unit.
8. Classify each of the following as a conductor, semiconductor, or insulator: air, gold, silicon, rubber, and aluminum.

Measuring voltage and current

Humans cannot normally sense voltage or current. Instead, we use a multimeter to find the voltage or current in a circuit. To measure voltage, the meter's probes are touched to two places in a circuit or across a battery. The meter shows the difference in voltage between the two places. To measure current, the circuit is broken and reconnected through the meter. The current then passes through the meter where it can be measured.

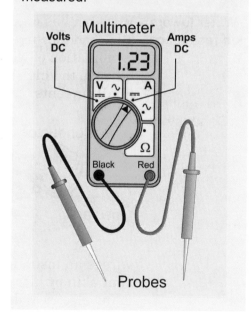

8.3 Properties of Magnets

 **VOCABULARY**

Magnetism has fascinated people since the earliest times. We know that magnets stick to refrigerators and pick up paper clips or pins. They are also found in electric motors, computer disk drives, burglar alarm systems, and many other common devices.

magnetic - the property of creating or responding to forces from magnets.

permanent magnet - a material that remains magnetic without outside energy being supplied.

What is a magnet?

Magnets and magnetic materials If a material is **magnetic**, it has the ability to exert forces on magnets or other magnetic materials. A magnet on a refrigerator is attracted to the steel in the refrigerator's door. A *magnet* is a material that can create magnetic effects by itself. *Magnetic materials* are affected by magnets but do not actively create their own magnetism. Iron and steel are magnetic materials that can also be magnets.

Permanent magnets A **permanent magnet** is a material that keeps its magnetic properties, even when it is not close to other magnets. Bar magnets, refrigerator magnets, and horseshoe magnets are good examples of permanent magnets.

Bar magnet

Horseshoe magnet

Magnetic materials

Poles All magnets have two magnetic poles (north and south). If a magnet is cut, each part will have its own north and south poles (Figure 8.15). It is impossible to have only a north or south pole by itself. The north and south poles are like the two sides of a coin. You can't have a one-sided coin, and you can't have a single magnetic pole either.

Magnetic forces Magnetic forces can pass through many materials with no apparent decrease in strength. For example, one magnet can drag another magnet even when there is a piece of wood between them (Figure 8.16). Plastics, wood, and most insulating materials are transparent to (have no effect on) magnetic forces.

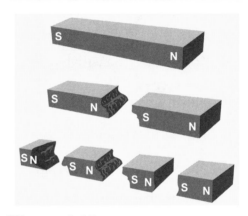

Figure 8.15: *If a magnet is cut, each piece has both a north and a south pole.*

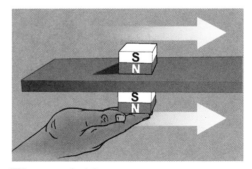

Figure 8.16: *The force between two magnets can pass through many solid materials.*

The magnetic field

How to describe magnetic forces

How does the force from one magnet get to another magnet? Does it happen instantly? How far does the force reach? These questions puzzled scientists for a long time. Eventually, they realized that the force between magnets acts in two steps. First, a magnet fills the space around itself with a kind of potential energy called the **magnetic field**. Second, the magnetic field makes forces that act on other magnets nearby (and back on the same magnet too).

The speed of magnetic forces

The magnetic field spreads out around the magnet at the speed of light. The speed of light is about 300 million meters *per second*. That means the force from one magnet reaches a nearby magnet so fast it *seems* like it happens instantly, though it actually takes a fraction of a second. Sensitive instruments can measure this small amount of time.

Magnetic forces get weaker with distance

The force from a magnet gets weaker as it gets farther away. You can feel this by comparing the force when you hold two magnets close together compared to holding them far apart (Figure 8.17). Try this and you will find that the force loses strength very rapidly with increasing distance. Separating a pair of magnets by twice the distance reduces the force by eight times or more.

Drawing the magnetic field

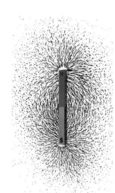

A special kind of diagram is used to show the magnetic field. The diagram shows an arrow in the direction of the force on the north pole of an imaginary test magnet. Since the test magnet is imaginary, we can allow it to have only a north pole. Figure 8.18 shows a drawing of the magnetic field around a small magnet. The force points away from the north pole because a north pole would be repelled from another north pole. The force points toward the south pole because a north pole magnet would be attracted to the south pole. You can model the pattern of a magnetic field by sprinkling iron filings on cardboard with magnets on it (shown left). Each tiny piece of iron filing is a tiny magnet with a north and south pole. Even though the actual magnetic field is invisible, you can see the pattern of its forces through the alignment of all the tiny magnets.

magnetic field - the influence created by a magnet that exerts forces on other magnets.

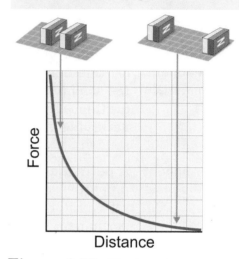

Figure 8.17: *The force between two magnets fades away quickly as the magnets are separated.*

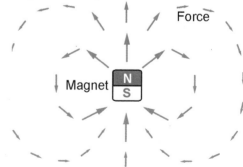

Figure 8.18: *The force on an imaginary north magnetic pole (test magnet) near a source magnet.*

How does a compass work?

A compass is a magnet

A compass needle is a magnet that is free to spin (Figure 8.19). The north pole of a compass needle always points toward the south pole of a permanent magnet. This is in the direction of the magnetic field lines. Because the needle aligns with the local magnetic field, a compass is a great way to "see" magnetic field lines.

North and south poles

The planet Earth has a magnetic field that comes from the core of the planet itself. The terms "north pole" and "south pole" come from the direction that a magnetized compass needle points. The end of the magnet that points toward geographic north was called the magnet's north pole and the opposite pole was called south. The names were decided long before people understood how a compass needle worked.

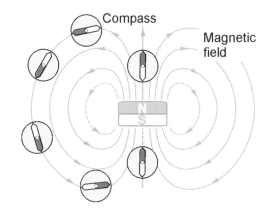

Figure 8.19: *A compass needle lines up with a magnetic field.*

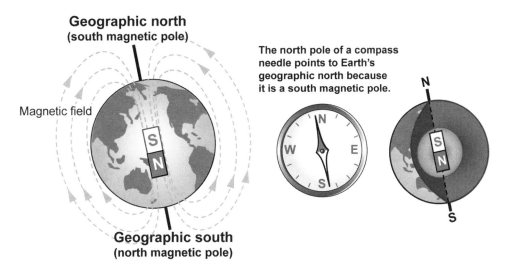

Geographic and magnetic poles

The true *geographic* North and South Poles are where the Earth's axis of rotation intersects its surface. Earth's *magnetic* poles are defined by the planet's magnetic field. When you use a compass, the north-pointing end of the needle points toward a spot near (but not exactly at) Earth's geographic north pole. That means the *south magnetic pole* of the planet is near the geographic North Pole.

Some animals have biological compasses

Many animals, including some species of birds, frogs, fish, turtles, and bacteria, can sense the planet's magnetic field. Migratory birds are the best known examples. Magnetite, a magnetic mineral made of iron oxide, has been found in bacteria and in the brains of birds. Tiny crystals of magnetite may act like compasses and allow these organisms to sense the small magnetic field of Earth. Samples of magnetite are common in rock collections or kits.

The effect of current on a compass

Finding the relationship between electricity and magnetism

For a long time, people believed electricity and magnetism were unrelated. As scientists began to understand electricity better, they searched for relationships between electricity and magnetism. In 1819, Hans Christian Ørsted placed a compass needle near a wire in a circuit. When a switch in the circuit was closed, the compass needle moved just as if the wire were a magnet. We now know that magnetism is created by electric current and that electricity and magnetism are two forms of the same basic force.

Magnetism is created by electric current.

An experiment with a wire and compasses

Imagine a variation on Ørsted's experiment. A long straight wire is connected to a battery and a switch. The wire passes through a board with a hole in it. Around the hole are many compasses that can detect any magnetic field. When the switch is off, the compasses all point north (Figure 8.20).

Compasses react to electric current

As soon as the switch is closed, current flows, and the compasses point in a circle (see illustration below). The compasses stay pointed in a circle as long as there is current in the wire. If the current stops, the compasses return to pointing north again. If the current is reversed in the wire, the compasses again point in a circle, but in the opposite direction.

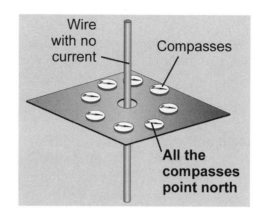

Figure 8.20: *When there is no current in a wire, all of the compasses point north.*

Permanent magnets

Magnetism is created by electric current. A permanent magnet stays magnetic even though there are no wires to carry current. How does a permanent magnet get its magnetism? Here's a hint: There are electric charges inside atoms and those charges have energy of motion.

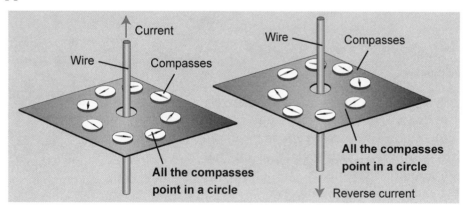

Magnetic forces and electric currents

Electromagnets

Simple electromagnet

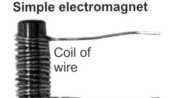

Coil of wire

Steel

A magnet made with wires and electric current is called an **electromagnet**. A simple electromagnet is made with a coil of wire wrapped around a steel rod. The electromagnet produces a magnetic field exactly the same as a permanent magnet with its north and south poles as shown in Figure 8.21. Two coils carrying electric current exert forces on each other, just as magnets do. The forces can be attractive or repulsive depending on the direction of current in the coils. If the current is in the same direction in both coils, they attract. If the currents are in opposite directions, they repel.

Coil carrying current

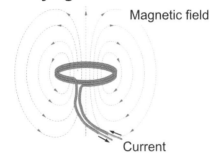

Magnetic field

Current

The poles of an electromagnet

The right hand rule

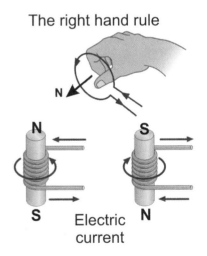

N

N   S

S   Electric   N
     current

The north and south poles of an electromagnet are on opposite ends of the coil. Which is north depends on the direction of the electric current. When the fingers of your right hand curl in the direction of current, your thumb points toward the electromagnet's north pole. This is called the *right hand rule*. You can switch the north and south poles of an electromagnet by reversing the direction of the current in the coil. This is a great advantage over permanent magnets.

Permanent magnet

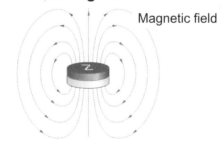

Magnetic field

The strength of an electromagnet

The magnetic force from an electromagnet depends on the total current going around the steel core. More current creates a stronger magnet. Increasing the number of turns in the coil also increases the magnetic force even with the same current. That's because each additional turn lets the current circle the coil one more time. In effect adding turns "reuses" the same current over and over, once per turn.

Figure 8.21: *The magnetic field from current flowing in a coil of wire and from a similar shaped permanent magnet.*

Magnetic materials

Magnetic materials The force from a magnet doesn't affect a plastic pen cap but attracts a steel paper clip. The same magnet doesn't stick to an aluminum pot but does stick to a cast iron pot. Why do some materials have strong magnetic properties while others do not? The metals iron, nickel, and cobalt have strong magnetic properties. Steel is mostly iron, which is why a steel paper clip is attracted to a magnet. A **ferromagnetic metal** such as iron is attracted to a magnet. It doesn't usually matter whether the south or north pole is facing the iron. Iron is attracted to both magnetic poles.

ferromagnetic metal - a material, like iron, which has strong magnetic properties.

How permanent magnets are made Both permanent magnets and iron owe their magnetic properties to their atoms. The electric charge inside an atom creates a current, making some atoms into tiny electromagnets. In ordinary matter the atoms are scrambled with their north and south poles pointing every different direction. On average, the magnetism of one atom cancels with the next atom so the material is not magnetic. In a permanent magnet however, the atoms have been partly locked into alignment. Their individual north and south poles stay pointing in about the same direction. That is why permanent magnets keep their magnetism.

Why iron always attracts a magnet Iron atoms can rotate their magnetic poles to line up with neighboring atoms. When the north pole of an external magnet gets near iron, the south pole of each atom in the iron is attracted to the magnet's north pole (Figure 8.22). Many atoms group together in south-pointing clusters. The iron becomes *magnetized* and is attracted to the magnet. The south pole of an external magnet magnetizes iron the opposite way. Clusters of atoms grow that have north poles facing the external magnet.

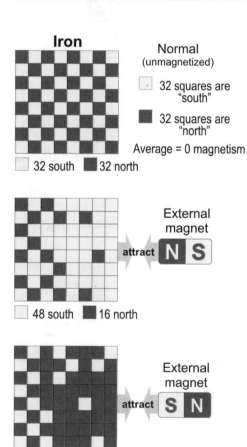

Figure 8.22: *How iron is magnetized so it always attracts an external magnet.*

Electric generators and induction

Magnetism and electricity
An electric current in a wire creates a magnetic field. The reverse is also true. If you move a magnet near a coil of wire, an electric current (or voltage) is *induced* in the coil. The word *induce* means "to cause to happen." The process of using a moving magnet to create electric current or voltage is called **electromagnetic induction**. A moving magnet *induces* electric current to flow in a circuit.

Making current flow
Figure 8.23 shows an experiment demonstrating electromagnetic induction. In the experiment, a magnet can move in and out of a coil of wire. The coil is attached to a meter that measures the electric current. When the magnet moves into the coil of wire, *as the magnet is moving,* electric current is induced in the coil and the meter swings to the left. The current stops if the magnet stops moving.

Reversing the current
When the magnet is pulled back out again, *as the magnet is moving,* current is induced in the opposite direction. The meter swings to the right as the magnet moves out. Again, if the magnet stops moving, the current also stops.

Current flows only when the magnet is moving
Current is produced only if the magnet is moving, because a *changing* magnetic field is what creates current. Moving magnets induce current because they create changing magnetic fields. If the magnetic field is not changing, such as when the magnet is stationary, the current is zero.

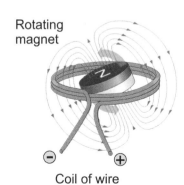

Rotating magnet

Coil of wire

Electric motors transform electrical energy into mechanical energy. Electric *generators* do the opposite. They transform mechanical energy into electrical energy. Generators are used to create the electricity that powers all of the appliances in your home. A simple electric generator is a magnet that spins inside a coil of wire. As the magnet spins, the changing magnetism induces electric current to flow in the coil.

electromagnetic induction - using a moving magnet to create electric current or voltage.

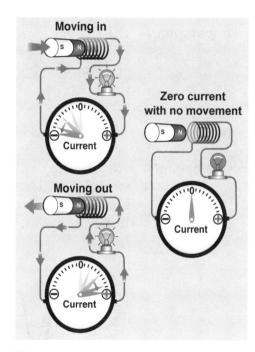

Figure 8.23: *A moving magnet produces a current in a coil of wire.*

Transformers

Electricity is transmitted at high voltage
It takes thick, heavy, and expensive wires to carry high current. For this reason, power companies use high voltage for transmitting electric power over long distances. The main power lines on a city street operate at 13,800 volts. Since power is current times voltage, each amp of current provides 13,800 watts of power. The problem is that you would *not* want your wall outlets to be at 13,800 volts. With a voltage this high, it would be dangerous to plug in your appliances!

Electric power transformers
A transformer changes the high voltage from the main power lines to the 120 volts your appliances use. Transformers can change voltage and current with very little loss of power. A series of transformers changes one amp at 13,800 volts into 115 amps at 120 volts (Figure 8.24). The total electrical power remains the same because 13,800 V × 1 A = 120 V × 115 A.

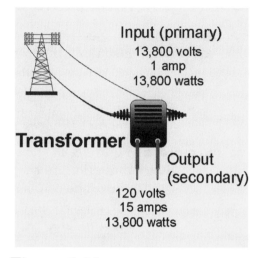

Figure 8.24: *A high-power transformer can reduce the voltage keeping the power constant.*

Transformers operate on electromagnetic induction
Figure 8.25 shows what a transformer looks like inside its protective box. You may have seen one inside a doorbell or an AC adapter. The two coils are called the *primary* and *secondary* coils. The input to the transformer is connected to the primary coil. The output of the transformer is connected to the secondary coil. The two coils have different numbers of turns to convert from one voltage to another.

DC and AC

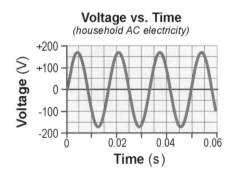

The current from a battery is called *direct current* or DC. In DC electricity, the positive terminal stays positive and the negative terminal stays negative. Your experiments in the lab are DC since they use batteries. *Transformers do not work with DC electricity.* For this reason, the electrical system in your house uses *alternating current* or AC. AC electricity constantly switches between positive and negative. In the electrical system used in the United States, the voltage reverses direction 60 times per second.

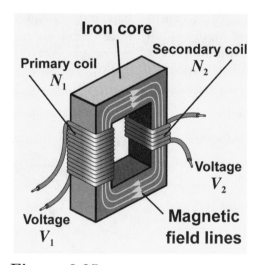

Figure 8.25: *A transformer contains coils wound around an iron core.*

8.3 Section Review

1. Which magnetic pole is attracted to a south magnetic pole?
2. Why can the magnetic force be either attractive or repulsive when gravity can only be attractive?
3. Name two materials which are magnetic and two that are not magnetic.
4. What is wrong with the picture below?

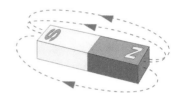 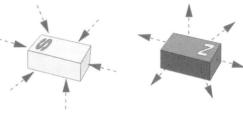

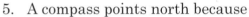

5. A compass points north because
   a. Earth's gravity is strongest at the North Pole.
   b. Earth's south magnetic pole is there.
   c. Earth's north magnetic pole is there.
6. Why does a compass change direction when it is near a current-carrying wire?
7. What is the difference between a permanent magnet and an electromagnet?
8. An electromagnet is shown in Figure 8.26. Use the right hand rule to tell whether the pointed end of the nail is a north pole or a south pole.
9. Iron attracts
   a. only the north pole of a magnet.
   b. only the south pole of a magnet.
   c. both north and south poles of a magnet.
10. An electric generator uses changing magnetism to
    a. induce current to flow in a coil.
    b. transform electrical energy into mechanical energy.

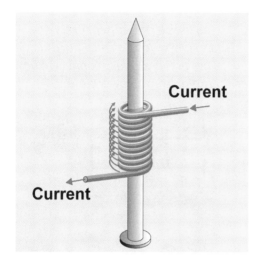

Current

Current

Figure 8.26: *Question 8.*

CHALLENGE

Anti-gravity magnets!

You can "float" a tethered magnet by attracting it to another magnet. See if you can do it! How far apart can you get the two magnets before the lower one falls?

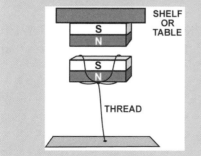

Household Electricity

You use electric current every day. When you plug in an electric appliance, you connect it to a circuit created by wires in the walls. The wires eventually connect to power lines outside that bring the current from a power station.

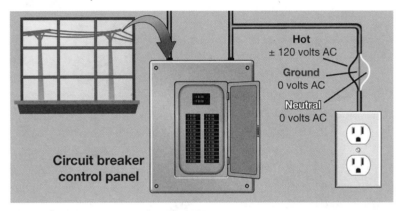

Hot
± 120 volts AC

Ground
0 volts AC

Neutral
0 volts AC

Circuit breaker
control panel

Where does electricity enter a building?

Electricity comes into a typical building through a circuit breaker panel. Circuit breakers are small devices that protect against overloaded or overheated wires. Each electrical circuit in the house has its own circuit breaker, which opens a circuit if too much current flows through it. This prevents electrical fires that can happen if wires overheat.

Circuit breaker

What if a circuit breaker switches the circuit off?

Have you ever had the lights go out in one room in your house but not other rooms? This usually happens because the circuit breaker for that room detected an overloaded circuit and opened, causing electricity to stop flowing to that area of the house. If you are using an extension cord, or a power strip that has several things plugged into it, you should unplug several items and reset the breaker at the control panel.

How does a wall socket work?

Each wall socket has three wires feeding it. The hot wire carries 120 volts. The neutral wire stays at zero volts. When you plug something in, current flows in and out of the hot wire, through your appliance (doing work) and back through the neutral wire. The ground wire is for safety and is connected to the ground (zero volts) near your house. If there is a short circuit in your appliance, the current flows through the ground wire rather than through you.

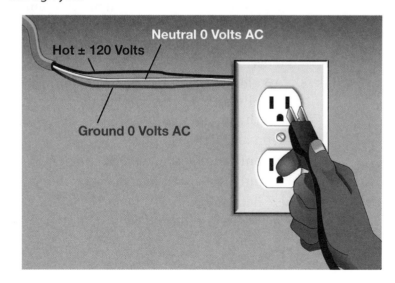

Neutral 0 Volts AC

Hot ± 120 Volts

Ground 0 Volts AC

Chapter 8 Connection

Why do some outlets have buttons on them?

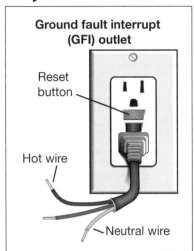

Ground fault interrupt (GFI) outlet

Reset button

Hot wire

Neutral wire

Special wall socket outlets are located in bathrooms, kitchens, and outside. These outlets have "test" and "reset" buttons located in between the sockets. These outlets, called Ground Fault Interrupt (GFI) outlets, are required in places where water may be near electricity. A GFI outlet contains a circuit that compares the current flowing out on the hot wire and back on the neutral wire. If everything is working properly, the two currents should be exactly the same. If they are different, some current must be flowing to ground through another path, such as through your hand. The ground fault interrupter detects any difference in current and immediately breaks the circuit. GFI outlets are excellent protection against electric shocks, especially in wet locations.

If you turn on an appliance that is plugged into a GFI, and you press the "test" button on the outlet, the appliance should immediately turn off. This means the GFI is working properly. Press the "reset" button to restore power to the outlet.

What if you plug too many things into a wall outlet?

Each room in a building usually has its own parallel circuit, protected by a circuit breaker. Each device connected to a room circuit will use as much electricity as it needs. If you plug in a toaster that needs 10 amps of electrical current and a coffee maker that uses 10 amps of electrical current, a total of 20 amps needs to come through the wire.

If you plug too many things into the same circuit or outlet, you will eventually use more electrical current than the wires can safely carry without overheating. If this happens, the circuit breaker at the control panel will click open and stop the flow of electricity. You should unplug things to reduce the current in the circuit before resetting the circuit breaker.

QUESTIONS

1. Explain two reasons why the electrical control panel in a building is important.

2. What is the purpose of the third, round hole in wall sockets?

3. Why is a GFI outlet important to have in a bathroom or kitchen?

4. Where is the electrical control panel located in your home? How many circuit breakers are there on your control panel?

Chapter 8 Connection

Make a Simple Motor

Electricity and magnetism are two forms of the same basic force. You will use this idea to create a small motor. The coil of wire will spin with no help from you. See if you can explain how this works!

Materials

D-cell; 3 to 4 meters of enameled copper wire; two large paperclips; one magnet (CPO-type or small neodymium); strong rubber band (not too large); small piece of sandpaper

What you will do

1. Make a circle out of your wire by winding 12 or so turns around a cardboard tube or similar-sized object. It is important to wind the coil as circular as possible, to distribute the mass of the wire evenly all the way around.

2. Use a small piece of sandpaper to remove the enamel completely from one end of your wire coil. With the coil in a vertical position, remove the enamel from the top half only of the other end of the wire.

Sand one wire end completely

Sand top half of the other wire end

3. Center the coil's "tails" and straighten them to form a shaft for the coil.

4. To form supports for the coil, open two jumbo paperclips and bend a hook in the large end as shown.

5. Use a sturdy rubber band to attach one support to each end of the D-cell. You may have to tape the paperclips to the cell terminals tightly with masking tape to achieve excellent connections. This is the most important factor in getting your motor to work.

6. Set a magnet on the cell as shown.

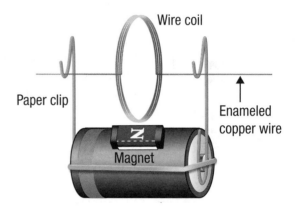

Wire coil

Paper clip

Enameled copper wire

Magnet

7. To operate the motor, set the coil in the supports. You might have to give the coil a gentle spin to get it started.

Troubleshooting

This project is extremely satisfying once you are able to get the motor to run. The main problem spots to watch out for are:

· unbalanced coil

· poor connections

· dead D-cell

· improperly sanded coil ends

Applying your knowledge

a. When electricity runs through the coil of wire, what type of force is created around the coil?

b. What is the purpose of the permanent magnet?

c. What interactions cause the coil of wire to spin?

d. What would happen if you created a coil with twice the number of winds? Try it and see if you are right!

Chapter 8 Assessment

Vocabulary

Select the correct term to complete the sentences.

ampere	electric current	electromagnet
electric circuit	ferromagnetic	insulator
conductor	Ohm's law	north, south
positive, negative	magnetic field	permanent magnet

Section 8.1

1. The two kinds of electric charge are ____ and ____.

2. The two kinds of magnetic poles are ____ and ____.

3. The flow of tiny particles that carry electrical energy is called ____.

4. The unit of measure for electric current is called the ____.

Section 8.2

5. A complete path through which electric current passes is called a(n) ____

6. A(n)____ has high electrical resistance.

7. The physical law relating electrical resistance, current, and voltage is known as ____.

8. A material, such as copper, with low electrical resistance is called a(n) ____.

Section 8.3

9. A magnet made using wires and electric current is a(n) ____.

10. Materials similar to iron that have strong magnetic properties are called ____.

11. The influence created by a magnet that exerts forces on other magnetic objects is known as a(n) ____.

12. A material that maintains its magnetic properties even when it is not close to another magnet is called a(n) ____.

Concepts

Section 8.1

1. A scientist says, "Magnetic poles of magnets and electric charges on objects apply forces in similar ways." Explain what is meant by this statement.

2. Why is it more difficult to determine the electric charge on an object than the mass of an object?

3. Explain how a cat's fur may become statically charged.

4. How does static electricity differ from current electricity?

5. Why don't you usually notice electric forces between objects?

6. How does voltage cause current to do work?

7. What does a battery do in an electrical circuit?

8. What is measured in units of amperes?

9. What is measured in units of volts?

Section 8.2

10. Explain the difference between an open circuit and a closed circuit?

11. Will a bulb light if it is in an open circuit? Why?

12. Is flipping a switch the only way to create an open circuit?

13. How are volts, amperes, and watts related?

14. Explain how volts, amperes, and ohms are related in a circuit.

15. Why is it more dangerous to touch a wire conducting electric current with wet hands than with dry hands?

Section 8.3

16. How does the force between two magnets differ from the force between two masses?

17. Large, electro-magnetic cranes are used in junk yards for moving scrap metal from one location to another. Why would an electromagnet be more useful in this application than a permanent magnet?

18. Suppose you stick a magnet on the door of your refrigerator. Is the magnet a magnetic material or a permanent magnet? Is the refrigerator door a magnetic material or permanent magnet?

19. Two magnetic north poles ____ each other. Two south poles ____ each other. A north pole and a south pole ____ each other.

20. Magnetic field lines outside a magnet point away from its ____ pole and toward its ____ pole.

21. Explain how to make current flow in a wire coil using a magnet.

22. Compare an electric motor to an electric generator.

Problems

Section 8.1

1. What happens when two positively charged objects are placed near each other?

2. Four 1.5-V AA batteries are connected end-to-end.
    a. What is the voltage difference across a single battery?
    b. What is the voltage difference across two batteries?
    c. What is the voltage difference across all four batteries?

Section 8.2

3. Household circuits in the United States typically run on 120 volts of electricity. Circuit breakers are commonly used to break a circuit if the current is greater than 15 amperes. What is the minimum amount of resistance needed in a circuit to prevent the circuit breaker from activating?

4. A hair dryer draws a current of 10 A when plugged into a 120-volt outlet. What is the resistance of the hair dryer?

5. Calculate the current produced if a 12-volt battery supplies 6 watts of power.

6. A television runs on 120 volts and has a resistance of 60 ohms. What current does it draw?

7. The current flowing through a 1,200-watt hair dryer is 10 amperes. Calculate the voltage that must be supplied to operate this hair dryer properly.

Section 8.3

8. A student knocked a ceramic permanent magnet off her desk, and it shattered when it hit the floor. Copy the broken pieces and label the north and south poles on each one.

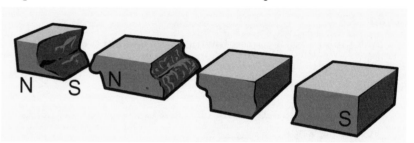

9. Copy the diagram of the wire shown to the right and draw the magnetic field lines in the region around the wire. Don't forget to show the field's direction.

10. When you plug in a cell phone, a transformer on the plug changes the outlet's 120 volts to the 6 volts needed by the battery. The transformer draws 1 amp of current from the electrical outlet.
    a. How much power does the wall outlet supply to the transformer?
    b. What current does the telephone draw?

Chapter 9

Waves and Sound

Humans were making musical instruments to produce sounds around 20,000 years before the wheel and axle were invented! Instruments gradually improved from simple flutes and drums to modern standards like the violin. A violin's sound is rich and complex because vibrations of its wooden parts create a unique blend of frequencies. Among instrument builders, perhaps Antonio Stradivari is the most famous. Stradivari built violins in the small town of Cremona, Italy, between 1667 and 1730.

Stradivari worked tirelessly trying different woods and different varnishes, searching for the perfect sound. Over time, he developed a secret formula for varnish, and special ways to carve and treat the all-important vibrating parts of the violin. In the 300 years since Stradivari lived and worked, no one has figured out how he did it. Today, a Stradivarius violin is the most highly prized of all musical instruments. Its rich sound has never been duplicated.

Key Questions:

1. How do we describe back and forth motions?

2. What is a wave?

3. What is sound and why is sound a wave?

Photo- courtesy of Geo.Heinl & Co. Toronto
Instrument Bank of the Canada Council for the Arts

9.1 Harmonic Motion

A runner passing you on the street moves in **linear motion**. Linear motion gets us from one place to another (Figure 9.1A). This chapter is about another kind of motion called harmonic motion (Figure 9.1B). **Harmonic motion** is motion that repeats over and over. The cycles of day and night and the seasons are caused by Earth's harmonic motion. Other examples of harmonic motion cause your heartbeat and create the sound of music.

Motion in cycles

What is a cycle?
To describe harmonic motion we need to learn some new ideas that describe the "over-and-over" repeating action. The first important idea is the **cycle**. One full back-and-forth swing of a child on a swing is one cycle. The motion of the swing is the same cycle, repeated over and over again.

Looking at one cycle
A **pendulum's** cycle is shown in the diagram below. Each box in the diagram is a snapshot of the motion at a different time in the cycle.

The cycle of a pendulum

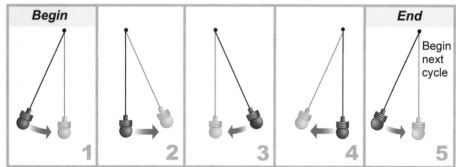

The cycle of a pendulum
The cycle starts with (1) the swing from left to center. Next, the cycle continues with (2) center to right, and (3) back from right to center. The cycle ends when the pendulum moves (4) from center to left because this brings the pendulum back to the beginning of the next cycle. Once a cycle is completed, the next cycle begins without any interruption in the motion.

VOCABULARY

linear motion - motion that goes from one place to another without repeating.

harmonic motion - motion that repeats in cycles.

cycle - a unit of motion that repeats.

pendulum - a device that swings back and forth due to the force of gravity.

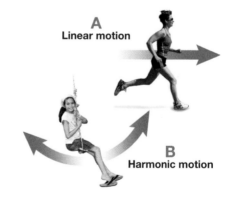

Figure 9.1: *(A) A sprinter is a good example of linear motion. (B) A person on a swing is a good example of harmonic motion.*

Oscillators

An **oscillator** is a physical system that has repeating cycles. A child on a swing is an oscillator, as is a vibrating guitar string. A wagon on a hill just rolls down and is not an oscillator. What properties determine whether a system will oscillate or not?

Equilibrium   Systems that oscillate always move back and forth around a center or *equilibrium* position. You can think of equilibrium as the system at rest, undisturbed, with zero net force. A wagon on a hill is *not* in equilibrium because the force of gravity is not balanced by another force. A child sitting *motionless* on a swing *is* in equilibrium because the force of gravity is balanced by the tension in the ropes.

Restoring forces   A **restoring force** is any force that always acts to pull a system back toward equilibrium. If a pendulum is pulled forward, gravity creates a restoring force that pulls it back, toward equilibrium. If the pendulum is moved backward, gravity pulls it forward, back to equilibrium again (Figure 9.2). *Systems with restoring forces are the ones that become oscillators.*

Inertia causes an oscillator to go past equilibrium   Gravity always pulls a pendulum toward equilibrium. Why doesn't the pendulum just stop at equilibrium? Newton's first law of motion explains why. According to the first law, an object in motion tends to stay in motion. The pendulum has inertia that keeps it moving forward. Inertia causes the pendulum to overshoot its equilibrium position every time. The result is harmonic motion.

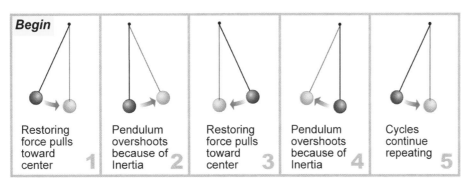

1 Restoring force pulls toward center
2 Pendulum overshoots because of Inertia
3 Restoring force pulls toward center
4 Pendulum overshoots because of Inertia
5 Cycles continue repeating

VOCABULARY

oscillator - a physical system that has repeating cycles.

restoring force - any force that always acts to pull a system back toward equilibrium.

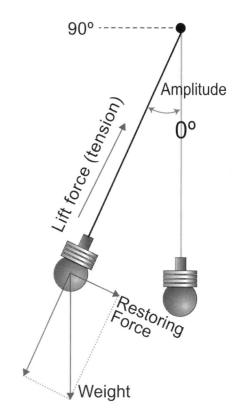

Figure 9.2: *Restoring force keeps a pendulum swinging. Restoring force is related to weight and the lift force (or tension) of the string of a pendulum.*

Frequency and period

A period is the time for one cycle

Harmonic motion can be fast or slow, but we don't use speed to tell the difference. This is because the speed of a pendulum constantly changes during its cycle. We use *period* and *frequency* to describe how quickly cycles repeat themselves. The time for one cycle to occur is called a **period**. A clock pendulum with a period of one second will complete one full back and forth swing each second.

period - the time it takes for each complete cycle.

frequency - how often something repeats, expressed in hertz.

hertz - the unit of frequency. One hertz is one cycle per second.

Frequency is the number of cycles per second

The **frequency** is the number of complete cycles per second. The unit of one cycle per second is called a **hertz** (Hz). Something that completes 10 cycles each second has a frequency of 10 Hz. A guitar string playing the note "A" vibrates back and forth at a frequency of 220 Hz (Figure 9.3). Your heartbeat has a frequency between one-half and two cycles per second (0.5 Hz–2 Hz).

Frequency is the inverse of period

Frequency and period are inversely related. The period is the number of seconds per cycle. The frequency is the number of cycles per second. For example, if the period of a pendulum is 2 seconds, its frequency is 0.5 cycles per second (0.5 Hz).

A guitar "A" string vibrates at 220 Hz

PERIOD AND FREQUENCY

$$\underset{\text{Frequency (hertz)}}{\overset{\text{Period}\ \text{(seconds)}}{\longrightarrow}}\ T = \frac{1}{f}$$

$$\overset{\text{Frequency (hertz)}}{\underset{}{f}} = \frac{1}{T} \underset{\text{Period}\ \text{(seconds)}}{\longleftarrow}$$

When to use period or frequency

While both period and frequency tell us the same information, we usually use period when cycles are slower than a few per second. The pendulum you use in the lab has period between 0.9 and 2 seconds. We use frequency when cycles repeat faster. The vibrations that make sound in musical instruments have frequencies between 20 and 20,000 Hz.

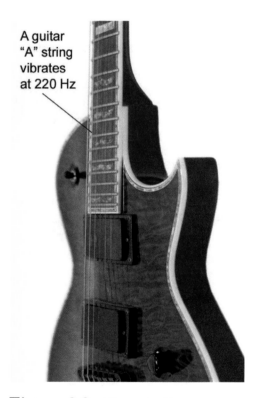

Figure 9.3: *All musical instruments use harmonic motion to create sound.*

Amplitude

Amplitude describes the "size" of a cycle
The **amplitude** describes the "size" of a cycle. Figure 9.4 shows a pendulum with small amplitude and one with a large amplitude. With a moving object like a pendulum, the amplitude is often a distance or angle. With other kinds of oscillators, the amplitude might be voltage or pressure. The amplitude is measured in units appropriate to the kind of harmonic motion being described.

How do you measure amplitude?
The amplitude is the maximum distance the oscillator moves away from its *equilibrium* position. For a pendulum, the equilibrium position is hanging straight down in the center. For the pendulum in Figure 9.5, the amplitude is 20 degrees, because the pendulum moves 20 degrees away from center in either direction.

Damping and friction
Look at the illustration above. Friction slows a pendulum down, just as it slows all motion. That means the amplitude slowly gets reduced until the pendulum is hanging straight down, motionless. We use the word *damping* to describe the gradual loss of amplitude. If you wanted to make a clock with a pendulum, you would have to find a way to keep adding energy to counteract the damping of friction so the clock's pendulum would work continuously.

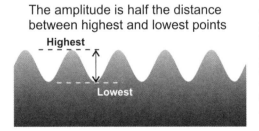

The amplitude is half the distance between highest and lowest points

A good way to find the amplitude is to measure the distance between the farthest points the motion reaches. The amplitude is half this distance. The amplitude of a water wave is often found this way.

amplitude - the amount that a cycle moves away from equilibrium.

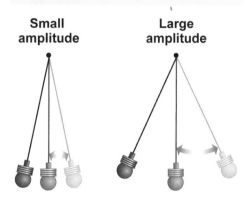

Figure 9.4: *Small amplitude versus large amplitude.*

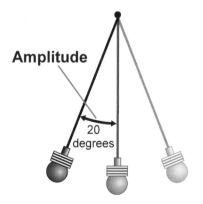

Figure 9.5: *A pendulum with an amplitude of 20 degrees swings 20 degrees away from the center in either direction.*

Graphs of Harmonic Motion

Graphing harmonic motion A graph is a good way to show harmonic motion because you can quickly recognize cycles (Figure 9.6). The most common type of graph puts position on the vertical (*y*) axis and time on the horizontal (*x*) axis. The graph below shows how the position of a pendulum changes over time. The repeating "wave" on the graph represents the repeating cycles of motion of the pendulum.

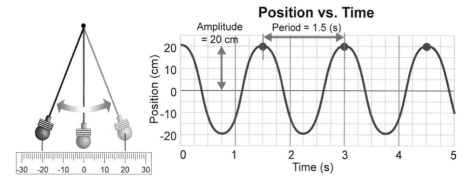

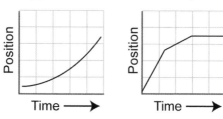

Typical Linear Motion Graphs

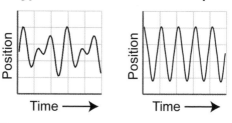

Typical Harmonic Motion Graphs

Figure 9.6: *Typical graphs for linear motion (top) and harmonic motion (bottom). Graphs of linear motion do not show cycles. Harmonic motion graphs show repeating cycles.*

Finding the period This pendulum has a period of 1.5 seconds, so the pattern on the graph repeats every 1.5 seconds. If you were to cut out any piece of the graph and slide it over 1.5 seconds it would line up exactly. You can tell the period is 1.5 seconds because the graph repeats itself every 1.5 seconds.

Showing amplitude on a graph The amplitude of harmonic motion can also be seen on a graph. The graph above shows that the pendulum swings from +20 centimeters to −20 centimeters and back. Therefore, the amplitude of the pendulum is 20 centimeters.

Using positive and negative positions Harmonic motion graphs often use positive and negative values to represent motion on either side of a center (equilibrium) position. Zero usually represents the equilibrium point. Notice that zero is placed halfway up the *y*-axis so there is room for both positive and negative values. This graph is in centimeters, but the motion of the pendulum could also have been graphed using the angle measured relative to the center (straight down) position.

Natural frequency and resonance

Natural frequency
A pendulum will have the same period each time you set it moving. Unless you change the pendulum itself (such as changing its length), it will always swing with the same period. The **natural frequency** is the frequency (or period) at which a system naturally oscillates. Every system that oscillates has a natural frequency. Musical instruments use natural frequency. For example, guitar strings are tuned by adjusting their natural frequency to match musical notes.

Changing natural frequency
Natural frequency depends on the balance between restoring force and inertia (mass). Any change that affects this balance will also change the natural frequency. The natural frequency of a vibrating guitar string increases when the string gets tighter. Tightening the string increases the force pulling the string back toward equilibrium. Higher force means higher acceleration, and higher natural frequency.

Periodic force
You can get a swing moving by pushing it at the right time every cycle. A force that is repeated over and over is called a **periodic force**. A periodic force has a cycle with an amplitude, frequency, and period, just like an oscillator. *To supply energy to an oscillator you need to use a periodic force.*

Resonance

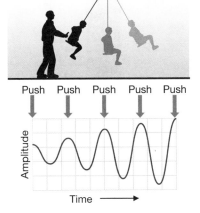

Resonance happens when a periodic force has the same frequency as the natural frequency. When this happens, each push adds to the next one and the amplitude of the motion grows. The big amplitude of a swing is an example of resonance. You get a big swing by using many small pushes applied at the right time each cycle, or, in other words, by applying a periodic force (repetitive pushes) at the natural frequency (once each cycle). In resonance, the response can grow very large compared to the strength of the force!

Harmonic motion can be created using an energy source to push or rotate parts. For example, the piston of a car engine goes up and down as the crank turns. The piston is in harmonic motion, but the motion is caused by the rotation of the crankshaft and the attachment of the connecting rod.

STEM

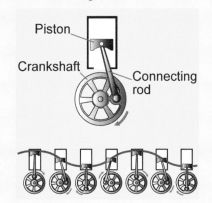

9.1 Section Review

1. Which is the best example of a cycle: a turn of a wheel or a slide down a ski slope?
2. Describe one example of an oscillating system you would find at an amusement park.
3. What is the relationship between period and frequency?
4. Every 6 seconds a pendulum completes 1 cycle. What are the period and frequency of this pendulum?
5. What is the difference between a graph of linear motion and a graph of harmonic motion?
6. A graph of the motion of a pendulum shows that it swings from +5 centimeters to –5 centimeters for each cycle. What is the amplitude of the pendulum?

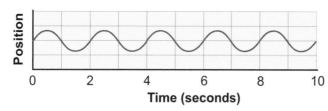

7. What is the period of the oscillation shown in the diagram above?
8. Figure 9.7 shows a sliding mass on a spring. Assume there is no friction. Will this system oscillate? Explain why or why not.
9. A student makes two oscillators with identical rubber bands that are stretched the same amount (Figure 9.8). One oscillator has a wooden bead in the middle. Which oscillator will have the higher natural frequency? Explain why you think so.
10. Resonance happens when
    a. a periodic force is applied at the natural frequency.
    b. an oscillator has more than one natural frequency.
    c. a force is periodic and not constant.
    d. the amplitude of an oscillator grows large over time.

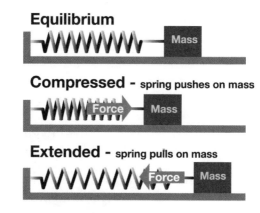

Figure 9.7: *Question 8.*

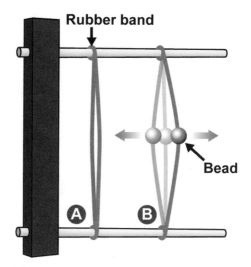

Figure 9.8: *Question 9.*

9.2 Waves

A **wave** is an oscillation that travels from one place to another. A musician's instrument creates waves that carry sound to your ears. When you throw a stone into a pond, the energy of the falling stone creates waves in the water that carry energy to the edge of the pond. In this section you will learn about waves.

Why learn about waves?

What is a wave? If you poke a floating ball, it oscillates up and down. But, something else happens to the water as the ball oscillates. The surface of the water oscillates in response and the oscillation spreads outward from where it started. *An oscillation that travels is a wave.*

Why do waves travel? When you drop a ball into water, some of the water is pushed aside and raised by the ball (A). The higher water pushes the water next to it (B). The water that has been pushed then pushes on the water next to *it*, and so on. The wave spreads through the connection between each drop of water and the water next to it (C).

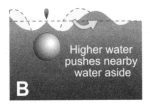
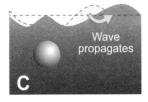

Water is displaced and pushed up | Higher water pushes nearby water aside | Wave propagates
A | B | C

Waves transmit energy and information Waves are present whenever information, energy, or motion is transmitted over a distance in a certain amount of time. Waves are used in many technologies because they can quickly carry energy and information over great distances. A TV remote control is one example. To change the channel, you can use the remote or get up and push the buttons on the TV. Both actions change the channel but one uses physical motion while the other uses an invisible electromagnetic wave called infrared light, which goes from the remote to the TV.

ã VOCABULARY

wave - a traveling oscillation that has properties of frequency, wavelength, and amplitude.

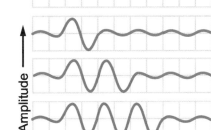

Figure 9.9: *One way to represent numbers using the waves.*

Frequency, amplitude, and wavelength

Waves are oscillators Like all oscillations, waves have cycles, frequency, and amplitude. The frequency of a wave is a measure of how often it goes up and down at any one place (Figure 9.10). The frequency of one point on the wave is the frequency of the whole wave. Distant points on the wave oscillate up and down *with the same frequency*. A wave carries its frequency to every place it reaches. Like other frequencies, the frequency of a wave is measured in *hertz* (Hz). A wave with a frequency of one hertz (1 Hz) causes everything it touches to oscillate at one cycle per second.

Wavelength You can think of a wave as a moving series of high points and low points. A *crest* is the high point of the wave, a *trough* is the low point. **Wavelength** is the distance from any point on a wave to the same point on the next cycle of the wave (Figure 9.11). The distance between one crest and the next crest is a wavelength. So is the distance between one trough and the next trough. We use the Greek letter *lambda* for wavelength. A lambda (λ) looks like an upside-down *y*.

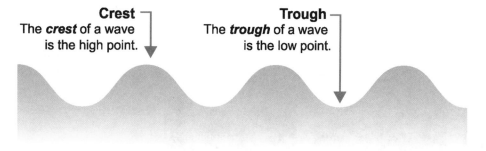

Crest — The *crest* of a wave is the high point.

Trough — The *trough* of a wave is the low point.

Amplitude and energy The amplitude of a wave is the maximum amount the wave causes anything to move away from equilibrium. Equilibrium is the average, or resting position (Figure 9.12). You can measure amplitude as one-half the distance between the highest and lowest points. The amplitude of a wave is related to the energy it carries. Waves with high amplitudes have more energy in them. Think about standing in the water on a beach while waves wash onshore. The bigger the amplitude of the wave, the more energy it has and the harder it crashes against you.

wavelength - the distance from any point on a wave to the same point on the next cycle of the wave.

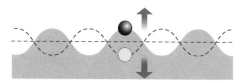

Figure 9.10: *The frequency of a wave is the rate at which every point on the wave moves up and down.*

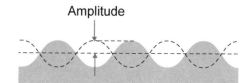

Figure 9.11: *The amplitude of a water wave is the maximum height the wave rises above the level surface.*

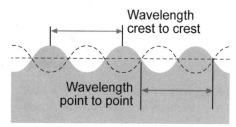

Figure 9.12: *The wavelength can be measured from crest to crest. This is the same as the distance from one point on a wave to the same point on the next cycle of the wave.*

The speed of waves

What is moving? The speed of a wave is different from the speed of a moving object, like a ball. The speed of a ball is the speed at which the ball itself moves. The speed of a wave is the speed at which the wave *spreads*. When a wave moves through water, *the water itself stays in the same average place.*

What is the speed of a wave? The illustration below shows how to measure the speed of a wave. You start a wave in one place and measure how long it takes the wave to affect a place some distance away. The speed of the wave is how fast the wave spreads, *not* how fast the water surface moves up and down. The speed of a water wave is a few miles per hour. Light waves are extremely fast—186,000 miles per *second* (300,000 km/s). Sound waves travel at about 660 miles per hour (about 1,000 km/h), faster than water waves and much slower than light waves.

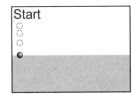 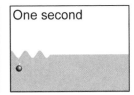 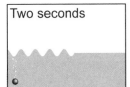 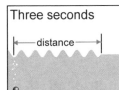

Speed is frequency times wavelength In one complete cycle, a wave moves forward one wavelength (Figure 9.13). The speed is the distance traveled (one wavelength) divided by the time it takes (one period). Actually, we usually calculate the speed of a wave by multiplying wavelength and frequency. This is mathematically the same since multiplying by frequency is the same as dividing by period. The result is true for all kinds of waves, including water waves, sound waves, light waves, and even earthquake waves!

$$Speed = \frac{\text{Distance traveled}}{\text{Time taken}} = \frac{\text{Wavelength}}{\text{Period}} = \left(\frac{1}{\text{Period}}\right) \times \text{Wavelength}$$

$$Speed = Frequency \times Wavelength$$

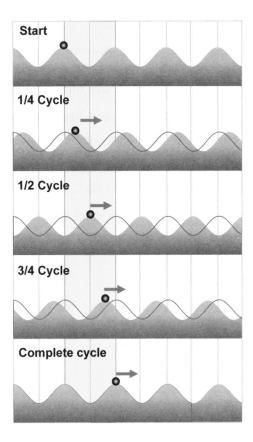

Figure 9.13: *A wave moves one wavelength in each cycle. Since a cycle takes one period, the speed of the wave is the wavelength divided by the period. Mathematically, this is the same as saying speed is frequency times wavelength.*

Transverse and longitudinal waves

Wave pulses A wave *pulse* is a short burst of a traveling wave. A pulse can just be a single up-down movement. The illustrations below show wave pulses in ropes and springs. It is sometimes easier to see the motion of wave pulses than it is to see long waves with many oscillations.

Transverse waves There are two basic kinds of waves. The oscillations of a **transverse** wave *are not* in the direction the wave moves. For example, the wave pulse in the illustration below moves from left to right. The oscillation (caused by the boy's hand) is up and down. Water waves are also transverse waves (Figure 9.14 top).

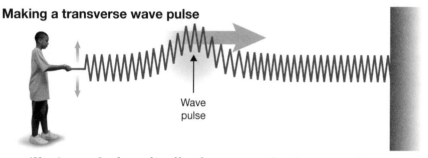

Making a transverse wave pulse

Wave pulse

Longitudinal waves The oscillations of a **longitudinal** wave *are* in the same direction that the wave moves (Figure 9.14 bottom). A large spring with one end fastened to a wall is a good way to make a longitudinal wave. A sharp push-pull on the end of the spring makes a traveling wave pulse as portions of the spring compress then relax. The direction of the compressions are in the same direction that the wave moves. Sound waves are longitudinal waves.

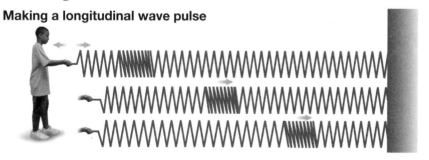

Making a longitudinal wave pulse

VOCABULARY

transverse - a wave is transverse if its oscillations *are not* in the direction it moves.

longitudinal - a wave is longitudinal if its oscillations *are* in the direction it moves.

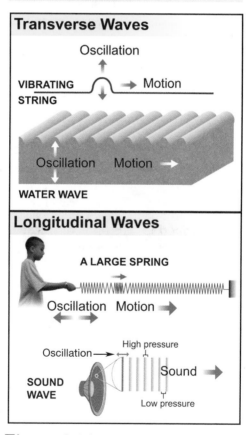

Figure 9.14: *Transverse (top) and longitudinal (bottom) waves.*

When a wave encounters objects

The four wave interactions

Have you ever heard a radio station fade out while driving into a tunnel or down into a valley? Radio signals are carried by radio waves. Like all waves, radio waves are affected by objects that get in their way. When a wave hits an object or a surface, four things can happen. The four are listed below and illustrated in Figure 9.15.

Reflection *The wave bounces and goes in a new direction.*

Refraction *The wave bends as it passes into and through an object.*

Diffraction *The wave bends around an object or through holes in the object.*

Absorption *The wave is absorbed and disappears.*

Boundaries

A *boundary* is an edge or surface where conditions change. The surface of a glass window is a boundary. If a wave traveling through air meets the sudden change of a glass window, it could be reflected, refracted, or diffracted as it crosses the boundary. Absorption can also occur at boundaries, but usually happens more within the body of a material.

Reflection

When a wave bounces off an object we call it **reflection**. A reflected wave is like the original wave but moving in a new direction. The wavelength and frequency are usually unchanged. An echo is an example of a sound wave reflecting from a distant object or wall. People who design concert halls pay careful attention to the reflection of sound from the walls and ceiling.

Refraction

Refraction occurs when a wave bends as it crosses a boundary. We say the wave is *refracted* as it passes through the boundary. Eyeglasses are a good example where refraction is used to bend light waves. People with poor eyesight have trouble focusing images. Glasses bend incoming light waves so that an image is correctly focused within the eye.

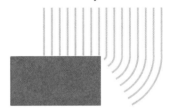

Reflection

The wave bounces and goes in a new direction.

Refraction The wave bends as it passes into and through and object.

Diffraction The wave bends around an object or through holes in the object.

Absorption The wave is absorbed and disappears.

Figure 9.15: *The four basic interactions between waves and boundaries.*

Constructive and destructive interference

Wave pulses Imagine stretching an elastic string over the back of a chair (see the illustration below). To make a wave pulse, you pull down a short length of the string behind the chair and let go. This creates a wave pulse in the string that races away from the chair. The wave pulse moves *on* the string, but each section of string returns to the same place after the wave pulse moves past.

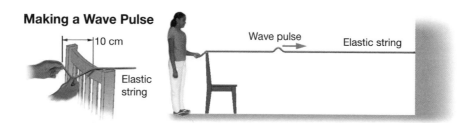

Constructive interference Suppose you make two wave pulses on a stretched string. One comes from the left and the other comes from the right. When the waves meet, they combine to make a single large pulse. **Constructive interference** happens when waves add up to make a larger amplitude (Figure 9.16).

Destructive interference There is another way to add two pulses. What happens when one pulse is on top of the string and the other is on the bottom? When the pulses meet in the middle, they cancel each other out (Figure 9.17). One pulse pulls the string up and the other pulls it down. The result is that the string flattens and both pulses vanish for a moment. In **destructive interference**, waves add up to make a wave with smaller or zero amplitude. After interfering, both wave pulses separate again and travel on their own. This is surprising if you think about it. For a moment, the middle of the cord is flat, but a moment later, two wave pulses come out of the flat part and race away from each other. Waves still store energy, even when they interfere. Noise-cancelling headphones are based on technology that uses destructive interference.

constructive interference - when waves add up to make a larger amplitude.

destructive interference - when waves add up to make a smaller, or zero, amplitude.

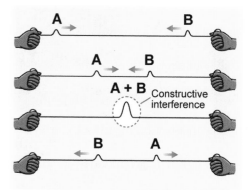

Figure 9.16: *This is an example of constructive interference.*

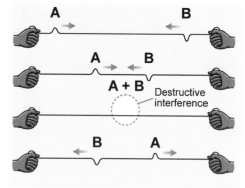

Figure 9.17: *This is an example of destructive interference.*

9.2 Section Review

1. Which is the fastest way to send information, using sound waves, light waves, or water waves?
2. What is the difference between longitudinal and transverse waves?
   a. longitudinal waves are faster
   b. transverse waves are faster
   c. longitudinal waves oscillate in the same direction they move
   d. transverse waves oscillate in the same direction they move
3. What is the speed of a wave that has a wavelength of 0.4 meters and a frequency of 10 hertz?
4. Is a wave that travels slower than 50 m/s most likely to be a sound wave, a light wave, or a water wave?
5. What is the period of a wave that has a wavelength of 1 meter and a speed of 20 m/s?

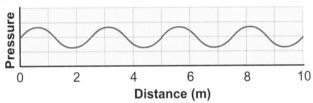

6. The wavelength of the wave shown in the graph above is about:
   a. 1.2 meters.
   b. 2.5 meters.
   c. 5.0 meters.
7. One of the four wave interactions is very important to how plants use light to grow. Guess which interaction this is, and write a couple of sentences justifying your answer.
8. Two waves combine to make a wave that is larger than either wave by itself. Is this constructive or destructive interference?
9. If a wave is being absorbed, what would you expect to happen to the amplitude of the wave? Explain using the idea of energy.

Waves and earthquakes

Earth's crust is not one shell, but is broken up into huge slabs called "plates." The plates float on top of a deep layer of softer, partly melted rock. When the plates hit each other they sometimes slip very suddenly, resulting in earthquakes. An earthquake releases powerful seismic waves that travel along the surface and also through the planet. One kind of seismic wave is a longitudinal wave. Another kind of seismic wave is transverse. The transverse wave shakes the ground sideways and causes damage to buildings and bridges. Because seismic waves travel through the planet, they are used to study what Earth is like deep below the surface. The refraction and reflection of seismic waves are like an x-ray of the Earth's internal structure.

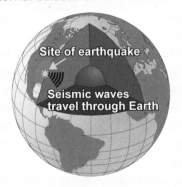

9.3 Sound

Like other waves, sound has frequency, wavelength, amplitude, and speed. Because sound is part of your daily experience, you already know its properties—but by different names. You may never hear anyone complain about *amplitude*, but you have heard about sound being too *loud*. The loudness of sound comes from the amplitude of a sound wave.

The frequency of sound

Frequency and pitch
Your ear is very sensitive to the frequency of sound. The **pitch** of a sound is how you hear and interpret its frequency. A low-frequency sound has a low pitch, like the rumble of a big truck or a bass guitar. A high-frequency sound has a high pitch, like the scream of a whistle or siren. Humans can generally hear frequencies between 20 Hz and 20,000 Hz. Animals may hear both higher and lower frequencies.

Most sound has more than one frequency
Almost all the sounds you hear contain *many frequencies at the same time*. In fact, the sound of the human voice contains thousands of different frequencies—all at once (Figure 9.18).

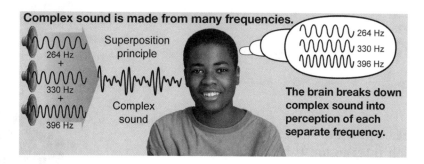

The frequency spectrum
Why is it easy to recognize one person's voice from another's, even when both are saying the same word? The reason is that people have different mixtures of frequencies in their voices. A *frequency spectrum* shows loudness on the vertical axis and frequency on the horizontal axis. Figure 9.18 shows the frequency spectrum for three people saying "hello." Can you see any difference between the graphs?

VOCABULARY

pitch - the perception of high or low that you hear at different frequencies of sound.

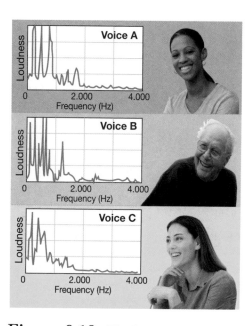

Figure 9.18: *The frequencies in three people's voices as they say the word* hello.

The loudness of sound

The decibel scale The loudness of sound is measured in **decibels** (dB). Loudness is determined mostly by the amplitude of a sound wave. However, almost no one (except scientists) uses amplitude to measure loudness. Instead, we use the decibel scale (Figure 9.19). Most sounds fall between 0 and 100 on the decibel scale, making it a very convenient number to understand and use.

decibel - measure of the loudness (amplitude) of sound.

Table 9.1: Common sounds and their loudness in decibels

0 dB	Threshold of human hearing; quietest sound we can hear
10–15 dB	A quiet whisper 3 feet away
30–40 dB	Background sound level at a house
45–55 dB	The noise level in an average restaurant
65 dB	Ordinary conversation 3 feet away
70 dB	City traffic
90 dB	A jackhammer cutting up the street 10 feet away
100 dB	MP3 player turned to its maximum volume
110 dB	The front row of a rock concert
120 dB	The threshold of physical pain from loudness

Comparing Decibels and Amplitude	
Decibels (dB)	Amplitude
0	1
20	10
40	100
60	1,000
80	10,000
100	100,000
120	1,000,000

Figure 9.19: *The decibel scale measures amplitude (loudness).*

The sensitivity of the ear How loud you *hear* a sound depends on both amplitude and frequency. The human ear is most sensitive to frequencies between 500 and 5,000 Hz. It is no surprise that these are the same the frequencies found in voices! An *equal loudness curve* compares how loud you hear sounds of different frequencies (Figure 9.20). Sounds near 2,000 Hz seem louder than sounds of other frequencies, even at the same decibel level. According to this curve, a 40 dB sound at 2,000 Hz sounds just as loud as an 80 dB sound at 50 Hz.

Acoustics Acoustics is the science and technology of sound. Knowledge of acoustics is important in many situations. For example, reducing the loudness of sound is important in designing libraries so that sounds are absorbed to maintain quiet. Recording studios are designed to prevent sound from the outside from mixing with the sound inside.

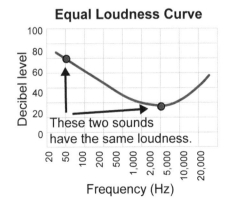

Figure 9.20: *All points on an equal loudness curve have the same loudness.*

The speed of sound

Sound moves about 340 m/s in air

The speed of sound in air is 343 m/s (600 mph). Do you think you could measure the speed of sound? One way to do so is to create an echo. If you make a loud sound toward a rock wall that is 100 meters away, the sound will bounce off the wall and return to you. You know the distance to and from the wall is 200 meters, so if you measure the time it takes for the sound to travel to the wall and back you can figure out its speed.

Subsonic and supersonic

Objects that move faster than sound are called **supersonic**. If you were on the ground watching a supersonic plane fly toward you, there would be silence (Figure 9.21). The sound would be *behind* the plane, racing to catch up. Some military jets fly at supersonic speeds. Passenger jets are *subsonic* because they travel at speeds from 400 to 500 miles per hour.

Sonic booms

A supersonic jet "squishes" the sound waves that are created as its nose cuts through the air. A cone-shaped *shock wave* forms where the waves "pile up" ahead of the plane. In front of the shock wave there is total silence. Behind the shock wave you can hear the noise from the plane. Right at the shock wave the amplitude changes abruptly, causing a very loud sound called a *sonic boom*.

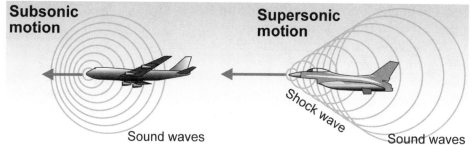

Subsonic motion

Sound waves

Supersonic motion

Shock wave

Sound waves

Sound in liquids and solids

Sound travels through most liquids and solids faster than through air (Figure 9.22). Sound travels about five times faster in water, and about 18 times faster in steel. This is because sound is a traveling oscillation that depends on restoring forces. The forces holding steel atoms together are much stronger than the forces between the molecules in air. Stronger restoring forces raise the speed of sound.

supersonic - faster than the speed of sound.

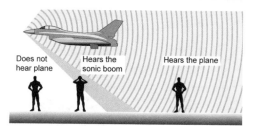

Does not hear plane   Hears the sonic boom   Hears the plane

Figure 9.21: *If a supersonic jet flew overhead, you would not hear the sound until the plane was far beyond you. The boundary between sound and silence is the "shock wave." The person in the middle hears a sonic boom as the shock wave passes over him. Because the sonic boom can shatter windows, planes are not allowed to fly over cities at supersonic speeds.*

Material	Sound speed (m/s)
Air	330
Helium	965
Water	1,530
Wood (average)	2,000
Gold	3,240
Steel	5,940

Figure 9.22: *The speed of sound in various materials (helium and air at 0°C and 1 atmospheric pressure).*

The Doppler effect

The Doppler effect is caused by motion If an object making sound is not moving, listeners on all sides will hear the same frequency. When the object is moving, the frequency will *not* be the same to all listeners. People moving with the object or to the side hear the frequency as if the object were at rest. People in front hear a higher frequency. People behind hear a lower frequency. The shift in frequency caused by motion is called the **Doppler effect**. The Doppler effect occurs at speeds *below* the speed of sound.

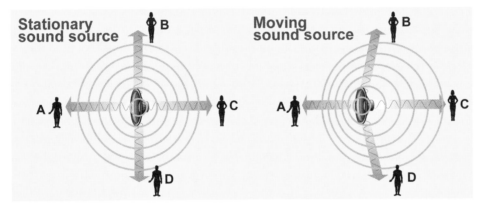

The cause of the Doppler effect The Doppler effect occurs because an observer hears the frequency at which wave crests arrive at his or her ears. Observer A in the graphic above hears a higher frequency. This is because the object's motion causes the crests in front to be closer together. The opposite is true behind a moving object, where the wave crests are farther apart. Observer C in back hears a lower frequency because the motion of the object makes more space between successive wave crests. The greater the speed of the object, the larger the difference in frequency between the front and back positions.

Hearing the Doppler effect You hear the Doppler effect when you hear a police or fire siren coming toward you, then going away from you. The frequency shifts up when the siren is moving toward you. The frequency shifts down when the siren is moving away from you.

Doppler effect - an increase or decrease in frequency caused by the motion of a source of sound

Doppler radar

The Doppler effect also happens with reflected microwaves. With Doppler radar, a transmitter sends a pulse of microwaves. The microwaves reflect from a moving object, such as a car. The frequency of the reflected wave is increased if the car is moving toward the source and decreased if the car is moving away.

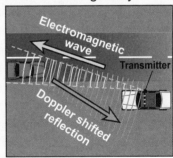

The difference in frequency between the reflected and transmitted wave is proportional to speed. Doppler radar is a way to accurately measure speed at a distance.

What is a sound wave?

How we know sound is a wave

You can see the water move in a water wave, but sound waves are invisible. We know sound is a wave because it does all the things other waves do. Sound can be reflected, refracted, and absorbed. Sound also shows interference and diffraction. What is really oscillating in a sound wave?

Sound in solids and liquids

Sound is a traveling oscillation of atoms. If you push on one atom, it pushes on its neighbor. That atom pushes on the next atom, and so on. The push causes atoms to oscillate back and forth like tiny beads on springs. The oscillation spreads through the connections between atoms to make a sound wave. This is how sound moves through liquids and solids.

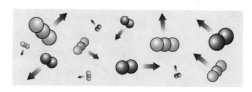

Figure 9.23: *Air is made of molecules in constant random motion, bumping off each other and the walls of their container.*

Sound in air and gases

In air the situation is different. Air molecules are spread far apart and interact by colliding with each other (Figure 9.23). The pressure is highest where atoms are close together and lowest where they are farthest apart (Figure 9.24). Imagine pushing the molecules on the left side of the picture below. Your push squeezes atoms together creating a layer of higher pressure. That layer pushes on the next layer, which pushes on the next layer, and so on. The result is a traveling oscillation in pressure, which is a sound wave. Sound is a *longitudinal* wave because the oscillations are along the same direction the wave travels.

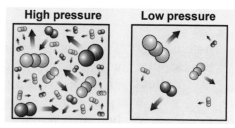

Figure 9.24: *At the same temperature, high pressure means more molecules per unit volume. Low pressure means fewer molecules per unit volume.*

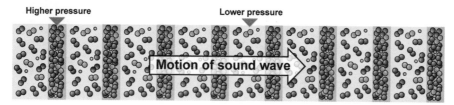

The frequency range of sound waves

Anything that vibrates creates sound waves, as long as there is contact with other atoms. However, not all "sounds" can be heard. Humans can hear only the range between 20 Hz and 20,000 Hz. Bats can hear high frequency sounds between 40,000 and 100,000 Hz and whales hear very low frequency sounds that are lower than 10 Hz.

The wavelength of sound

Range of wavelengths of sound

The wavelength of sound in air is similar to the size of everyday objects. The table below gives some examples. As with other waves, the wavelength of a sound is inversely related to its frequency (Figure 9.25). A low-frequency, 20-Hz sound has a wavelength the size of a large classroom. At the upper range of hearing, a 20,000-Hz sound has a wavelength about the width of your finger.

Table 9.2: Frequency and wavelength for some typical sounds

Frequency (Hz)	Wavelength	Typical source
20	17 m	rumble of thunder
100	3.4 m	bass guitar
500	70 cm (27")	average male voice
1,000	34 cm (13")	female soprano voice
2,000	17 cm (6.7")	fire truck siren
5,000	7 cm (2.7")	highest note on a piano
10,000	3.4 cm (1.3")	whine of a jet turbine
20,000	1.7 cm (0.67")	highest-pitched sound you can hear

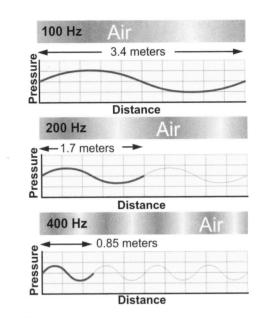

Figure 9.25: *Wavelength and frequency are inversely related.*

Wavelengths of sounds are important

Although we usually think about different sounds in terms of frequency, wavelength is also important. Suppose you wanted to make a sound of a certain wavelength (or frequency). You often need to have a vibrating object that is similar in size to the wavelength of that sound. That is why instruments like French horns have valves. A French horn makes sound by vibrating the air trapped in a long coiled tube. Short tubes only fit short wavelengths and make higher frequency sounds. Long tubes fit longer wavelengths and make lower frequency sounds (Figure 9.26). Opening and closing the valves on a French horn allows the player to add and subtract different length tubes, changing the frequency of the sound.

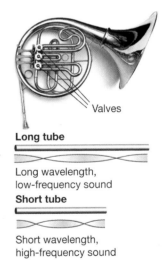

Figure 9.26: *How a French horn works.*

How we hear sound

The inner ear
The inner ear has two important functions—providing our sense of hearing and our sense of balance (Figure 9.27). The sense of balance comes from the three semicircular canals. Fluid moving in each of the three canals tells the brain whether the body is moving left-right, up-down, or forward-backward.

How the cochlea works
The "hearing" of sound starts with the eardrum. The eardrum vibrates in response to sound waves in the ear canal. The three delicate bones of the inner ear transmit the vibration of the eardrum to the side of the cochlea. We get our sense of hearing from the *cochlea*. Fluid in the spiral of the cochlea vibrates and creates waves that travel up the spiral. The spiral channel starts out large and gets narrower near the end. The nerves near the beginning see a relatively large channel and respond to longer-wavelength, lower-frequency sound. The nerves at the small end of the channel respond to shorter-wavelength, higher-frequency sound.

The range of human hearing
The combination of the eardrum, bones, and the cochlea limit the range of human hearing to between 20 Hz and 20,000 Hz. Animals, such as cats and dogs, can hear much higher frequencies because their ears have evolved slightly differently.

Hearing ability changes with time
Hearing varies greatly with people and changes with age. Some people can hear sounds above 15,000 Hz and other people can't. On average. people gradually lose high-frequency hearing with age. Most adults cannot hear frequencies above 15,000 Hz, while children can often hear to 20,000 Hz.

Hearing can be damaged by loud noise
Hearing is affected by exposure to loud or high-frequency noise. The nerves in the cochlea have tiny hairs that shake when the fluid in the cochlea vibrates. Listening to loud sounds for a long time can cause the hairs to weaken or break off. It is smart to protect your ears by keeping the volume of noise reasonable and wearing ear protection if you have to stay in a loud place. In concerts, many musicians wear earplugs on-stage to protect their hearing!

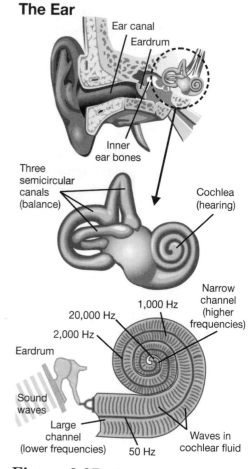

The Ear

Figure 9.27: *The structure of the inner ear. When the eardrum vibrates, three small bones transmit the vibrations to the cochlea. The vibrations make waves inside the cochlea, which vibrates nerves in the spiral. Each part of the spiral is sensitive to a different frequency.*

9.3 Section Review

1. What is the relationship between pitch and frequency?
2. The sound that you hear around you usually
   a. occurs one frequency at a time.
   b. contains many frequencies at the same time.
3. If one sound wave has twice the amplitude of another, the first sound is
   a. louder.
   b. softer.
   c. higher pitched.
   d. lower pitched.
4. Do two sound waves that seem equally loud always have the same amplitude? Explain.
5. Would a car driving at 800 mph be supersonic or subsonic?
6. A paramedic in an ambulance does not experience the Doppler effect of the siren. Why?
7. How could you increase the air pressure inside a bag containing a group of air molecules?
8. Is sound a longitudinal or transverse wave?
9. A 200-Hz sound has a wavelength about equal to the height of an adult. Would a sound with a wavelength equal to the height of a 2-year-old child have a higher or lower frequency than 200 Hz?
10. Explain how the cochlea allows us to hear both low-frequency and high-frequency sound.
11. What is the range of frequencies for human hearing?

Ultrasound

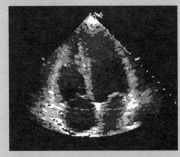

We cannot hear ultrasound, but it can pass through the human body. Doctors may use ultrasound images to see "inside" patients, like x-rays. The ultrasound image pictured above is a heart.

What is ultrasound?

How does do the frequency and wavelength of ultrasound compare to sounds you can hear?

Sound All Around

Acoustics is the science and technology of sound. Sound is greatly affected by reflections in enclosed spaces. Your living room or bedroom at home is an enclosed space, but so is your school cafeteria or auditorium. Physicists who specialize in acoustics study how sound acts in these spaces.

Your school spaces

Think about the sound you hear in a school cafeteria or gymnasium versus the school library. From experience, you know that a cafeteria and gym are often loud places, and libraries are quiet. Now, think about the design of these spaces and the types of materials used in them. What comes to mind?

Most libraries and auditoriums have carpet on the floors. The walls and ceilings of these spaces may also have special materials that absorb sound. Of course, the sound in a library or auditorium is also controlled by rules and what types of events are happening. People study quietly in libraries, but might listen to loud speeches or music in an auditorium.

School cafeterias tend to be large spaces with hard floors and bare ceilings. The flooring is easier to clean, but also provides a surface that reflects sound. The floor of a gymnasium is good for bouncing basketballs and for bouncing sound. When sound is reflected rather than absorbed by a surface, the space tends to be noisy rather than quiet.

Is the space dead or alive?

Sound travels through a medium (solid, liquid, or gas) until the energy is absorbed by the medium. The sound waves move through a room and reflect off surfaces they run into. The time for this varies, depending upon many variables including the strength of the initial sound, the absorption rate of the walls of the room, and the size of the room. A *live room* is one whose materials have a low absorption rate. Live rooms include gymnasiums and cafeterias where sounds easily reflect off walls and last a long time, even while many news sounds are made. A library or auditorium is an example of a *dead room*. In these rooms, the absorption rate of the materials is much higher. Sounds are absorbed, and they don't last a long time, causing the space to be quieter.

Cancel the noise!

In a library, passive noise reduction (PNR) is used to help make this enclosed space quiet. Carpet, heavy curtains, or even ear plugs are examples of passive noise reduction items. These materials absorb sound.

Another way to reduce sound is by active noise reduction (ANR). ANR technology tries to cancel rather than absorb sound that is unwanted. Have you ever heard of noise reduction headphones? Specially-designed headphones are one part of the growing technology of ANR. There are three basic parts of ANR in these special headphones: a microphone, processing electronics, and a speaker. These parts, which must all fit into the ear pieces, work together to cancel unwanted sound waves.

With carefully-designed ANR, the microphone very near the ear canal continually detects noise. The frequency and amplitude profile of the noise is detected. The processing electronics create another noise that is just the opposite of the original. This new noise—or anti-noise—is sent into the ear canal by the speaker and cancels the offending sound.

ANR headsets for MP3 players are safe to wear because they only cancel the lower frequencies of sound, and not speech or warning sirens.

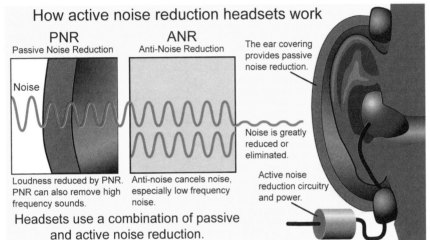

How active noise reduction headsets work

PNR Passive Noise Reduction

ANR Anti-Noise Reduction

Noise

The ear covering provides passive noise reduction.

Noise is greatly reduced or eliminated.

Loudness reduced by PNR. PNR can also remove high frequency sounds.

Anti-noise cancels noise, especially low frequency noise.

Active noise reduction circuitry and power.

Headsets use a combination of passive and active noise reduction.

Which is better: ANR or PNR?

Scientists have learned that passive and active noise reduction are effective in different ways. ANR seems to work better with low frequency sounds. PNR is better at absorbing the higher frequencies. For example, studies have shown that the noise produced by propellers in airplanes is in the low frequency range. Therefore, specialized ANR headphones work well for airplane pilots. Extra soundproofing for passive noise reduction, although it would lessen high frequency noise, would add too much weight to a plane to be practical.

Presently, ANR technology is being tested to lower the noise from the cooling fans inside electronic devices like your computer, tailpipes of cars, or inside the cabin of the car. As ANR technology grows, new uses for ANR will be discovered. Can you think of a new use for ANR technology?

QUESTIONS

1. What is the difference between a live room and a dead room in terms of sound?

2. If you wanted to create a recording studio for recording a new CD for your band, what would you do? You may want to do research on the Internet to find out the design features of recording studios.

3. Compare and contrast passive and active noise reduction.

4. Does active noise reduction work using constructive or destructive interference?

Make Your Own Speaker

Almost all speakers contain magnets and coils of wire that interact to create mechanical vibrations out of pulsating electric currents. You can make your own speaker to hear music from your MP3 player—it's simple!

Materials

a source of music (mp3 player, or anything that takes a 1/8-inch plug); mono earbud with 1/8-inch plug with earbud cut off and wire stripped back about 4 inches; copper wire coil with at least 20 turns or so (made from enameled copper wire); tape; sandpaper; magnet (CPO-type or small neodymium); rubber band; plastic drinking cup

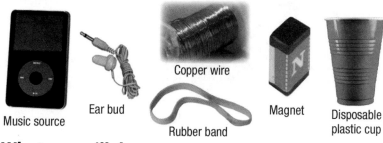

Music source   Ear bud   Copper wire   Rubber band   Magnet   Disposable plastic cup

What you will do

1. Sand about 1 inch of the enamel coating from the two ends of the wire coil.

2. Bend the very end of each coil "tail" back on itself to form a little eye hook.

3. Where the wire coating was stripped back from cutting off the earbud, there will be either two or three wires inside. Separate the two strands. If there are three wires, one is a ground and can be stuck together with either of the other strands.

4. Thread one of the stripped wire strands from the earbud cord through the eye hook of one of the coil ends, and pull it halfway through. Twist the stripped wire around and around

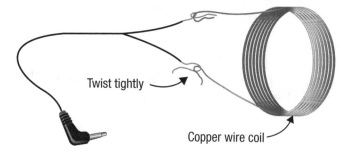

Twist tightly

Copper wire coil

so it tightens up against the eye hook. Fasten with tape to make a good connection.

5. Repeat steps 3 and 4 with the other free wire strand.

6. Place the wire coil on the bottom of the plastic cup and fasten with a rubber band.

7. Plug your speaker into the music source.

8. Rest the magnet on top of the rubber band, inside the wire coil, and hold it there while you place the open end of the cup against your ear.

9. Listen for the music! Make sure the volume is on *loud*.

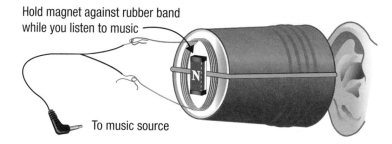

Hold magnet against rubber band while you listen to music

To music source

Applying your knowledge

a. Do some research to see how speakers work.

b. What is the purpose of the plastic cup? Explain.

c. How could you improve the strength of your sound without turning up the volume on the music source?

Chapter 9 Activity

Chapter 9 Assessment

Vocabulary

Select the correct term to complete the sentences.

wavelength	supersonic	amplitude
pendulum	reflection	constructive interference
longitudinal	harmonic	frequency
decibels	transverse	

Section 9.1

1. A device that swings back and forth due to the force of gravity is called a(n) ____.

2. Motion that repeats in cycles is called ____ motion.

3. The number of cycles an oscillator completes in each second is called its ____.

4. The amount that a cycle moves away from equilibrium is called ____.

Section 9.2

5. The distance from one point on a wave to the same point in the next cycle of the wave is known as the ____.

6. When a wave bounces off a surface, the interaction is called ____.

7. When waves combine to produce a wave of larger amplitude, ____ has occurred.

8. A(n) ____ wave has oscillations in the same direction as its motion.

9. A(n) ____ wave has oscillations that are not in the same direction as its motion.

Section 9.3

10. Units for measuring the loudness of sound are ____.

11. Objects that move faster than sound are referred to as ____.

Concepts

Section 9.1

1. Of the following, which are examples of harmonic motion (*H*), linear motion (*L*), or both?
   a. a child on a moving swing
   b. a skateboard moving down the sidewalk
   c. a blinking directional signal on a car
   d. a bouncing basketball
   e. a child sliding down a playground slide one time

2. For each object, determine if it is in equilibrium (**E**) or not in equilibrium (**N**).
   a. a car moving with constant velocity
   b. a ball at rest on the floor
   c. a child sitting motionless in a swing
   d. a bicyclist rolling down a hill

3. If a periodic force is applied to a swing at the natural frequency of the swing, what happens to the swing's period and amplitude?

Section 9.2

4. For the wave in the diagram, which measurement shows the amplitude? Which measurement shows the wavelength?

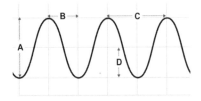

5. Rank the following waves from fastest to slowest.
   a. sound waves
   b. water waves
   c. light waves

6. Below are diagrams representing interactions between waves and boundaries. Identify each interaction by name.

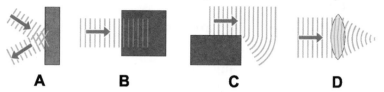

A   **B**   **C**   **D**

7. What happens if two waves are in the same place at the same time? Use the term *interference* in your answer.

Section 9.3

8. Imagine you are cruising in outer space in a spaceship when you notice an asteroid hurtling towards your ship. You fire a missile and score a direct hit. The asteroid explodes into a billion pieces. Would you hear the explosion? Explain your answer.

9. Why do we see lightning before we hear the thunder from it?

10. What happens when the inner ear is exposed to very loud noises? (Some musicians wear earplugs when playing in concerts.)

11. How are the pitch and frequency of a sound related?

12. Which part of the ear vibrates in response to sound in the ear canal?

Problems

Section 9.1

1. A bicycle wheel spins 25 times in 5 seconds. Calculate the period and frequency of the wheel.

2. The piston in a gasoline engine goes up and down 3,000 times per minute. For this engine, calculate the frequency and period of the piston.

3. Calculate the period and frequency for the second hand, minute hand, and hour hand of a clock.

Section 9.2

4. A water wave with a frequency of 2 Hz has a wavelength of 3 meters. What is the speed of the wave?

5. What is the wavelength of a sound wave whose frequency is 200 Hz (speed of sound = 340 m/s)?

6. A water wave hits the beach every 2.5 seconds. The distance between wave crests is 5 meters. For these waves, calculate:

   a. wavelength

   b. period

   c. speed

7. Draw at least one cycle of a transverse wave with an amplitude of 4 cm and a wavelength of 8 cm. If the frequency of this wave is 10 Hz, what is its speed?

Section 9.3

8. If the loudness of a sound increases by 40 decibels, how is the amplitude of the sound wave changed?

9. A whistle is used to create a sound with a wavelength of 1.0 centimeter.

   a. Calculate the frequency of this sound.

   b. Can this sound be detected by the human ear?

10. The Doppler effect is used by astronomers to determine if stars are moving away from or toward Earth. Red light has a lower frequency than blue light. If light from a star is shifted to the red, does that mean the star is moving toward or away from Earth?

11. The range of human hearing is between 20 Hz and 20,000 Hz. If the speed of sound is 340 m/s, what is the longest wavelength you can hear? What is the shortest?

Light and Color

Television brings you images of objects and places that you may not otherwise have ever seen. What's more, the images move with full sound and color as if you really were there. Skies on TV are blue, flowers are bright, and colors appear as if the actual objects were right in front of you.

What creates color? Does the flower give off red and orange light like a neon sign? How is color seen by our eyes? How is it created in a television?

To answer these questions, start with a short experiment. Take a colorful object like a shirt or a toy. Look at the object in the light. Then, look at the same object in a totally dark room. What do you see? How do the colors compare in the light versus in the dark? Your answer and your observations will prepare you for this chapter, where you will learn about light and color.

Key Questions:

1. What is light?

2. What is color and how do we see it?

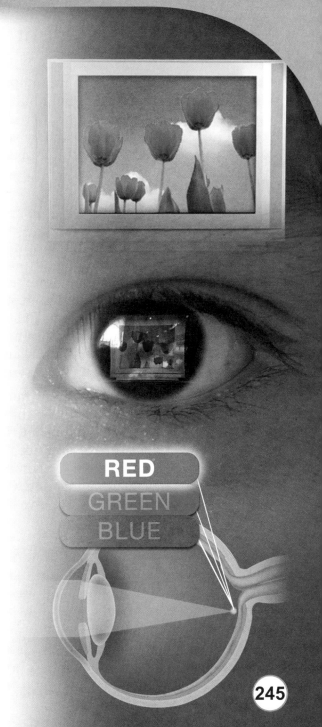

RED
GREEN
BLUE

10.1 Properties of Light

Every time you "see," you are using **light**. You can't see *anything* in complete darkness! Whether you are looking at a light bulb, or a car, or this book, light brings information to your eyes. In fact, the very act of "seeing" means receiving light and forming images in your mind from the light received by your eyes. This chapter is about light—where it comes from, its many and useful properties, and how it is related to color.

What is light?

Light is a form of energy   Light, like sound and heat, is a form of energy. Our understanding of light starts with what light does and what its properties are (Figure 10.1). We know that:

- light travels extremely fast and over long distances;
- light carries energy and information;
- light travels in straight lines;
- light bounces and bends when it comes in contact with objects;
- light has color; and
- light has different intensities, and can be bright or dim.

Seeing with reflected light   What happens when you "see" this page? Light in the room reflects off the page and into your eyes. The reflected light carries information about the page that your brain uses to make a mental picture of the page. You see because light in the room *reflects* from the page into your eyes. If you were sitting in a perfectly dark room with no light, you would not be able to see this page at all because the page does not give off its own light. *We see most of the world by reflected light.*

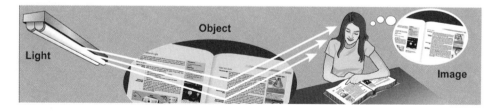

light - a form of energy that travels at 300,000 km/s and includes all the colors that can be seen by the human eye.

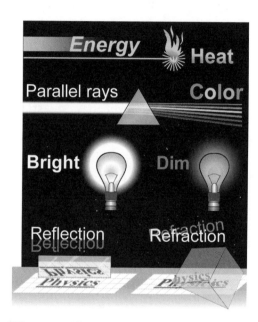

Figure 10.1: *Some words and properties that are associated with light. What words do you use to describe light?*

Most light comes from atoms

The electric light For most of human history, people relied on the Sun, the Moon, and fire to provide light. Thomas Edison's electric light bulb (1879) changed our dependence on fire and daylight forever. The electric light is one of the most important inventions in the progress of human development.

Light is produced by atoms Whether in an electric bulb or in the Sun, light is mostly produced by atoms. Here's an analogy. When you stretch a rubber band, you give the rubber band elastic energy. You can use that energy to launch a paper airplane. In this case, the energy is released as kinetic energy of the flying airplane. Unlike a rubber band, an atom releases the extra energy usually—but not always—as light!

Incandescent light bulbs In order to get light out of an atom, you must first put some energy into the atom. One way to do this is with heat. Making light with heat is called **incandescence**. Incandescent bulbs use electric current to heat a thin metal wire called a *filament*. The atoms of the filament convert electrical energy to heat and then to light. Unfortunately, incandescent bulbs are not very efficient. Only a fraction of the energy of electricity is converted into light. Most of the energy becomes heat. In restaurants, this feature of incandescent bulbs is used to warm food.

Compact fluorescent light bulbs Another common kind of electric light is a compact fluorescent light (CFL). CFLs are much more efficient than and provide four times as much light as incandescent bulbs. CFLs consists of a thin tube coiled into a bulb. High-voltage electricity is used to energize atoms of gas inside the tube. These atoms release the electrical energy as light (not heat) in a process called **fluorescence**. The atoms in the tube emit high-energy ultraviolet light—the same kind that gives you a sunburn. The ultraviolet light is absorbed by other atoms in a white coating on the inside surface of the tube. The atoms that make up this coating re-emit the energy as white light (Figure 10.2). Even with this two-step process, CFLs are still more efficient at producing light than incandescent bulbs.

LED bulbs LED stands for light-emitting diode. A diode is an electronic device used in circuits to allow electricity to flow in one direction while blocking current from flowing in the other direction (Figure 10.3). Diodes are found in almost every electronic device in use today. The advantage of LEDs is that they need very little current to produce light. Arrays of LEDs are assembled into bulb shapes that are even more efficient than CFLs.

VOCABULARY

incandescence - a process that makes light with heat.

fluorescence - a process that makes light directly from electricity.

Compact fluorescent lamp

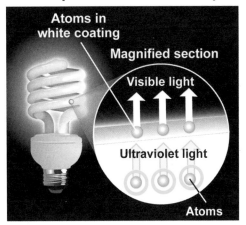

Figure 10.2: *Fluorescent lights generate light by exciting atoms with electricity in a two-step process.*

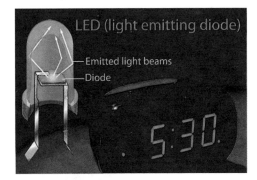

Figure 10.3: *The display on this alarm clock is made of LEDs.*

Color and energy

White light When all the colors of the rainbow are combined, we see light without *any* color. We call the combination of all colors **white light**. The light that is all around us most of the time is white light. The light from the Sun and the light from most electric lights is white light.

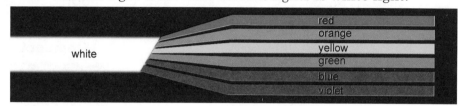

What is color? Not all light has the same energy. **Color** is how we perceive the energy of light. This definition of color was proposed by Albert Einstein. All of the colors in the rainbow are light of different energies. Red light has the lowest energy we can see, and violet light the highest energy. As we move through the rainbow from red to yellow to blue to violet, the energy of the light increases.

Color and energy What do we mean when we talk about the energy of light? Think about the hot, blue flame from a blow torch or gas stove compared to the orange flame of a match. The hot gas flame has more energy than the cooler flame of the match. The light from a gas flame is blue (high energy) and the light from a match is red-orange (low energy) (Figure 10.4).

Photons

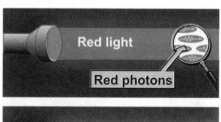

Just as matter is made of atoms, light energy comes in tiny wave-bundles called **photons**. In some ways, photons act like jellybeans of different colors. Each photon has its own color (energy), no matter how you mix them up. The lowest-energy photons we can see are dull red and the highest-energy photons are blue-violet.

Blue flames = High energy

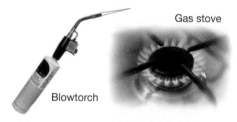

Gas stove

Blowtorch

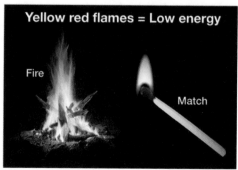

Yellow red flames = Low energy

Fire

Match

Figure 10.4: *High-energy flames such as the ones from a blow torch produce blue light. Flames from a match or campfire are lower energy and produce reddish-yellow light.*

The speed of light

Comparing the speeds of sound and light

Think about what happens when you shine a flashlight on a wall that is far away. You don't see a time delay as the light leaves your flashlight, travels to the wall, bounces off, and comes back to your eyes. But that is exactly what happens. You don't notice because it because it happens so *fast*. Suppose the wall is 170 meters away. The light travels to the wall and back in about one millionth of a second (0.000001 s). Sound travels much slower than light. If you shout, you will hear an echo one full second later from the sound bouncing off the wall and back to your ears. Light travels almost a million times faster than sound!

Light is faster than sound

The speed of light is about 300 million meters per second or 186,000 miles per second. At 15°C, the speed of sound is about 340 meters per second or 1 mile every 5 seconds. You can use the speed of sound to determine how far away a lightning strike has occurred.

When you see lightning, begin counting seconds until you hear thunder. Divide the number of seconds you count by 5. The result is the distance in miles between where you are and where the lightning struck.

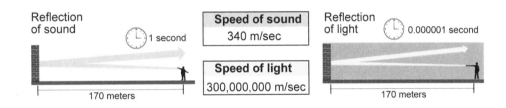

The speed of light, $c = 3 \times 10^8$ m/s

The speed at which light travels through air is about 300 million meters per second. Light is so fast it can travel around the entire Earth 7 1/2 times in 1 second. The *speed of light* is so important in physics that it is given its own symbol, a lower case c. When you see this symbol in a formula, remember that it means the speed of light ($c = 300,000,000$ m/s).

Why you hear thunder after you see lightning

The speed of light is so fast that when lightning strikes a few miles away, we hear the thunder several seconds after we see the lightning. At the point of the lightning strike, the thunder and lightning are simultaneous. But just a mile away from the lightning strike, the sound of the thunder is already about 5 seconds behind the flash of the lightning. You can use this information to calculate how far you are away from a thunderstorm (see the sidebar at right).

The wavelength and frequency of light

Wavelength of light   The wavelength of visible light is very small. For example, waves of orange light have a length of only 0.0000006 meters. Because the wavelength of light is so small, scientists use **nanometers**. One nanometer (nm) is one billionth of a meter (0.000000001 m). Figure 10.5 shows the size of a light wave relative to other small things. Thousands of wavelengths of red light would fit in the width of a single hair on your head!

Frequency of light   The frequency of light waves is very high. For example, red light has a frequency of 460 trillion, or 460,000,000,000,000, cycles per second. To manage these large numbers, scientists use units of terahertz (THz) to measure light waves. One THz is 1 trillion Hz (1,000,000,000,000 Hz).

Wavelength, frequency, color, and energy   Like other waves, the wavelength and frequency of light are inversely related. As frequency increases, wavelength decreases. Red light has a lower frequency and longer wavelength than blue light. Blue light has a higher frequency and shorter wavelength than red light.

nanometer - a unit of length equal to one billionth of a meter (0.000000001 m).

Energy	Color	Wavelength (nanometers)	Frequency (THz)
Low	Red	650	462
	Orange	600	500
	Yellow	580	517
	Green	530	566
	Blue	470	638
High	Violet	400	750

As you can see from the table above, energy and frequency are directly related. The higher the frequency, the higher the energy. Since color is related to energy, the table also shows the relationships between color, frequency, and wavelength.

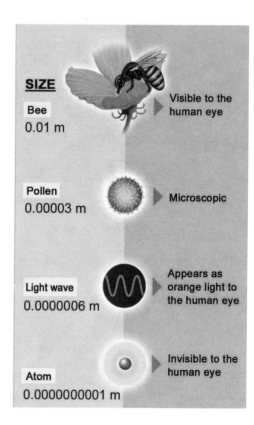

Figure 10.5: *The sizes of some objects compared to the wavelength of a light wave.*

What kind of wave is light?

Light comes from electricity and magnetism

A sound wave is a oscillation of air. A water wave is an oscillation of the surface of water. What is oscillating in a light wave? The answer is electricity and magnetism! Imagine you have two magnets. One hangs from a string and the other is in your hand. If you wave the magnet in your hand back and forth, you can make the magnet on the string sway back and forth (Figure 10.6). How does the oscillation of one magnet get to the other one? In Chapter 8 you learned that magnets create an invisible magnetic field around them. When you move a magnet in your hand back and forth, you make a change in the magnetic field. The changing magnetic field makes the other magnet move. In a similar way, the force between two electric charges is carried by an *electric field*.

Electromagnetic waves

Any change in the electric or magnetic field travels at the speed of light. If you could shake your magnet (or charge) back and forth *100 million times per second* you would make an **electromagnetic wave**. In fact, it would be an FM radio wave at 100 million Hz (100 MHz). An electromagnetic wave is a traveling oscillation in the electric and magnetic field.

The hard way to make red light

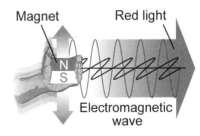

If you could shake the magnet up and down 450 *trillion* times per second, you would make waves of red light. Red light is a traveling oscillation (wave) in the electric and magnetic fields with a frequency of about 450 THz.

Oscillations of electricity or magnetism create light waves

Anything that creates an oscillation of electricity or magnetism also creates electromagnetic waves. If you switch electricity on and off repeatedly in a wire, the oscillating electricity makes an electromagnetic wave. This is exactly how radio towers make radio waves. Electric currents oscillate up and down the metal towers and create electromagnetic waves of the right frequency to carry radio signals.

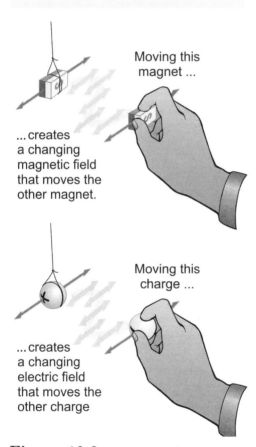

Figure 10.6: *Magnets influence each other through the magnetic field. Charges influence each other through the electric field.*

The electromagnetic spectrum

Waves in the electromagnetic spectrum
The entire range of electromagnetic waves, including all possible frequencies, is called the **electromagnetic spectrum**. The electromagnetic spectrum includes radio waves, microwaves, infrared light, ultraviolet light, X-rays, and gamma rays. As you can see from the chart below, we use electromagnetic waves for all kinds of human technologies.

The electromagnetic spectrum

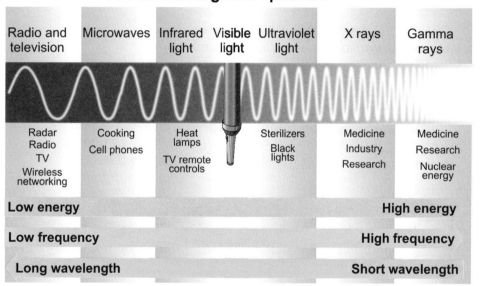

Radio and television	Microwaves	Infrared light	Visible light	Ultraviolet light	X rays	Gamma rays
Radar Radio TV Wireless networking	Cooking Cell phones	Heat lamps TV remote controls		Sterilizers Black lights	Medicine Industry Research	Medicine Research Nuclear energy

Low energy — **High energy**

Low frequency — **High frequency**

Long wavelength — **Short wavelength**

Properties of electromagnetic waves
You can see that visible light is a small group of frequencies in the middle of the spectrum, between infrared and ultraviolet. The rest of the spectrum is invisible for the same reason you cannot see the magnetic field between two magnets. The energies are either too low or too high for the human eye to detect. Visible light includes only the electromagnetic waves with the range of energy that can be detected by the human eye. Some insects and animals can see other frequencies, including some infrared and some ultraviolet light.

X-rays

X-rays are high-energy electromagnetic waves used in medicine and industry. The wavelength range is from about 10 nm to about 0.001 nm (or 10-trillionths of a meter). When you get a medical x-ray, digital sensors detect the amount of energy that passes through your body. X-rays can show the extent of a broken bone because calcium and other elements in your bones absorb the x-rays before they reach the detector. Information from the digital x-ray sensors can be stored on a computer and then manipulated with software to improve the quality of the image.

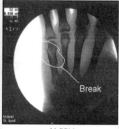

x ray

10.1 **Section Review**

1. Which of the following is *not* a property of light?
    a. Light is a form of matter less dense than air.
    b. Light travels in straight lines.
    c. Light has different colors.
    d. Light has different intensities, and can be bright or dim.
2. If a room were completely dark, could you see your hand? Could you see a television screen? Explain the difference.
3. List three observations that show how light carries energy.
4. Most light comes from
    a. vibrating surfaces.
    b. atoms.
    c. conversion of frequency to wavelength.
5. Compared to sound waves, the frequency of light waves is
    a. much lower.
    b. about the same.
    c. much higher.
6. Which electromagnetic wave has less energy than visible light and more energy than radio waves?
    a. microwaves
    b. ultraviolet light
    c. gamma rays
    d. x-rays
7. According to the table on page 250:
    a. What is the relationship between the wavelength of light and energy?
    b. What is the relationship between the frequency of light and energy?

CHALLENGE

Who discovered that white light contains all colors? How was the discovery made? When was it made? You might be surprised what you find out. This famous scientist is mentioned in this book, but not in connection with light!

SOLVE IT!

The speed of light is frequency multiplied by wavelength, the same as other waves. Suppose you make light with a frequency of 600 THz.

a) What is the wavelength of this light?

b) Describe what color the light would appear to your eye.

You will have to use scientific notation to solve this problem with your calculator. If necessary, ask your teacher or a friend who knows how to do this to help you.

10.2 Color and Vision

The energy of light explains how different colors are physically different. But it doesn't explain how we *see* colors. How does the human eye see color? The answer explains why computers and TVs can make virtually all colors with combinations of only three colors!

How the human eye sees light

Photoreceptors Light enters your eye through the lens then lands on the retina. On the surface of the retina are light-sensitive cells called *photoreceptors* (Figure 10.7). When light hits a photoreceptor cell, the cell releases a chemical signal that travels along the optic nerve to the brain. In the brain, the signal is translated into a perception of color.

Cone cells respond to color Our eyes have two kinds of photoreceptors, called *cones* and *rods*. *Cones* (or *cone cells*) respond to color (Figure 10.8). There are three types of cone cells. One type responds best to low-energy (red) light. Another type responds best to medium-energy (green) light. The third type responds best to higher-energy (blue) light.

Rod cells respond to light intensity The second kind of photoreceptors are called *rods* or *rod cells*. Rods respond to differences in light intensity, but not to color (Figure 10.8). Rod cells "see" black, white, and shades of gray. However, rod cells are much more sensitive than cone cells. At night, colors seem washed out because there is not enough light for cone cells to work. When the light level is very dim, you see "black and white" images from your rod cells.

Black and white vision is sharper than color vision A human eye has about 130 million rod cells and 7 million cone cells. Each cell contributes a "dot" to the image assembled by your brain. Because there are more rod cells, things look sharpest when there is a big difference between light and dark. That's why black and white letters are easier to read than colored letters. Each cone cell "colors" the signals from the surrounding rod cells. Because there are fewer cone cells, our color vision is much less sharp than our black-and-white vision.

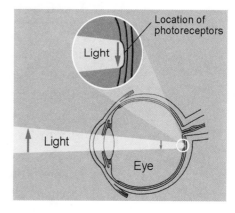

Figure 10.7: *The photoreceptors that send color signals to the brain are in the back of the eye.*

Photoreceptors in the eye

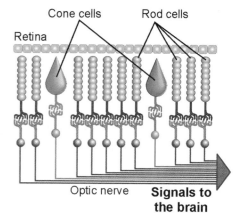

Figure 10.8: *The human eye has two types of photoreceptors—cones and rods. Cones respond to color and rods respond to the intensity of light.*

How we see colors

The additive color process
Our eyes work according to an **additive color process**—three photoreceptors (red, green, blue) in the eye operate together so that we see millions of different colors. The color you "see" depends on how much energy is received by each of the three different types of cone cells. The brain thinks "green" when there is a strong signal from the green cone cells but no signal from the blue or red cone cells (Figure 10.9).

How we perceive color

The additive primary colors

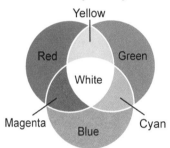

We perceive different colors as a combination of percentages of the three **additive primary colors**: *red*, *green*, and *blue*. For example, we see yellow when the brain gets an equally strong signal from both the red and the green cone cells at the same time. Whether the light is actually yellow or a combination of red and green, the cones respond the same way and we perceive yellow. If the red signal is stronger than the green signal, we see orange (Figure 10.10). If all three cones send an equal signal to the brain, we interpret the light we see as white light.

Two ways to see a color
The human eye can see any color by adding different percentages of the three additive primary colors. Mixing red and green light is one way the eye sees the colors yellow or orange, for example. Keep in mind that you perceive these colors even though the light istself is still red and green. You can also see pure yellow light or orange light that is not a mixture of red and green.

Do animals see colors?
To the best of our knowledge, primates such as chimpanzees and gorillas are the only animals with three-color vision similar to that of humans. Birds and fish—in particualr, tropical varieties—have three or more kinds of photoreceptors. Some birds and insects can see ultraviolet light, which humans cannot detect. Dogs, cats, and some squirrels are thought to have at least two color photoreceptors. Although both octopi and squid can *change* color better than any other animal, they cannot *see* color.

Color signals from only the green cones tell the brain the leaf is green.

Figure 10.9: *If the brain gets a signal from only the green cone, we see green.*

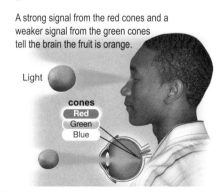

A strong signal from the red cones and a weaker signal from the green cones tell the brain the fruit is orange.

Figure 10.10: *If there is a strong red signal and a weak green signal, we see orange.*

Making a color image

Full color image

Figure 10.11: *To be printed by a full-color press, an image is separated into cyan, magenta, yellow, and black images.*

Making a color photograph
Modern printing presses use the CMYK color process to produce vivid colors from only four inks. To print a color photograph, the image is converted into four separate images in cyan, magenta, yellow, and black. Each separate image represents what will be printed with its matching CMYK ink. The cyan separation is printed with cyan ink, the magenta separation with magenta ink, and so on. Figure 10.11 shows the four color separations from a color image.

The RGB color process
Color images are created using the RGB color process, an additive process that uses red, green, and blue light. The RGB process is used by television screens and computer monitors, which make different colors by lighting red, green, and blue pixels to different percentages (Figure 10.12). For example, a light brown tone is 88 percent red, 85 percent green, and 70 percent blue. Each pixel (or dot) has three numbers that tell how much red, green, and blue to use. A digital video image is 720 dots wide times 480 dots high. If each dot has three numbers (R, G, B), a single image takes 1,036,800 numbers to store!

Video cameras create color images
A video camera-recorder (also called a camcorder) uses the RGB process differently than a TV. Like the rods and cones in your retina, a video camcorder has 300,000–500,000 sensors on a small chip called a CCD (charge-coupled device). The sensors on the CCD measure the light intensity as percentages of red, green, and blue in the light coming through the camera lens. This information is recorded 30 times per second. The CCDs in most video camera-recorders are typically 1 centimeter square or less.

Figure 10.12: *A television makes colors by using tiny dots of red, green, and blue.*

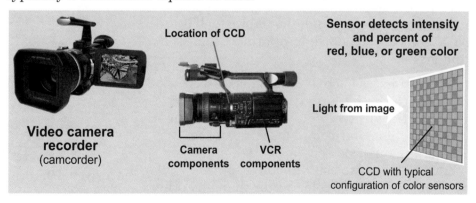

How objects appear to be different colors

What gives objects their color?

Your eye creates a sense of color by responding to red, green, and blue light. You don't see objects in their own light, you see them in reflected light! A blue shirt looks blue because it *reflects blue light into your eyes*. However, the shirt did not *make* the blue light. The color blue is not *in* the cloth! The blue light you see is the blue light mixed into white light that shines on the cloth. You see blue because the other colors in white light have been subtracted out (Figure 10.13).

The subtractive color process

Colored fabrics and paints get color from a **subtractive color process**. Chemicals known as *pigments* in the dyes and paints absorb some colors and reflect other colors. Pigments work by taking away colors from white light, which is a mixture of all the colors.

The subtractive primary colors

To make all colors by subtraction we need three primary pigments. We need one that absorbs blue (reflects red and green). This pigment is called *yellow*. We need another pigment that absorbs green (reflects red and blue). This is a pink-purple pigment called *magenta*. The third pigment is *cyan*, which absorbs red (reflects green and blue). Cyan is a greenish shade of light blue. Magenta, yellow, and cyan are the three **subtractive primary colors** (see illustration above). Different proportions of the three subtractive primary colors change the amount of reflected red, green, and blue light.

How "white" is white?

A blue shirt won't look blue in red light! It will look *black*! The subtractive color model assumes a painted or dyed surface is seen in white *sunlight* containing a precise mix of colors. If the "white" has a different mix than sunlight, colors don't look right. This is why home videos made under fluorescent lights often look greenish. The white from fluorescent lights has a slightly different mix of colors than the white from sunlight.

VOCABULARY

subtractive color process - a process that uses absorption to create color by subtracting colors from white light.

subtractive primary colors - cyan, magenta, and yellow.

The subtractive primary colors

Red

Magenta   Yellow

Black

Blue   Green

Cyan

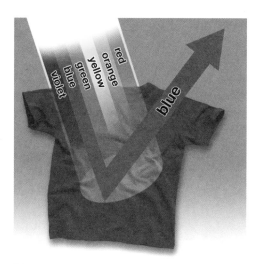

Figure 10.13: *The pigments in a blue cloth absorb all colors except blue. You see blue because blue light is reflected to your eyes.*

The CMYK color process

A subtractive color process Another name for the subtractive color process is the *CMYK color process*. CMYK stands for cyan, magenta, yellow, and black. The letter *K* stands for black because the letter *B* is used to represent the color blue.

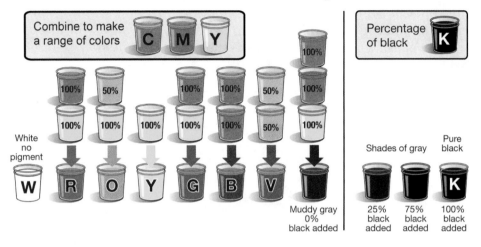

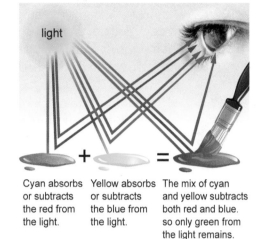

Figure 10.14: *Creating the color green using cyan and yellow.*

CMYK are pigments The CMYK color process is used for making all colors seen in reflected light, including printing inks and fabric dyes. The three pigments—cyan, magenta, and yellow—are combined in various proportions to make any color. Figure 10.14 shows how CMYK pigments can be combined to make green. You might think that mixing cyan, magenta, and yellow would make black, but in reality the result is a muddy gray. This is why a fourth color, pure black, is included in the CMYK process. Figure 10.15 shows how the CMYK process works with an ink-jet printer.

To make	Mix	Because
Red	Magenta and yellow +	Magenta absorbs green Yellow absorbs blue Red is reflected
Blue	Magenta and cyan +	Magenta absorbs green Cyan absorbs red Blue is reflected
Green	Cyan and yellow +	Cyan absorbs red Yellow absorbs blue Green is reflected

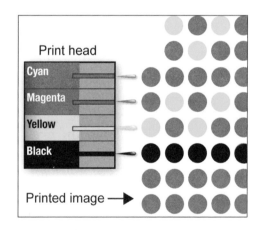

Figure 10.15: *An ink-jet printer makes tiny dots of cyan, magenta, yellow, and black to print a full-color image. The dots are so small that your eye sees only colors. Look at an ink-jet print under a magnifying glass and you will see these dots.*

Why plants are green

Light is necessary for photosynthesis

Plants absorb energy from light and convert it to chemical energy in the form of sugar. This process is called *photosynthesis*. The vertical (*y*) axis of the graph in Figure 10.16 shows the percentage of different colors of light that are absorbed by a plant. The *x*-axis on the graph shows the colors of light. The graph line shows how much and which colors of visible light are absorbed by plants. Based on this graph, can you explain why plants look green?

Why most plants are green

The important molecule that absorbs light in a plant is called *chlorophyll*. There are several forms of chlorophyll. They absorb mostly blue and red light, and reflect green light. This is why most plants look green. The graph in Figure 10.16 shows that plants absorb red and blue light to grow. A plant will die if placed under only green light!

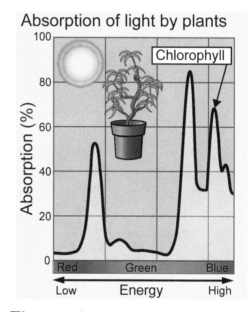

Figure 10.16: *Plants absorb energy from light. The plant pigment chlorophyll absorbs red and blue light, and reflects green light. This is why plants look green!*

Plants reflect some light to keep cool

Why don't plants absorb all colors of light? The reason is the same reason you wear light-colored clothes when it is hot outside. Like you, plants must reflect some light to avoid absorbing too much energy and overheating. Plants use visible light because the energy is just enough to change certain chemical bonds, but not enough to completely break them. Ultraviolet light has more energy but would break chemical bonds. Infrared light has too little energy to change chemical bonds.

Why leaves change color

The leaves of some plants, such as sugar maple trees, turn brilliant red or gold in the fall. Chlorophyll masks other plant pigments during the spring and summer. In the fall, when photosynthesis slows down, chlorophyll breaks down and red, orange, and yellow pigments in the leaves are revealed!

CHALLENGE

What about red plants?

All plants that use sunlight to grow have chlorophyll, but some do not look green. Come up with a hypothesis to explain this observation.

10.2 **Section Review**

1. If humans have only three kinds of color photoreceptors, how can we see so many different colors?
2. Why is it easier to read black and white text compared to green text or text of any light color?
3. Why might it be a good idea to put a light in your clothes closet? (*Hint*: What kind of vision do we have in dim light?)
4. Do you think this textbook was printed using the CMYK color process or the RGB color process? Explain your answer.
5. If you were going to design the lighting for a play, would you need to understand the CMYK color process, the RGB color process, or both? Explain your answer.
6. Suppose you have cyan, magenta, yellow, and black paint. Which colors would you mix to get blue?
7. Why does static on a television set appear white?
8. How is the color black produced in the CMYK color process versus the RGB color process?
9. A red shirt appears red because
   a. the shirt emits red light.
   b. the shirt absorbs red light.
   c. the shirt emits green and blue light.
   d. the shirt absorbs green and blue light.
10. Some plants that grow in shady areas have dark green or even purple leaves. Come up with a hypothesis to explain this observation.
11. What would happen if you tried to grow a green plant in pure green light? Would the plant live? Explain your answer.
12. Propose an explanation for how the top image in Figure 10.17 is related to the four images below it.

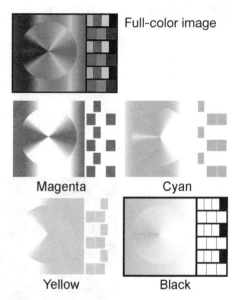

Figure 10.17: *Question 12.*

Pictures from dots

A color printer, like an inkjet printer, makes color images by printing small dots. If there were only four dots per inch, your eye would see the individual dots instead of the picture the dots are supposed to make. How many dots must there be (per inch) to trick the eye into seeing a smooth image? How many dots per inch do printers around your home or office use?

10.3 Optics

Optics is the science and technology of light. Almost everyone has experience with optics. For example, trying on new glasses, checking your appearance in a mirror, or admiring the sparkle from a diamond ring all involve optics.

Basic optical devices

Lenses A **lens** bends light in a specific way. A *converging lens* bends light so that the light rays come together in a point. This is why a magnifying glass makes a hot spot of concentrated light (Figure 10.18). A *diverging lens* bends light so it spreads light apart instead of bringing it together. An object viewed through a diverging lens appears smaller than it would look without the lens.

Mirrors A **mirror** reflects light and allows you to see yourself. Flat mirrors show a true-size image. Curved mirrors distort images. The curved surface of a fun house mirror can make you look appear thinner, wider, or even upside down!

Prisms A **prism** is usually made of a solid piece of glass with flat polished surfaces. A common triangular prism is shown in the picture below. Prisms can both bend and/or reflect light. Telescopes, cameras, and supermarket laser scanners use prisms of different shapes to bend and reflect light in precise ways. A diamond is a prism with many flat, polished surfaces. The "sparkle" that makes diamonds so attractive comes from light being reflected many times as it bounces around the inside of a cut and polished diamond.

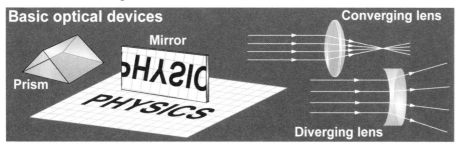

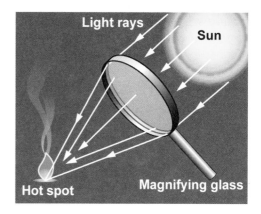

Figure 10.18: *A magnifying glass is a converging lens. This is why a magnifying glass can be used to make a hot spot of concentrated light. You should* not *try this yourself—the science is interesting, but can be unsafe.*

How light is affected by matter

Interactions Since light rays travel through oscillating electric and magnetic fields, they do not need matter to propagate. What happens when light does encounter matter? How light responds to an object or a surface is called an interaction. Light has interactions whenever it meets matter, whether the matter is a leaf, a glass, or a mirror.

Some materials bounce or scatter light **Reflection** occurs when light bounces off a material and goes in a new direction. Almost all surfaces reflect some light. A mirror is a very good reflector, but a sheet of white paper is also a good reflector. The difference is in how they reflect. Sometimes light is bounced back, and sometimes light is scattered in different directions.

Some materials allow light to pass through **Refraction** occurs as light bends and changes direction. If you look at your thumb through a magnifying glass, it looks huge (Figure 10.19). That's because a magnifying glass is curved in order to bend and change the direction of light to make an image look bigger. Materials that allow light to transmit through are called *transparent*. Air is transparent, and so is window glass.

Some materials can take energy from light **Absorption** happens when light's energy is transferred to the material it is passing through. A black road surface gets hot on a sunny day because it absorbs energy from sulight. A pair of sunglasses is also an example of a material that absorbs light. Tinted glass lenses absorb some of the bright light to keep it from reaching your eyes. Different color tints absorb different wavelengths of light.

More than one interaction at once

Most of the time, all three interactions happen together. Light waves can partly bounce off, partly pass through, and be partly absorbed by the same material. A polished glass window aborbs about 10 percent of light, while still reflecting bright sunlight back outside and transmitting light through to the inside. The type of interactions light has with matter depends on the type of material and the frequency (color) of light. Materials that do not absorb light well look white; those that absorb all colors appear black. Most materials have a combination of absorption and reflection that appear as different colors. Look at the illustration above. Green paper absorbs some light, and reflects some light. Can you tell which colors are absorbed and which colors are reflected?

Figure 10.19: *When you look through a magnifying glass, your thumb appears huge.*

Light rays

What are light rays? When light moves through a material, it travels in straight lines. Diagrams that show how light travels use straight lines and arrows to represent **light rays**. Think of a light ray as a thin beam of light, like a laser beam. The arrow models the direction the actual light is moving.

Reflection and refraction When light moves from one material to another, it may bounce or bend. Light rays can be used to show exactly how the light travels in its interaction with a material. Refraction occurs when light bends while crossing a surface or moving through a material. Reflection occurs when light meets the surface of a material. Reflection and refraction cause many interesting changes in the images we see.

light ray - an imaginary line that represents a beam of light.

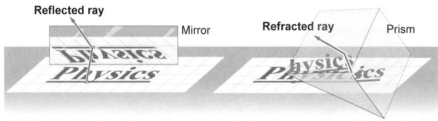

Light rays are reflected in a mirror, causing an inverted image.

Light rays are refracted (or bent) by a prism, causing the image to be distorted.

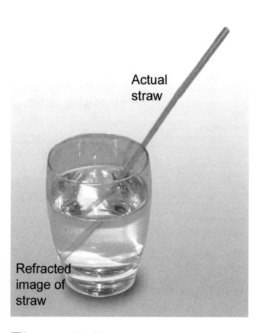

Figure 10.20: *Refraction bends light rays so the straw appears to be in a different place.*

Reflection creates images in mirrors When you look in a mirror, objects that are in front of the mirror appear as if they are behind the mirror. Light from the object strikes the mirror and reflects to your eyes. The image reaching your eyes appears to your brain as if the object really *was* behind the mirror. This illusion happens because your brain "sees" the image where it would be if the light reaching your eyes had traveled in a straight line.

Refraction changes how objects look When light rays travel from air to water, they refract. This is why a straw in a glass of water looks broken or bent at the water's surface (Figure 10.20). Look at some objects through a glass of water; move the glass closer and farther away from the objects. What strange illusions do you see?

Reflection

The image in a mirror
When you look at yourself in a mirror, you see your own image as if your exact twin were standing in front of you. The image appears to be the same distance from the other side of the mirror as you are on your side of the mirror (Figure 10.21). If you step back, so does your image. Images form in mirrors because of how light is reflected.

Specular reflection
Light is reflected from all surfaces, not just mirrors. But not all surfaces form images. The reason for this is that there are two types of reflections. A ray of light that strikes a shiny surface (like a mirror) creates a single reflected ray. This type of reflection is called **specular reflection**. Specular reflection is why you see an image in a polished surface, like a mirror. In fact, a surface which has perfect specular reflection is *invisible*. If you look at that surface, you see reflections of other things, *but you don't see the surface itself.*

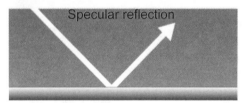 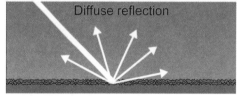

Diffuse reflection
A surface that is dull, (not shiny) creates **diffuse reflection**. In diffuse reflection, each reflected ray of light scatters in many directions creating multiple reflected rays. Diffuse reflection is caused by the roughness of a surface. Even if a surface feels smooth to the touch, on a microscopic level it may be rough. For example, the surface of a wooden board creates a diffuse reflection. When you look at a diffuse reflecting surface *you see the surface itself.*

One surface can create both types of reflection
Many surfaces are in between rough and smooth. These kinds of surfaces create both kinds of reflection. For example, a polished wood tabletop can reflect some light in specular reflection, and the rest of the light in diffuse reflection. The specular reflection creates a faint reflected image on the table surface. You also see the table surface itself by light from diffuse reflection.

specular reflection - "shiny" surface reflection, where each incident ray produces only one reflected ray.

diffuse reflection - "dull" surface reflection, where each incident ray produces many scattered rays.

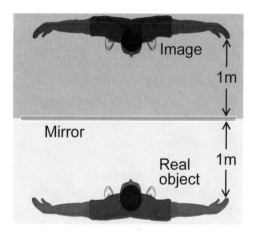

Figure 10.21: *The image you see in a flat mirror appears to be the same distance behind the mirror as you are in front of it.*

Refraction

The index of refraction
Light rays may bend as they cross a boundary from one material to another. Refraction is the bending of light rays. Eyeglasses, telescopes, binoculars, and fiber optics are a few inventions that use refraction to change the direction of light rays. Different materials have different abilities to bend light. Materials with a higher **index of refraction** bend light by a greater angle. The index of refraction for air is approximately 1.00. Water has an index of refraction of 1.33; for a diamond it is 2.42. Diamonds sparkle because of their high index of refraction. Table 10.1 lists the index of refraction for some common materials.

Table 10.1: The index of refraction for some common materials

Material	Index of refraction
Air	1.00
Water	1.33
Ice	1.31
Glass	1.45–1.65
Diamond	2.42

The direction a light ray bends
When light goes from air into glass (A), it bends toward the normal line because glass has a higher index of refraction than air. When the light goes from glass into air again (B), it bends away from the normal line. Coming out of the glass, the light ray is going into air with a lower index of refraction than glass.

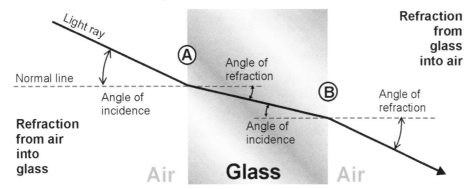

index of refraction - a number that measure how much a material is able to bend light.

A trick of refraction

If two materials have the same index of refraction, light doesn't bend at all. Here's a neat trick you can do with a glass rod. You see the edges of a glass rod because of refraction. The edge appears dark because light is refracted away from your eyes.
Vegetable oil and glass have almost the same index of refraction. If you put a glass rod into a glass cup containing vegetable oil, the rod disappears because light is *not* refracted around its edges!

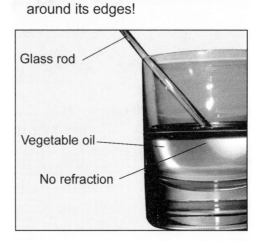

Lenses

A lens and its optical axis

An ordinary lens is a polished, transparent disc, usually made of glass. The surfaces are curved to refract light in a specific way. The exact shape of a lens's surface depends on how strongly and in what way the lens needs to bend light.

How light travels through a converging lens

The most common lenses have surfaces shaped like part of a sphere. Any radius of a sphere is also a normal line to the surface. When light rays fall on a spherical surface from air, they bend *toward* the normal line (Figure 10.22). For a converging lens, the first surface (air to glass) bends light rays toward the normal line. At the second surface (glass to air), the rays bend *away* from the normal line. Because the second surface "tilts" the other way, it also bends rays toward the focal point.

Focal point and focal length

Light rays that enter a converging lens parallel to its axis bend to meet at a point called the *focal point* (see illustration below). Light can go through a lens in either direction so there are always two focal points, one on either side of the lens. The distance from the center of the lens to the focal point is the *focal length*. The focal length is usually (but not always) the same for both focal points of a lens.

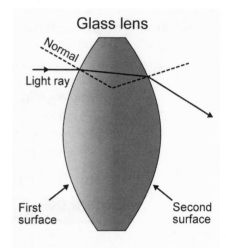

Figure 10.22: *Most lenses have spherically-shaped surfaces.*

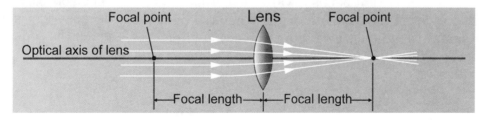

Converging and diverging lenses

Figure 10.23 shows how light rays enter and exit two types of lenses. The entering rays are parallel to the optical axis. A *converging lens* bends exiting rays toward the focal point. A *diverging lens* bends the rays outward, away from the focal point.

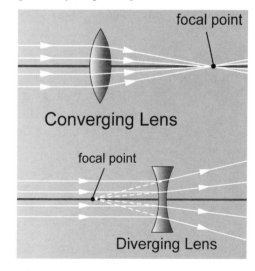

Figure 10.23: *Converging and diverging lenses.*

10.3 Section Review

1. A lens uses what process to deflect light rays passing through it?
   a. reflection
   b. refraction
   c. absorption
   d. transparency
2. Can light be reflected and refracted at the same time? If so, give an example.
3. Make a list of all the optical devices you use on an average day.
4. Name an object that is mostly transparent, one that is translucent, one that is mostly absorbent, and one that is mostly reflective.
5. Windows that look into bathrooms are often translucent instead of transparent. Why?
6. Why can you see your own reflected image in a mirror but not on a dry, painted wall?
7. Why is the true surface of a perfect mirror invisible?
8. The index of refraction determines (pick the best fit)
   a. the color of glass.
   b. the ratio of thickness to focal length for a lens.
   c. the amount a material bends light rays.
   d. whether a material is transparent or translucent.
9. A clear plastic rod seems to disappear when it is placed in water. Based on this observation and Table 10.1, predict the index of refraction for the plastic.
10. Fill in the blank. When light travels from water into the air, the refracted light ray bends _____ (away from or toward) the normal line.
11. What is the difference between a converging lens and a diverging lens?

Twinkling of stars

Another example of the refraction of light is the twinkling of a star in the night sky. To reach your eyes, starlight must travel from space through Earth's atmosphere which varies in temperature and density. Cold pockets of air are more dense than warm pockets. Starlight is refracted as it travels through the various air pockets. Since the atmosphere is constantly changing, the amount of refraction also changes. The image of a star appears to "twinkle" or move because the light coming to your eye follows a zig-zag path due to refraction.

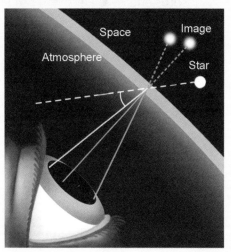

Bioluminescence

Imagine you could make your hands glow like living flashlights. No more fumbling around for candles when the power goes out! You could read in bed all night, or get a job directing airplanes to their runways.

Although a glowing hand might sound like something from a science fiction movie, many living things can make their own light. On warm summer evenings, fireflies flash signals to attract a mate. A fungus known as foxfire glows in decaying wood. While there are only a few kinds of glowing creatures that live on land, about *90 percent* of the animals that live in the deep parts of the ocean make their own light!

How do they do that?

Almost everything that creates light is made of atoms. If an atom absorbs energy, an electron can move to a higher energy level. When the electron moves back down to its original energy level, the atom could give off visible light.

Atoms can absorb energy from a number of sources. Electrical energy is used in ordinary light bulbs. Mechanical energy can be used, too. Hit two quartz rocks together in a dark room, and you'll see flashes of light as the energized electrons fall back down to lower energy levels and give off light. You can also use the energy from a chemical reaction. When you bend a glow stick, you break a vial inside so that two chemicals can combine. When they react, energy is released and used to make light.

Bioluminescence

Like a glow stick, living things produce their own light using a chemical reaction. We call this process *bioluminescence* (*bio-* means "living" and *luminesce* means "to glow").

Bioluminescence is "cold light" because it doesn't produce a lot of heat. While it takes a lot of energy for a living thing to produce light, almost 100 percent of the energy becomes visible light. In contrast, only 10 percent of the used by an "incandescent" electric light bulb is converted to visible light. 90 percent of the energy is wasted as heat.

The chemical reaction

Three ingredients are usually needed for a bioluminescent reaction to occur: an organic chemical known as *luciferin*, a source of oxygen, and an enzyme called *luciferase*.

Luciferin and luciferase are categories of chemicals with certain characteristics. Luciferin in a firefly is not exactly the same as the luciferin in foxfire fungus. However, both luciferin chemicals are carbon-based and have the ability to give off light under certain conditions.

Firefly light

In a firefly, luciferin and luciferase are stored in special cells in the abdomen called photocytes. To create light, fireflies push oxygen into the photocytes. When the luciferin and luciferase are exposed to oxygen, they combine with ATP (a chemical source of energy) and magnesium. This chemical reaction drives some of the luciferin electrons into a higher energy state. As they fall back down to their "ground state," energy is given off in the form of visible light.

Why make light?

Living creatures don't have an endless supply of energy. Since it takes a lot of energy to make light, there must be good reasons for doing it.

Fireflies flash their lights in patterns to attract a mate. The lights also warn predators to stay away, because the light-producing chemicals taste bitter. They can also be used as a distress signal, warning others of their species that there is danger nearby. The female of one firefly species has learned to mimic the signal of other types of fireflies. She uses her light to attract males of other species and then she eats them!

It's a little harder to figure out why foxfire fungus glows. Some scientists think that the glow attracts insects that help spread around the fungus spores.

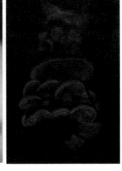

Photos by Garth Fletcher

Bioluminescent ocean creatures use their lights in amazing ways. The deep-sea angler fish has a glowing lure attached to its head. When a smaller fish comes to munch on the lure, it instead is gobbled up by the angler fish.

Photo by E. Widder

Comb jellies (shown below) are some of the ocean's most beautiful glowing creatures. When threatened, they release a cloud of bioluminescent particles into the water, temporarily blinding the attacker.

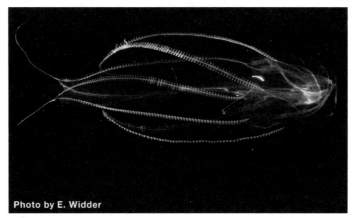

Photo by E. Widder

So far we know that living creatures use bioluminescence to attract mates, to communicate, to find food, and to ward off attackers. Perhaps someday you will be part of a research team that discovers even more uses for bioluminescence.

QUESTIONS

1. Find out more about what is inside a glow stick. Make a poster to explain how glow sticks work, or prepare a demonstration for your classmates.

2. Bioluminescence is found in a wide range of living organisms, including bacteria, fungi, insects, crustaceans, and fish. However, no examples have been found among flowering plants, birds, reptiles, amphibians, or mammals. Why do you think this is so?

3. Use the Internet or a library to find out more about bioluminescent sea creatures. Here are some questions to pursue: What is the most common color of light produced? What other colors of bioluminescence have been found?

Make a Pinhole Viewer

A pinhole viewer is fun to use. Light travels in straight lines through the tiny opening. When you aim the viewer at a brightly-lit object, the object's image will appear on the little screen in your viewer. You will notice something unusual about the image!

Materials:

black film canister; tack or pushpin; semi-opaque tape; piece of black construction paper, about 5 by 12 inches

What you will do

Poke a tiny hole

Tape over opening

1. Poke a hole in the bottom of the film canister with a tack or pushpin.

2. Place tape over the open end of the film canister. You will need to put two pieces side-by-side to cover the opening. This will be your viewing screen.

3. Form a tube out of the construction paper and place around the opening of the canister (the taped end) so no light can get into the sides of your viewer. You will be looking down the long black paper tube, and the screen is between the eye opening and the pinhole in the bottom of the film canister.

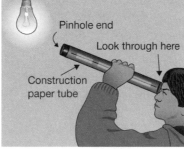

Pinhole end

Look through here

Construction paper tube

4. Point the viewer at a well-lit object. The object's image will appear on your screen. What is unusual about the image?

Viewing Tips

* The size of the pinhole is important. A small hole produces sharp images, but the image will be very dim unless the object is *very* brightly lit. A larger hole will give brighter but blurry images.

* For viewing objects in the classroom, your teacher can put an object on an overhead projector. The bright light will allow lots of light to enter your viewer through the pinhole, and the image will be brighter.

* You are looking for an image formed on the screen of the viewer. Try looking at a brightly colored, moving object, like one of your classmates jumping up and down.

Pinhole

Image

Object

How it works

Light coming from an object travels in straight lines through the tiny opening in your pinhole viewer. The light that starts on the left of the pinhole passes through the hole and ends up on the right, and vice versa. The upside down image is formed on the screen, where you can see it with your eye.

Applying your knowledge

a. What is unusual about the image formed on the tape screen in your pinhole viewer?

b. What would you see through the pinhole viewer if there was no tape placed over the open end of the can? Try it and describe the results.

c. Why does a very small opening make images that are crisp and clear?

Chapter 10 Assessment

Vocabulary

Select the correct term to complete the sentences.

RGB color model	color	diffuse
CMYK color model	photon	index of refraction
lens	light	specular reflection
pixel	nanometer	refraction
translucent	transparent	incandescence
white light	light ray	electromagnetic wave
fluorescence	normal	electromagnetic spectrum

Section 10.1

1. A process that produces light using heat energy is ____.

2. A process that makes light with electrical energy is known as ____.

3. A form of energy, including all the colors we see, that travels at 300,000 km/s in a vacuum is referred to as ____.

4. The smallest possible amount of light is a(n) ____.

5. The sensation created by the different energies of light falling on your eye is called ____.

6. A unit of length equal to one-billionth of meter is a(n) ____.

7. Light containing an equal mix of all colors is ____.

8. The entire range of electromagnetic waves, including all possible frequencies is known as the ____.

Section 10.2

9. A theory used to explain how any color of light may be produced mixing proportions of red, green, and blue light is known as the ____.

10. A single dot that forms part of an image made using many dots is a(n) ____.

11. Another name for the reflected light model or the subtractive color process is ____.

Section 10.3

12. An optical device used to bend light rays is a(n) ____.

13. A material that allows light to pass through without scattering the light would be described as ____.

14. A material that allows light to pass through but scatters the light rays would be described as ____.

15. Shiny, mirror surfaces produce images by ____.

16. Surface reflection that scatters light is called ____ reflection.

17. An imaginary line that represent a beam of light is a(n) ____.

18. The process of bending a light ray as it crosses the boundary between two different materials is called ____.

19. A number indicating how much a material is able to bend light is named the ____.

Concepts

Section 10.1

1. List four properties of light.

2. Describe the difference between the light you would see from a flashlight and the light you see from this printed page.

3. What is the source of most light?

4. Explain the difference between production of light by an incandescent light bulb and a fluorescent bulb.

5. Compare the speed, energy, wavelength and frequency of red light and blue light.

6. Compare the speed of light to the speed of sound; what symbol is used to represent the speed of light?

7. How can an electromagnetic wave be produced?

8. Name five different parts of the electromagnetic spectrum and arrange them from lowest to highest energy.

9. How are the frequency and wavelength of light related?

10. How are the frequency and energy of light related?

Section 10.2

11. Compare the sensitivity and number of the photoreceptors called rods and cones.

12. Which work better in dim light, rods or cones? Why?

13. Why do you think that color vision is better in the center of your field of view?

14. In the CMYK color process, why is black pigment used instead of mixing cyan, magenta, and yellow pigments?

15. What color of light is produced by the following combinations of light?

    a. red + blue   b. blue + yellow   c. green + red

16. What is difference between an ordinary TV screen and an HDTV screen?

17. Compare the way color is produced by a TV screen compared with the color of an illustration in this book.

18. Many years ago, material called "bluing" was added to wash water for soiled white shirts and white sheets. Offer a possible explanation. (*Hint*: Soiled cloth often takes on a yellow appearance.)

19. What colors of sunlight are most useful for green plants in making food?

20. What determines the color of an object that does not make its own light?

21. What are the three subtractive primary colors?

22. What colors of light are reflected by the color magenta?

Section 10.3

23. What is a light ray?

24. Name four ways in which light may interact with matter. Give an example of a situation where more than one interaction happens at the same time.

25. Describe the difference between *refraction* and *reflection*.

26. How does a transparent material differ from a translucent material?

27. Diamond has a higher index of refraction than water. What does this mean?

28. What is the focal point of a lens? What is the focal length of a lens?

29. What is the difference between a converging lens and a diverging lens? For each lens, discuss the shape and how each bends parallel light rays.

30. How does the image position in a flat mirror compare to the object's position?

Problems

Section 10.1

1. Frequencies of 462 THz, 517 THz, and 638 THz represent the frequencies of three colors: blue, red, and yellow. Match the frequencies to the appropriate color.

2. Lightning strikes in the distance and 6 seconds later the thunder is heard. How far away is the lightning strike?

3. The Sun is about 150 million kilometers away from Earth. How long does it take for light to travel from the Sun to Earth?

4. Red light may have a wavelength of 0.00000078 meters. What is this wavelength in units of nanometers?

5. What color of star is hottest: red, yellow, or blue?

6. Arrange the following in order of speed from fastest to slowest: sound waves, light waves, water waves.

Section 10.2

7. What color will a blue shirt appear in red light?

8. Which of the CMYK colors would you mix if you wanted to produce the following colors of ink?

a. red   b. green   c. blue

9. For the stage lighting for a play in a theater, light from a magenta spotlight is combined with light from a cyan spotlight. What color light is produced?

10. What primary additive colors of light will be allowed to pass through a cyan filter?

11. Answer the following questions using the absorption graph shown.

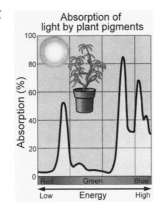

a. Which colors of light are most absorbed by plants?

b. Which colors of light are reflected the most by plants?

c. Based on the information from the absorption graph, explain why a plant will grow more quickly if it is grown in white light rather than green light.

d. When green pigments in the plants break down in the fall, you can see that leaves have other pigments like red and orange pigments. This effect is very noticeable in the northeastern United States. Come up with a hypothesis to explain why plants might have other pigments in addition to green.

12. Identify the color process (RGB or CMYK) used in each step.

a. taking a photograph with a digital camera

b. transferring the image from the camera to a computer the image appears on a computer monitor

c. printing the image using a laser printer

d. seeing the image on the paper with your eyes

Section 10.3

13. A clear plastic ball seems to disappear when placed in a liquid. What does this tell you about the indices of refraction for the clear plastic and the liquid?

14. What happens to light rays exiting a converging lens?

15. Glare from headlights can make it harder to see when driving at night. Glare is worse when the roads are wet from rain versus when roads are dry. Explain why, in terms of the two types of reflection.

16. Your body contains a lens. Where is this lens found? Is this lens converging or diverging?

17. Why do ambulances often have the letters for *ambulance* reversed on the front of the vehicle?

18. If you stand two meters in front of a mirror, what is the apparent distance between you and your image?

19. A light ray crosses from a piece of glass into a liquid. You observe that the light ray bends closer to the normal when passing from the glass to the liquid. Based on this observation, how does the index of refraction for the liquid compare to the index of refraction for the glass?

UNIT 5

MATTER

CHAPTER 11
Temperature, Heat, and the Phases of Matter

CHAPTER 12
The Physical Properties of Matter

Exploring on Your Own

Find a photograph of an automobile built at least 30 years ago. How is the design of modern automobiles different from older models? Engineering design is often inspired by nature. This process is called *biomimicry*. The lighter, but stronger materials currently used in automobile manufacturing imitate the strength of human bones and the ease with which they carry our body weight from place to place. Use the Internet to find at least two other examples of natural influences on engineered materials.

Chapter 11

Temperature, Heat, and the Phases of Matter

So much of life depends on temperature! The other planets of the solar system combined contain 2,000 times the surface area of Earth. Yet, our two closest neighbors are hardly comfortable. Venus is so hot that lead melts on the ground. Mars is so cold that everything is frozen on its barren, dusty surface. Life is best suited to the range of temperatures where water is liquid. It would be hard to survive in a place where the only water was in the form of ice or steam! Our search for life on other worlds has focused on the need to find water that stays liquid. The best candidates for extraterrestrial life in the solar system are underground on Mars and on Jupiter's moon, Europa. Astronomers believe Europa has a vast ocean of liquid water below a thick ice crust.

Key Questions:

1. What is temperature?

2. How can one material, like water, be solid, liquid, and gas?

3. What is heat? Are heat and temperature the same thing?

Images - courtesy of NASA/JPL

11.1 Temperature and the Phases of Matter

On a hot day, a glass of iced tea develops water droplets on the *outside*. The water does not seep from inside the glass to the outside. So, where does the water come from? It comes from the air. The cold glass causes water vapor in the air—a *gas*—to condense into *liquid* water. You are seeing direct evidence that water exists in three *phases*—solid (ice), liquid, and gas. The phase that water takes depends on the temperature.

Measuring temperature

Fahrenheit There are two common temperature scales. On the **Fahrenheit** scale, water freezes at 32 degrees and boils at 212 degrees (Figure 11.1). There are 180 Fahrenheit degrees between the freezing point and the boiling point of water. Temperature in the United States is commonly measured in Fahrenheit; 72°F is a comfortable room temperature.

Celsius The **Celsius** scale divides the interval between the freezing and boiling points of water into 100 degrees (instead of 180). Water freezes at 0°C and boils at 100°C. Most scientists and engineers use Celsius because 0 and 100 are easier to work with than 32 and 212.

Converting between the scales A weather report that says 21°C in London, England, predicts a pleasant day, good for shorts and a T-shirt. A weather report predicting 21°F in Minneapolis, Minnesota, means a heavy winter coat, gloves, and a hat. Because the United States is one of a few countries that use the Fahrenheit scale, it is useful to know how to convert between Fahrenheit and Celsius.

CONVERTING BETWEEN FAHRENHEIT AND CELSIUS

$$T_{Fahrenheit} = \frac{9}{5} T_{Celsius} + 32 \qquad T_{Celsius} = \frac{5}{9}(T_{Fahrenheit} - 32)$$

VOCABULARY

Fahrenheit - a temperature scale in which water freezes at 32 degrees and boils at 212 degrees.

Celsius - a temperature scale in which water freezes at 0 degrees and boils at 100 degrees.

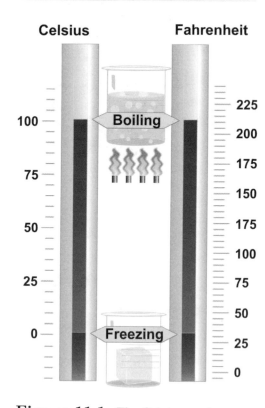

Figure 11.1: *The Celsius and Fahrenheit temperature scales.*

Thermometers

Thermometers   We can sense hot and cold, but not very accurately. A **thermometer** is an instrument that measures temperature. A type of thermometer you have likely seen uses colored liquid alcohol to sense temperature. As the temperature increases, the alcohol expands and rises up a long, thin tube. You tell the temperature by the height the alcohol rises. The tube is long and thin so a small change in volume makes a large change in the height (Figure 11.2).

How thermometers work   All thermometers are based on a physical property (such as color or volume) that changes with temperature. A *thermistor* is a device that changes its electrical resistance as the temperature changes. Some electronic thermometers sense temperature by measuring the resistance of a thermistor. There are some chemicals that change color at different temperatures. These are used for aquarium "sticker" thermometers that are placed on the outside of a fish tank.

Converting between temperature scales

A friend in Paris sends you a recipe for a cake. The French recipe says to bake the cake at a temperature of 200°C for 45 minutes. At what temperature should you set your oven, which uses the Fahrenheit scale?

1. Looking for: You are asked for the temperature in degrees Fahrenheit.

2. Given: You are given the temperature in degrees Celsius.

3. Relationships: Use the conversion formula: $T_F = \frac{9}{5}T_C + 32$.

4. Solution: $T_F = (\frac{9}{5})(200) + 32 = 392°F$.

Your turn...

a. You are planning a trip to Iceland where the average July temperature is 11.2°C. What is this temperature in Fahrenheit? **Answer:** 52.2°F

b. You are doing a science experiment with a Fahrenheit thermometer. Your data must be in degrees Celsius. If you measure a temperature of 125°F, what is this temperature in degrees Celsius? **Answer:** 51.7°C

How a thermometer works

Molecules move around more as the temperature increases. So, the same number of molecules takes up more space at higher temperatures.

Alcohol molecules at 0°C

Alcohol molecules at 75°C

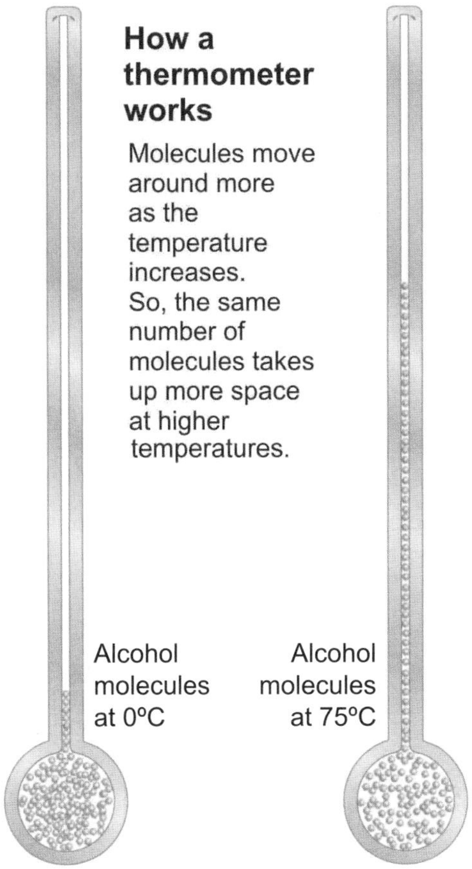

Figure 11.2: *The expansion of the liquid in an alcohol thermometer is proportional to the increase in temperature.*

What temperature really is

Atoms are always in motion

Imagine you had a microscope powerful enough to see individual atoms. You would see that atoms are in constant motion, even in a solid object. The atoms are not fixed in place, but act like they are connected by springs (Figure 11.3). Each atom stays in the same average place, but constantly jiggles back and forth in all directions. As you might guess, the "jiggling" means motion and motion means *energy*. The back-and-forth jiggling of atoms is caused by **thermal energy**, which is a kind of kinetic energy.

Temperature and energy

Thermal energy is proportional to temperature. When the temperature goes up, the energy of motion increases. That means the atoms jiggle around more vigorously. The higher the temperature, the more thermal energy atoms have and the faster they move around. Temperature measures a particular kind of kinetic energy per atom.

> *Temperature measures the kinetic energy per atom due to random motion.*

Random versus average motion

If you throw a rock, the rock gets more kinetic energy, but the temperature of the rock does *not* go up. How can temperature measure kinetic energy then? The answer is the difference between **random** and average. For a collection of many atoms (like a rock), the kinetic energy has two parts. The kinetic energy of the thrown rock comes from the average motion of the whole collection; the whole rock. This kinetic energy is *not* what temperature measures.

Random motion

Each atom in the rock is also jiggling back and forth independently of the other atoms in the rock. This jiggling motion is *random*. Random motion is motion that is scattered equally in all directions. On average, there are as many atoms moving one way as there are moving the opposite way. *Temperature measures the kinetic energy in the random motion.* Temperature is not affected by any kinetic energy associated with average motion. That is why throwing a rock does not make it hotter (Figure 11.4).

VOCABULARY

thermal energy - energy due to temperature.

random - scattered equally in all directions.

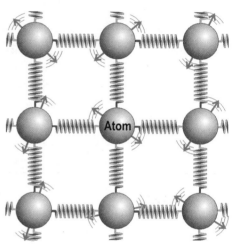

Figure 11.3: *Atoms in a solid are connected by bonds that act like springs.*

Random motion of atoms	Average motion of atoms

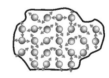

21 °C (70° F)   50 m/s

Figure 11.4: *A collection of atoms can have both average motion and random motion. That is why a moving rock has both a velocity and a temperature.*

Absolute zero

Absolute zero   There is a limit to how cold matter can get. As the temperature is reduced, molecules move more and more slowly. When the temperature gets down to **absolute zero**, molecules have the lowest energy they can have and the temperature cannot get any lower. You can think of absolute zero as the temperature where molecules are completely frozen, with no motion. Technically, molecules never become absolutely motionless, but the kinetic energy is so small it might as well be zero. Absolute zero occurs at –273°C (–459°F). *You cannot have a temperature lower than absolute zero.*

The Kelvin scale   A temperature in Celsius measures only *relative* thermal energy, relative to zero Celsius. The **Kelvin** temperature scale is useful in science because it starts at absolute zero. A temperature in Kelvins measures the actual energy of atoms relative to zero energy.

Converting to Kelvin

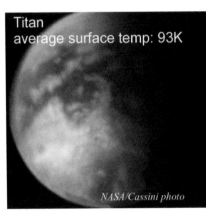

Titan
average surface temp: 93K

NASA/Cassini photo

The Kelvin (K) unit of temperature is the same size as the Celsius degree. However, water freezes at 273 K and boils at 373 K. Most of the outer planets and moons have temperatures closer to absolute zero than to the freezing point of water. To convert from Celsius to Kelvins you add 273 to the temperature in Celsius. For example, a temperature of 21°C is equal to 294 K (21 + 273).

High temperatures   While absolute zero is the lower limit for temperature, there is no practical upper limit. Temperature can go up almost indefinitely. As the temperature increases, exotic forms of matter appear. For example, at 10,000°C, atoms start to come apart and become a *plasma*. In a plasma, atoms are broken apart into separate positive ions and negative electrons. Plasma conducts electricity and is formed in lightning and inside stars.

VOCABULARY

absolute zero - lowest possible temperature, at which thermal energy is as close to zero as it can be, approximately –273°C.

Kelvin scale - a temperature scale that starts at absolute zero and has units the same as Celsius degrees.

Plasmas

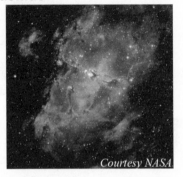

Courtesy NASA

At temperatures greater than 10,000°C the atoms in a gas start to break apart. In the plasma state, matter becomes ionized as electrons are broken loose from atoms. Because the electrons are free to move independently, plasma can conduct electricity. The Sun is made of plasma, as is most of the universe, including the Eagle nebula in the picture.

The phases of matter

Solid, liquid, and gas

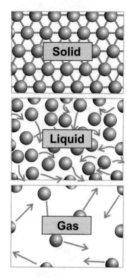

Most matter around you is either solid, liquid, or gas. A **solid** holds its shape and does not flow. The molecules in a solid vibrate in place, but on average, don't move far from their places. A **liquid** holds its *volume*, but does not hold its shape—it flows. The molecules in a liquid are about as close together as they are in a solid, but they have enough energy to change positions with their neighbors. Liquids flow because the molecules can move around. A **gas** flows like a liquid, but can also expand or contract to fill a container. A gas does not hold its volume. The molecules in a gas have enough energy to completely break away from each other and are much farther apart than molecules in a liquid or a solid.

Intermolecular forces

When they are close together, molecules are attracted through **intermolecular forces**. These forces are not as strong as the chemical bonds between atoms, but are strong enough to attach neighboring molecules to each other (Figure 11.5). Intermolecular forces have different strengths in different elements and compounds. Iron is a solid at room temperature. Water is a liquid at room temperature. This tells you that the intermolecular forces between iron atoms are stronger than those between water molecules.

Temperature vs. intermolecular forces

Within all matter, there is a constant competition between temperature and intermolecular forces. The kinetic energy from temperature tends to push atoms and molecules apart. When temperature wins the competition, molecules fly apart and you have a gas. Intermolecular forces tend to bring molecules together. When intermolecular forces win the competition, molecules clump tightly together and you have a solid. Liquid is somewhere in the middle. Molecules in a liquid are not stuck firmly together, but they cannot escape and fly away either.

 VOCABULARY

solid - a phase of matter that holds its shape and does not flow.

liquid - a phase of matter that flows and easily changes shape.

gas - a phase of matter that flows and also expands or contracts to fill any container.

intermolecular forces - forces between atoms or molecules that determine the phase of matter.

● Hydrogen atom   ● Oxygen atom

The forces in chemical bonds are strong

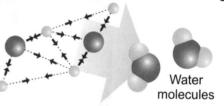

Water molecules

Intermolecular forces are weaker, and connect molecules to each other

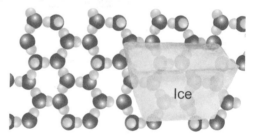

Ice

Figure 11.5: *The difference between bond forces and intermolecular forces.*

Changing phase

Melting and freezing

The **melting point** is the temperature at which a substance changes from solid to liquid (melting) or liquid to solid (freezing). Different substances have different melting points because intermolecular forces vary. When these forces are strong, it takes more energy to separate molecules from each other. Water melts at 0°C. Iron melts at a much higher temperature, about 1,500°C. The difference in melting points tells us the forces between iron atoms are stronger than between water molecules.

Boiling and condensing

When enough energy is added, the intermolecular forces are completely pulled apart and the liquid becomes a gas. The **boiling point** is the temperature at which a substance changes from liquid to gas (boiling) or from gas to liquid (condensation). When water boils, you can easily see the change within the liquid as bubbles of water vapor (gas) form and rise to the surface. The bubbles in boiling water are *not air*, they are water vapor.

Changes in phase require energy

It takes energy to break the bonds created by intermolecular forces. This explains a peculiar thing that happens when you heat an ice cube. As you add heat energy, the temperature increases. Once it reaches 0°C, *the temperature stops increasing* as ice starts to melt and form liquid water (Figure 11.6). As you add more heat energy, more ice becomes liquid but the temperature stays the same. This is because the energy you are adding is being used to break the intermolecular forces and change solid into liquid. Once all the ice has become liquid, the temperature starts to rise again as more energy is added. The graph at the right shows the temperature change in an experiment. When heat energy is added or subtracted from matter, either the temperature changes, or the phase changes, but usually not both at the same time.

Start with ice at –20°C

Add heat energy at a constant rate

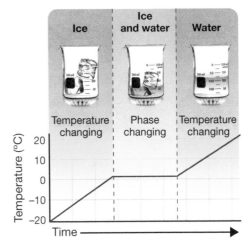

Figure 11.6: *Notice how the temperature stays constant as the ice is melting into water?*

11.1 Section Review

1. People in the United States know that water boils at 212°F. In Europe, people know that water boils at 100°C. Is the water in the United States different than the water in Europe? What explains the two different temperatures?

2. A comfortable room temperature is 20°C. What is this temperature in degrees Fahrenheit?

3. Which is colder, 0°C or 20°F?

4. In which system are the molecules moving faster, a cold glass of tea or a hot cup of tea?

5. Describe what happens at the atomic level during melting.

6. Explain the scientific meaning of the word *random*.

7. One student is trying to explain what *random* means to another student. The "explainer" takes a piece of paper outside and puts it on the ground in the rain. After 10 drops of rain fall on the paper, the explainer brings the paper back inside. The explainer then lets 10 drops of water fall from a faucet onto a similar piece of paper lying in the sink. How does the difference in the pattern of the drops illustrate the idea of "random"?

8. Put the following in order from lowest energy to highest energy. Assume the type of matter is the same for each phase.
    a. liquid
    b. solid
    c. gas

9. Explain why particles in a gas are free to move far away from each other.

10. Would you expect a substance to be a solid, liquid, or gas at absolute zero? Explain your answer.

11. Why can't there be a temperature lower than absolute zero?

12. When you add 100 joules of heat to a glass of water, the temperature goes up. When you add 100 joules of heat to water with ice cubes in it, the temperature stays the same. Why?

SOLVE IT!

What is absolute zero in degrees Fahrenheit?

CHALLENGE

There is a metal that is liquid at room temperature. What metal is this?

One of the ways to make car engines more efficient is to let them reach higher temperatures. Unfortunately, steel melts at about 1,500°C. Steel gets soft before it melts, so engines typically can't operate at temperatures even close to the melting point. Some new engine technologies use cylinders and pistons made of ceramic. Ceramic stays hard and strong at a much higher temperature than steel.

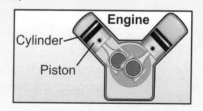

11.2 Heat

To change the temperature, you usually need to add or subtract energy. For example, when it's cold outside, you turn up the *heat* in your house or apartment and the temperature goes up. You know that adding heat increases the temperature, but have you ever thought about exactly what "heat" is? What does "heat" have to do with temperature?

heat - thermal energy that is moving or is capable of moving.

Heat, temperature, and thermal energy

What is heat?

What makes chocolate melt in your hand?

What happens when you hold a chocolate bar in your hand? Thermal energy flows from your hand to the chocolate and it begins to melt. We call this flow of thermal energy **heat**. Heat is really just another word for thermal energy that is moving. In the scientific sense, heat flows any time there is a difference in temperature. Heat flows naturally from the warmer object (higher energy) to the cooler one (lower energy). In the case of the melting chocolate bar, the thermal energy lost by your hand is equal to the thermal energy gained by the chocolate bar.

Thermal energy depends on mass and temperature

Heat and temperature are related, but are not the same thing. The amount of thermal energy depends on the temperature but it also depends on the *amount* of matter you have. Think about heating up two pots of water. One pot contains 1,000 grams of water and the other contains 2,000 grams of water. Both pots are heated to the same final temperature (Figure 11.7). Which takes more energy? Or, do both require the same amount of energy? The pot holding 2,000 grams of water takes twice as much energy as the pot with 1,000 grams, even though both start and finish at the same temperature. The two pots illustrate the difference between temperature and thermal energy. The one with more mass has more energy, even though both are at the same temperature.

Both pots of water boil at 100°C

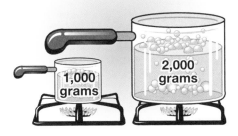

Figure 11.7: *It takes twice as much energy to heat a 2,000-gram mass of water compared to a 1,000-gram mass.*

Like many words used in science, the word *heat* has many other meanings besides the one above. Write down three sentences that use the word *heat*. Try to have each sentence use *heat* with a different meaning.

Units of heat and thermal energy

The joule The metric unit for measuring heat is the *joule*. This is the same joule used to measure all forms of energy, not just heat. A joule is a small amount of heat. The average hair dryer puts out 1,200 joules of heat every second!

The calorie One *calorie* is the amount of energy (heat) needed to increase the temperature of 1 gram of water by 1 degree Celsius. One calorie is a little more than 4 joules (Figure 11.8). You may have noticed that most food packages list "Calories per serving." The unit used for measuring the energy content of the food we eat is the *kilocalorie*, which equals 1,000 calories. The kilocalorie is often written as Calorie (with a capital *C*). If a candy bar contains 210 Calories, it contains 210,000 calories, or 897,060 joules!

The British thermal unit Still another unit of heat energy you may encounter is the *British thermal unit*, or Btu. The Btu is often used to measure the heat produced by heating systems or heat removed by air-conditioning systems. A Btu is the quantity of heat it takes to increase the temperature of 1 pound of water by 1 degree Fahrenheit. One Btu is a little more than 1,000 joules.

Unit	Is Equal To
1 calorie	4.186 joules
1 kilocalorie	1,000 calories
1 Btu	1,055 joules
1 Btu	252 calories

Figure 11.8: *Conversion table for units of heat.*

Heat and Work

Work can be done whenever heat flows from a higher temperature to a lower temperature. Since heat flows from hot to cold, to get output work you need to maintain a temperature difference. Many human inventions use heat to do work. The engine in your car uses the heat released by the burning of gasoline. In a car engine, the high temperature is inside the engine and comes from the burning gasoline. The low temperature is the air around the car. The output work produced by the engine is extracted from the flow of heat. Only a fraction of the heat is converted to work, and that is why a running car gives off so much heat through the radiator and exhaust.

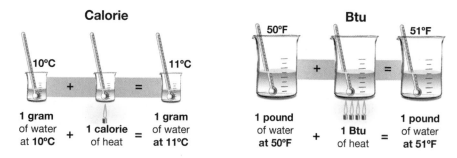

Why so many units? The calorie and Btu units were being used to measure heat well before scientists knew that heat was really energy. The calorie and Btu are still used, even 100 years after heat was shown to be energy, because people give up familiar ways very slowly!

Specific heat

Temperature and mass

If you add heat to an object, how much will its temperature increase? It depends in part on the mass of the object. If you double the mass of the object, you need twice as much energy to get the same increase in temperature. The temperature increase also depends on what substance you are heating up. It takes different amounts of energy to raise the temperature of different materials.

Temperature and type of material

You need to add 4,184 joules of heat to one kilogram of water to raise the temperature by 1°C. (Figure 11.9). You only need to add 470 joules to raise the temperature of a kilogram of steel by 1°C. It takes nine times more energy to raise the temperature of water by 1°C than it does to raise the temperature of the same mass of steel by 1°C.

Specific heat

Specific heat is a property of a substance that tells us how much heat is needed to raise the temperature of one kilogram by one degree Celsius. Specific heat is measured in joules per kilogram per degree Celsius (J/kg°C). A large specific heat means you have to put in a lot of energy for each degree increase in temperature.

Specific heat is the amount of energy that will raise the temperature of one kilogram of a substance by one degree Celsius.

Uses for specific heat

Knowing the specific heat tells you how quickly the temperature of a material will change as it gains or loses energy. If the specific heat is *low* (like steel), then temperature will change relatively quickly because each degree of temperature change takes less energy. If the specific heat is *high* (like water), then the temperature will change relatively slowly because each degree of temperature change takes more energy. Hot apple pie filling stays hot for a long time because it is mostly water, and therefore has a large specific heat. Pie crust has a much lower specific heat and cools much more rapidly. The table in Figure 11.10 lists the specific heat for some common materials.

VOCABULARY

specific heat - the amount of heat needed to raise the temperature of one kilogram of a material by one degree Celsius.

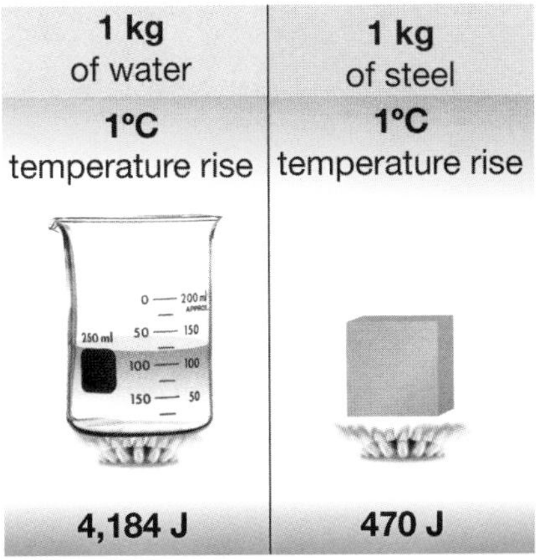

1 kg of water	1 kg of steel
1°C temperature rise	1°C temperature rise
4,184 J	470 J

Figure 11.9: *Water and steel have different specific heats.*

Material	Specific heat (J/kg°C)
water	4,184
wood	1,800
aluminum	900
concrete	880
glass	800
steel	470

Figure 11.10: *Specific heat values of some common materials.*

Why is specific heat different for different materials?

Why specific heat varies   In general, materials made up of heavy atoms or molecules have low specific heat compared with materials made up of lighter ones. This is because temperature measures the average kinetic energy *per particle*. Heavy particles mean fewer particles per kilogram. Energy that is divided between fewer particles means more energy per particle, and therefore more temperature change.

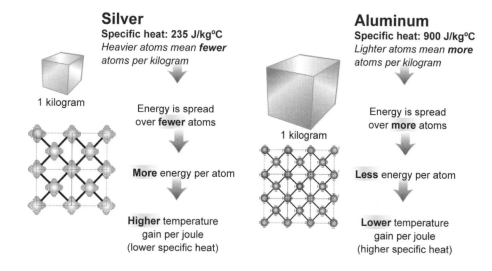

Silver
Specific heat: 235 J/kg°C
*Heavier atoms mean **fewer** atoms per kilogram*

1 kilogram

Energy is spread over **fewer** atoms

More energy per atom

Higher temperature gain per joule
(lower specific heat)

Aluminum
Specific heat: 900 J/kg°C
*Lighter atoms mean **more** atoms per kilogram*

1 kilogram

Energy is spread over **more** atoms

Less energy per atom

Lower temperature gain per joule
(higher specific heat)

An example: silver and aluminum   Suppose you add 4 joules of energy to a kilogram of silver and 4 joules to a kilogram of aluminum. Silver's specific heat is 235 J/kg°C and 4 joules is enough to raise the temperature of the silver by 17°C. Aluminum's specific heat is 900 J/kg°C. Four joules only raises the temperature of the aluminum by 4.4°C. The silver has fewer atoms than the aluminum because silver atoms are heavier than aluminum atoms. When energy is added, each atom of silver gets more energy than each atom of aluminum because there are fewer silver atoms in a kilogram. Because the energy per atom is greater, the temperature increase in the silver is also greater.

Water's high specific heat helps stabilize Earth's temperature.

Water has a higher specific heat than many other common materials. Its specific heat is more than four times greater than the specific heat of rocks and soil. The high specific heat of water is very important to our planet. Water covers about 75 percent of Earth's surface. One of the fundamental reasons our planet is habitable is that the huge amount of water on it helps regulate the temperature. Land, because it has a low specific heat, experiences large changes in temperature when it absorbs heat from the Sun. Water tends to have smaller changes in temperature when it absorbs the same amount of heat. During the day, oceans help keep Earth cool, while at night, they keep Earth warm by slowing the rate at which heat is emitted back into space.

Heat Transfer

<table>
<tr>
<td>The three ways heat flows</td>
<td>Thermal energy flows from higher temperature to lower temperature. This process is called heat transfer. How is heat transferred from material to material, or from place to place? It turns out there are three ways heat flows; conduction, convection, and radiation.</td>
</tr>
</table>

VOCABULARY

heat conduction - the transfer of heat by the direct contact of particles of matter.

thermal equilibrium - when things are at the same temperature and no heat flows.

What is conduction? **Heat conduction** is the transfer of heat by the direct contact of particles of matter. If you have ever held a warm mug of hot cocoa, you have experienced conduction. Heat is transferred from the mug to your hand. Conduction only occurs between two materials at different temperatures and when they are touching each other. In conduction, heat can also be transferred *through* materials. If you stir hot cocoa with a metal spoon, heat is transferred *from* the cocoa, *through* the spoon, and *to* your hand.

Conduction is the transfer of heat by the direct contact of particles of matter.

How does conduction work? Imagine placing a cold spoon into a mug of hot cocoa (Figure 11.11). The molecules in the cocoa have a higher average kinetic energy than those of the spoon. The molecules in the spoon exchange energy with the molecules in the cocoa through collisions. The molecules within the spoon itself spread the energy up the stem of the spoon through the intermolecular forces between them. Heat conduction works both through collisions and also through intermolecular forces between molecules.

Thermal equilibrium As collisions continue, the molecules of the hotter material (the cocoa) lose energy and the molecules of the cooler material (the spoon) gain energy. The kinetic energy of the hotter material is transferred, one collision at a time, to the cooler material. Eventually, both materials are at the same temperature. When this happens, they are in **thermal equilibrium**. Thermal equilibrium occurs when two bodies have the same temperature. No heat flows in thermal equilibrium because the temperatures are the same.

Cold spoon

Hot cocoa

➡ **Flow of heat energy**

Figure 11.11: *Heat flows by conduction from the hot cocoa into, and up, the spoon.*

Thermal conductors and insulators

Which state of matter conducts best? Conduction can happen in solids, liquids, and gases. Solids make the best conductors because their particles are packed closely together. Because the particles in a gas are spread so far apart, relatively few collisions occur, making air a poor conductor of heat. This explains why many materials used to keep things warm, such as fiberglass insulation and down jackets, contain air pockets (Figure 11.12).

Thermal conductors and insulators Materials that conduct heat easily are called *thermal conductors* and those that conduct heat poorly are called *thermal insulators*. For example, metal is a thermal conductor, and a foam cup is a thermal insulator. The words *conductor* and *insulator* are also used to describe a material's ability to conduct electrical current. In general, good electrical conductors like silver, copper, gold, and aluminum are also good thermal conductors.

Air spaces

Figure 11.12: *Because air is a poor conductor of heat, a down jacket keeps you warm in the cold of winter.*

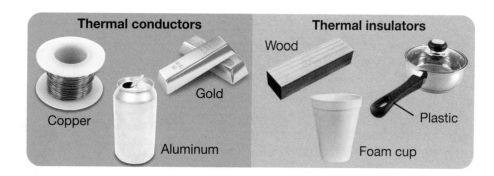

Thermal conductors
Copper
Gold
Aluminum

Thermal insulators
Wood
Plastic
Foam cup

Heat conduction cannot occur through a vacuum Conduction happens only if there are particles available to collide with one another. Conduction does not occur in the vacuum of space. One way to create an excellent thermal insulator on Earth is to make a *vacuum*. A vacuum is empty of everything, including air. A thermos bottle keeps liquids hot for hours using a vacuum. A thermos is a container consisting of a bottle surrounded by a slightly larger bottle. Air molecules have been removed from the space between the bottles to create a vacuum (Figure 11.13).

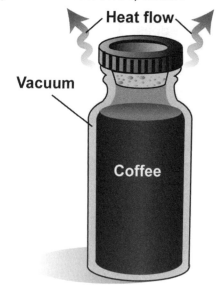

Heat flow
Vacuum
Coffee

Figure 11.13: *A thermos bottle uses a vacuum to prevent heat transfer by conduction and convection.*

Convection

What is convection?

Have you ever watched water boil in a pot? Bubbles form on the bottom and rise to the top. Hot water near the bottom of the pan circulates up, forcing cooler water near the surface to sink. This circulation carries heat through the water (Figure 11.14). This heat transfer process is called **convection.** Convection is the transfer of heat through the motion of matter such as air and water.

Natural convection

Fluids expand when they heat up. Since expansion increases the volume, but not the mass, a warm fluid has a lower mass-to-volume ratio (called *density*) than the surrounding cooler fluid. In a container, warmer fluid floats to the top and cooler fluid sinks to the bottom. This is called *natural convection.*

Forced convection

In many houses a boiler heats water and then pumps circulate the water to rooms. Since the heat is being carried by a moving fluid, this is another example of convection. However, since the fluid is *forced* to flow by the pumps, this is called *forced convection.* Both natural and forced convection often occur at the same time. Forced convection transfers heat to a hot radiator. The heat from the hot radiator then warms the room air by natural convection. Convection is mainly what distributes heat throughout the room.

VOCABULARY

convection - the transfer of heat by the motion of matter, such as by moving air or water.

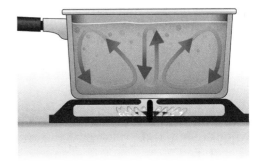

Figure 11.14: *Convection currents in water. The hot water at the bottom of the pot rises to the top and replaces the cold water.*

Thermal radiation

Definition of thermal radiation

If you stand in a sunny area on a cold, calm day, you will feel warmth from the Sun. Heat from the Sun is transferred to Earth by thermal radiation. **Thermal radiation** is electromagnetic waves (including light) produced by objects because of their temperature. All objects with a temperature above absolute zero (–273°C or –459°F) emit thermal radiation. To *emit* means to give off.

Thermal radiation is heat transfer by electromagnetic waves, including light.

Thermal radiation comes from atoms

Thermal radiation comes from the thermal energy of atoms. The power in thermal radiation increases with higher temperatures because the thermal energy of atoms increases with temperature (Figure 11.15). Because the Sun is extremely hot, its atoms emit lots of thermal radiation. Unlike conduction or convection, thermal radiation can travel through the vacuum of space. *All the energy the Earth receives from the Sun comes from thermal radiation.*

Objects emit and absorb radiation

Thermal radiation is also *absorbed* by objects. An object constantly receives thermal radiation from everything else in its environment. Otherwise all objects would eventually cool down to absolute zero by radiating their energy away. The temperature of an object rises if more radiation is absorbed. The temperature falls if more radiation is emitted. The temperature adjusts until there is a balance between radiation absorbed and radiation emitted.

Some surfaces absorb more energy than others

The amount of thermal radiation absorbed depends on the surface of a material. Black surfaces absorb almost all the thermal radiation that falls on them. For example, black asphalt pavement gets very hot in the summer Sun because it effectively absorbs thermal radiation. A silver mirror surface reflects most thermal radiation, absorbing very little (Figure 11.16). You may have seen someone put a silver screen across their windshield after parking their car on a sunny day. This silver screen can reflect the Sun's heat back out the car window, helping the parked car stay cooler on a hot day.

thermal radiation - electromagnetic waves produced by objects because of their temperature.

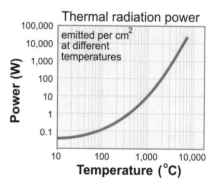

Figure 11.15: *The higher the temperature of an object, the more thermal radiation it emits.*

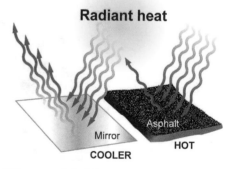

Figure 11.16: *Dark surfaces absorb most of the thermal radiation they receive. Silver or mirrored surfaces reflect thermal radiation.*

11.2 Section Review

1. What is the difference between temperature and heat?
2. Relative to 0°C, the amount of thermal energy in a quantity of water is its mass × temperature × specific heat. The specific heat of water is 4,184 joules per kilogram per degree Celsius.

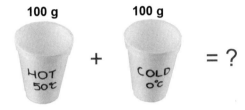

100 g   **100 g**

a. How much thermal energy is in 100 grams of water at 50°C?
b. How much thermal energy is in 100 grams of water at 0°C?
c. How much energy is there when both quantities of water are mixed together?
d. How much mass is this energy spread out over (in the mixture)?
e. What do you think the temperature of the mixture should be?
3. What conditions are necessary for heat to flow?
4. How much heat energy is required to raise the temperature of 20 kilograms of water from 0°C to 35°C?
5. What is thermal equilibrium?
6. How does heat from the Sun get to Earth?
   a. conduction
   b. convection
   c. radiation
7. A down jacket keeps your body warm mostly by stopping which two forms of heat transfer? (Pick two.)
   a. conduction
   b. convection
   c. radiation

Thermal energy
(relative to 0°C)

Energy =
mass × temperature × specific heat

Solving heat and temperature problems

How much heat does it take to raise the temperature of 5 kg of steel by 100°C?

1. Looking for:
Amount of heat (energy)

2. Given:
Mass, and material (steel)

3. Relationships:
Relative to 0°C, energy equals
mass × temperature × specific heat

4. Solution:
energy = (5kg) × (100°C) × (470 J/kg°C)
= 235,000 joules

Your turn...

a. How much heat does it take to warm 1 kg of water by 10°C?
Answer: 41,840 J

Extraordinary Materials

Materials scientists spend their time learning about the properties of different materials, and also designing, creating, or discovering new materials. Many materials you may be familiar with were discovered accidentally, while others were created in a laboratory with a particular use in mind.

Vulcanized Rubber

Most natural rubber comes from one species of tree that grows in South America and Southeast Asia. Natural rubber becomes sticky when heated and cracks when it freezes. These properties make natural rubber difficult to use for tires! In the mid-1800s, inventors sought to discover a more durable form of rubber, knowing it could be used in a variety of products if the properties were changed.Perhaps none tried as hard as Charles Goodyear. He only discovered the secret to improving the properties of rubber after years of research and poverty. Though many historians consider his discovery an accident (an experimental rubber mixture he spilled on a hot stove turned out to be very durable), it was his attention to detail that made him realize that burned rubber was actually the substance he was looking for.

Goodyear's experimental mixture contained sulfur, and exposing the rubber/sulfur mixture to heat caused a chemical change. Heating rubber in the presence of sulfur causes the long chains of rubber molecules to bond together. Vulcanized rubber, as it is called, doesn't break down when exposed to hot or cold temperatures. Have you heard of Goodyear automobile tires?

Now that materials scientists better understand the interaction of the molecules in rubber, they've applied this knowledge to other materials to make a variety of plastics and synthetic rubber.

Carbon Nanotubes

There is a material so strong, you could hang from a hair-like thread of it! Can you imagine that? As amazing as it seems, this super-strong material really exists.Scientists discovered that one form of carbon, called a nanotube, has some amazing properties. Nanotubes are very narrow, tube-shaped molecules that form under special conditions.Nanotubes conduct heat very well, they are incredibly strong. They have a lot of potential for use as small wires in electronic devices. Materials scientists are working hard to figure out how to create and use carbon nanotubes.

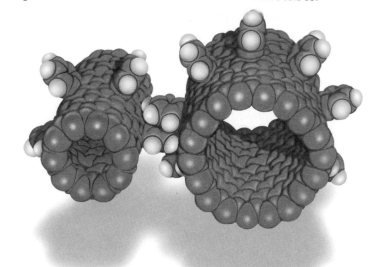

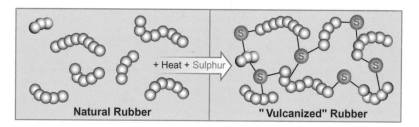

+ Heat + Sulphur

Natural Rubber   **"Vulcanized" Rubber**

Chapter 11 Connection

Memory Wire

Nitinol, or memory wire, was "accidentally" discovered. While searching for a metal that wouldn't rust, a US Navy lab discovered that one of its test materials had the unique property of "remembering" its shape. After bending the material into a new shape, they exposed it to heat and it snapped back in to the original form. Of course the metal doesn't really remember its original shape. When deformed, the molecules in the material undergo a transition from an orderly, crystalline arrangement to a more random form. Heating the material causes a transition back to the crystal form, returning the original shape. Some uses for nitinol include medical devices, eyeglass frames, temperature control devices, and cellular telephone antennas.

Aerogel

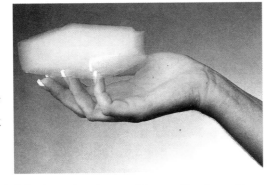

Would you believe that someone has made a solid material that has about the same density as air? If someone put a chunk of it your hand, you might not even notice. Silica aerogel is a foam that is like solidified smoke. Aerogel is mostly air and has remarkable thermal, optical and acoustical properties.

Aerogels are fantastic insulators. You could hold a flame under a chunk of the material and touch the top without being burned. Aerogels have the potential to replace a variety of materials in everyday life. If researchers could make a transparent version of an aerogel, it would almost certainly be used in double-pane windows to keep heat inside your house in the winter and outside in the summer. Opaque aerogels are already being used as insulators. Aerogels have been put to use by NASA in several projects, including the Mars Pathfinder Sojourner Rover and the Stardust mission.

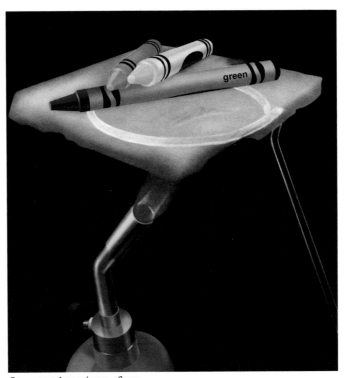

Crayons on Aerogel over a flame

QUESTIONS

1. Can you think of some new uses for vulcanized rubber? How about some uses for natural (sticky) rubber?

2. Can you think of some uses for carbon nanotubes if they could be easily manufactured? What existing materials could they replace? Why might one material be better than another?

3. Can you think of some uses for memory wire and aerogel?

Aerogel images courtesy of NASA.

Modeling Thermal Radiation

In this activity you will model how energy travels from the Sun to Earth's surface through thermal radiation.

Materials you will need

two 16- or 24-ounce soda bottles with some sand for stability; two digital thermometers; sheets of black and white paper; stopwatch (or use the CPO Science timer); tape, pencil, scissors, paper towels, metric ruler, light source

What you will do

1. Pour a handful of sand into each of the soda bottles. The sand steadies the empty bottle by adding a little weight.

2. Wrap a strip of paper towel around the thermometers at the zero degree mark. Insert a thermometer into each bottle so that it snugly fits into the neck.

3. Practice fitting a piece of black paper around one of the bottles so that the bottle is completely surrounded, but with no overlap. Mark the paper with a pencil, and cut the paper as necessary so that there is no overlap.

4. Wrap the paper snugly around the bottle, and tape it in place.

5. Repeat steps 3 and 4 for the other bottle, using white paper instead of black.

6. Place each bottle 10 cm away from the light source.

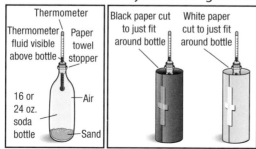

7. Copy the table below into your notebook. Check both thermometers and record the initial temperature of both bottles in the table.

8. Turn on the light source and record temperatures for both bottles every minute for 10 minutes.

9. Graph your data. Use time as the *x*-axis data and temperature as the *y*-axis data.

10. Label each curve on your graph to indicate which one is for the black bottle and which is for the white bottle. Remember to label your axes, indicate units, and title your graph.

	Temperature at each minute (°C)										
	0	1	2	3	4	5	6	7	8	9	10
Black Bottle											
White Bottle											

Applying your knowledge

a. What form of thermal energy transfer occurs between the light source and the bottles?

b. Which of the bottles reached a higher temperature?

c. What was the difference in the final temperatures of the two bottles?

d. Which bottle absorbed more energy from the light source? How do you know this?

e. Describe what happened to the energy from the light source when it reached the black bottle and the white bottle. Think about how the two bottles each absorbed and reflected radiation.

Chapter 11 Assessment

Vocabulary

Select the correct term to complete the sentences.

absolute zero	conduction	Celsius
Fahreheit	gas	heat
liquid	thermal energy	intermolecular forces
solid	thermal radiation	thermal equilibrium

Section 11.1

1. The temperature scale on which the freezing point of water is at 32° is the ____ scale.

2. The temperature scale on which the boiling point of water is at 100° is the ____ scale.

3. Energy that an objects possesses due to temperature is called ____.

4. The lowest possible temperature; objects contain the lowest amount of thermal energy at ____.

5. The phase of matter that flows and expands to fill its container is the ____ phase.

6. Forces between atoms or molecules that determine the phase of matter are ____.

7. The phase of matter that maintains its volume but not its shape is the ____ phase.

Section 11.2

8. When thermal energy is moving it is called ____.

9. When two objects are at the same temperature, heat will not flow between them because they are in a state of ____.

10. The transfer of heat from particle to particle by direct contact is called ____.

11. Heat energy transfer that may take place through a vacuum is called ____.

Concepts

Section 11.1

1. Compare the Celsius temperature scale with the Fahrenheit scale by answering the following questions.s
   a. Which is the larger change in temperature, 1°C or 1°F?
   b. What are the freezing points and boiling points of water on each scale?
   c. Why are two different scales used?

2. How can the Fahrenheit and Celsius scales be converted from one to another?

3. Since it is fairly easy to tell when the temperature is high or low, why do we need thermometers, thermistors, and other devices for measuring temperature?

4. Compare the Celsius temperature scale with the Kelvin scale by answering the following questions:
   a. Which is the larger change in temperature, 1 K or 1°C?
   b. What are the freezing points and boiling points of water on each scale?
   c. Why are two different scales used?

5. What is the difference between 0° on the Celsius scale and absolute zero?

6. Identify the phase represented by each diagram below and describe its basic properties.

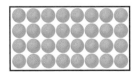 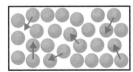 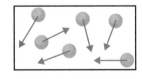

A   B   C

7. Absolute zero is considered the lowest possible temperature. What is the highest possible temperature?

Section 11.2

8. Thermal energy depends on what two factors?

9. Name three units for measuring heat.

10. What is the relationship between the calorie used by scientists and the Calorie used by nutritionists?

11. Compare the size of a calorie to a joule.

12. Why does specific heat vary for different substances?

13. Name the three methods by which heat can be transferred and give an example of each.

14. A metal cup containing water at 100°F is placed in an aquarium containing water at 80°F.

   a. Which way will heat flow? Why?

   b. When will the flow of heat stop?

   c. What is it called when heat no longer flows?

15. Why do thermos bottles keep cold beverages inside from getting warm?

16. Name three good thermal insulators.

17. How do we know that we receive heat from the Sun by thermal radiation and not by conduction or convection?

18. Explain the difference between natural and forced convection. Give an example of each.

Problems

Section 11.1

1. Calculate the average human body temperature, 98.6°F, on the Celsius scale.

2. Convert –20°C to the Kelvin scale.

3. What is the Celsius equivalent of 100 K?

4. The diagram to the right shows a graph of temperature vs. time for a material that starts as a solid. Heat is added at a constant rate. Using the diagram, answer the following questions.

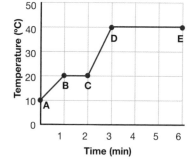

   a. During which time interval does the solid melt?

   b. During which time interval is the material all liquid?

   c. What is the boiling point of the substance?

   d. Does it take more heat energy to melt the solid or boil the liquid?

5. What does 104°F equal on the Kelvin scale?

Section 11.2

6. Which requires more heat?

   a. raising the temperature of a 450-gram steel pan from 40°C to 60°C

   b. raising the temperature of a 900-gram steel pan from 10°C to 25°C

7. If 50 joules of heat is added to raise the temperature of an object 20°C, how much heat will be given off if the object is cooled 20°C?

8. Compared to the heat required to raise 5 kg of wood 5°C, how much heat would be required to raise the temperature of 5 kg of aluminum 5°C? (*Hint*: The specific heat of wood is 1,800 J/kg°C; the specific heat of aluminum is 900 J/kg°C.)

9. The specific heat of steel is 470 J/kg°C. Calculate the amount of heat required to raise the temperature of a 2-kg steel block from 2°C to 5°C.

Chapter 12

The Physical Properties of Matter

Will it float or will it sink? If you are designing ships, this is a crucial question. One of the largest ships in the world is the *Barzan*, classified as an ultra-large container ship. This super-sized ship is 400 meters (1,312 feet) long, and 58.6 meters (192 feet) wide. If the Empire State Building was laid on its side, the *Barzan* would be longer by almost 20 meters. The *Barzan* can carry up to 199,714 metric tons, which is the equivalent of eight Statues of Liberty. Designed to be environmentally friendly, the *Barzan* is known as the greenest container vessel in the world due to its very low carbon dioxide emissions. The *Barzan* is largely constructed of steel. How can a big, heavy ship like this actually float, let alone carry all that cargo? By the time you finish studying this chapter, you will be able to explain how ships and boats of all sizes can float.

Key Questions:

1. What is density and how can you measure it?

2. What two things does density depend on?

3. How does a steel ship float when a steel marble sinks?

12.1 Density

When you think about the many kinds of matter you come into contact with every day, what properties come to mind? Some matter is solid and hard, like steel and wood. Some matter is liquid like water, or a gas like air. Within the category of solid matter, there are many varying properties. For instance, a block of wood and a block of steel may be the same size, but one has a lot more mass than the other. Because of that difference in mass, wood floats in water and steel sinks. Whether an object floats or sinks in water is related to the object's density. This chapter will explain density, a property of all matter.

ⓐ VOCABULARY

density - the mass of matter per unit volume; density is typically expressed in units of grams per milliliter (g/mL), grams per cubic centimeter (g/cm³), or kilograms per cubic meter (kg/m³).

Density is a property of matter

Density is mass per unit volume   **Density** describes how much mass is in a given volume of a material. Steel has high density; it contains 7.8 grams of mass per cubic centimeter. Aluminum, as you might predict, has a lower density; a 1-centimeter cube has a mass of only 2.7 grams.

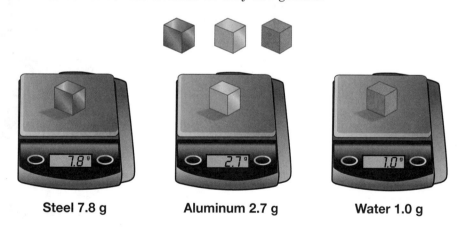

Steel 7.8 g   Aluminum 2.7 g   Water 1.0 g

Comparative densities
(vary with temperature and pressure)

Steel
7.8 g/mL

Aluminum
2.7 g/mL

Water
1.0 g/mL

Air
0.001 g/mL

The density of water and air   Liquids and gases are matter and have density. The density of water is about 1 gram per cubic centimeter. The density of air is lower, of course—much lower. The air in your classroom has a density of about 0.001 grams per cubic centimeter (Figure 12.1).

Figure 12.1: *The density of steel, aluminum, water, and air expressed in grams per milliliter (1 mL = 1 cm³).*

Volume

Volume

Volume is the amount of space an object takes up. The units used to measure volume depend on whether the object is solid or liquid. The volume of solids is measured in cubic centimeters (cm^3) or cubic meters (m^3). The volume of liquids is measured in milliliters (mL) or liters (L). One cubic centimeter is the same volume as one milliliter.

Measuring the volume of liquids

You can measure the volume of liquids by pouring them into a *graduated cylinder*. The graduated cylinder has markings that show volume. To read a graduated cylinder correctly, follow these two rules:

1. Read the mark at eye level.
2. You will notice that the surface of the liquid forms a curve rather than a straight line (Figure 12.2). This curve is called the *meniscus*. Read the volume at the center of the meniscus.

Volume of solids

You have probably already learned to measure the volume of some solid shapes. The volume of a rectangular solid (a shoebox shape), for example, is found by multiplying length times width times height. The volume of a sphere is $4/3\pi r^3$, with r equal to the radius of the sphere.

The displacement method

You can find the volume of an irregular shape using a technique called *displacement*. To *displace* means to "take the place of" or to "push aside." You can find the volume of an irregularly-shaped object by putting it in water and measuring the amount of water displaced.

How you make the measurement

You can use the displacement method to find the volume of an ordinary item like a house key. Fill a 100-mL graduated cylinder with 50 mL of water (Figure 12.3). Gently slide the key into the water. The water level in the container will rise, because the key displaced, or pushed aside, some water. If the level now reads 53.0 mL, you know that the key displaced 3.0 mL of water. The volume of the key, or of any object you measure in this way, is equal to the volume of the water it displaces. The key has a volume of 3.0 milliliters (mL), or 3.0 cubic centimeters (cm^3).

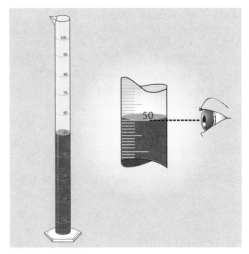

Figure 12.2: *The meniscus of water has a concave shape. Read the mark at the center of the meniscus, which is the bottom of the curve.*

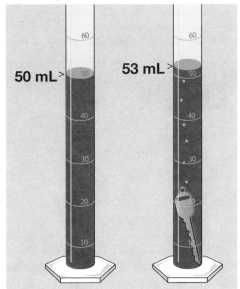

Figure 12.3: *The key displaced 3.0 mL of water.*

Units of density

Density in units of grams per milliliter

Your laboratory investigations will typically use density in units of grams per milliliter (g/mL). The density of water is one gram per milliliter. That means 1 milliliter of water has a mass of 1 gram, and 100 milliliters of water a mass of 100 grams.

Density in g/cm³ and kg/m³

Some problems use density in units of grams per cubic centimeter (g/cm³). Since one milliliter is exactly the same volume as one cubic centimeter, the units of g/cm³ and g/mL are actually the same. For measuring large objects, it is more convenient to use density in units of kilograms per cubic meter (kg/m³). Table 12.1 gives the densities of some common substances in both units.

Converting units of density

To convert from one unit of density to the other, remember that 1 g/cm³ is equal to 1,000 kg/m³. To go from g/cm³ to kg/m³, you multiply by 1,000. For example, the density of ice is 0.92 g/cm³. This is the same as 920 kg/m³.

To go from kg/m³ to g/cm³, you divide by 1,000. For example, the density of aluminum is 2,700 kg/m³. Dividing by 1,000 gives a density of 2.7 g/cm³.

Table 12.1: Densities of common substances

Material	(kg/m³)	(g/cm³)
Platinum	21,500	21.5
Lead	11,300	11.3
Steel	7,800	7.8
Titanium	4,500	4.5
Aluminum	2,700	2.7
Glass	2,700	2.7
Granite	2,600	2.6
Concrete	2,300	2.3
Plastic	2,000	2.0
Rubber	1,200	1.2
Liquid water	1,000	1.0
Ice	920	0.92
Oak (wood)	600	0.60
Pine (wood)	440	0.44
Cork	120	0.12
Air (avg.)	0.9	0.0009

Convert between units of density

A reference book lists the density of ceramic tile as 2,650 kg/m³. Estimate the mass of 1 cm³ of tile.

1. Looking for: Mass of 1 cm³, which is the density in g/cm³

2. Given: Density of 2,650 kg/m³

3. Relationships: 1 g/cm³ = 1,000 kg/m³

4. Solution: Divide by 1,000 to get the density in g/cm³.
2,650 ÷ 1,000 = 2.65 g

Your turn...

a. A bronze statue has a density of 6,000 kg/m³. What is the density in g/mL?
Answer: 6 g/mL

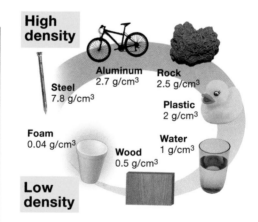

Figure 12.4: *The density range of common materials.*

Density of common materials

Material density is independent of shape

Density is a property of material independent of quantity or shape. For example, a steel nail and a steel cube have different amounts of matter and therefore different masses (Figure 12.5). They also have different volumes. But they have the same density. Dividing mass by volume gives the same result for the nail and the cube.

Strong solids typically have higher density

Solids that are strong, such as steel, typically have high density. High density means there are many atoms per cubic centimeter. Many atoms in a material means many bonds between atoms, and those bonds are what ultimately create strength.

Soft materials typically have lower density

Solids with low density, such as cork or foam, are often used as cushioning material. Low density means there are relatively large spaces between atoms. That means materials may be compressed relatively easily, which is why foam and other low-density substances make good packing materials.

Liquids tend to be less dense than solids of the same material

The density of a liquid is usually a little less than the density of the same material in solid form. For example, the density of solid solder is 10 g/mL. The density of liquid solder is 9.5 g/mL. The density of a liquid is lower because the atoms are not packed as uniformly as they are in the solid. Picture a brand-new box of toy blocks. When you open the box, you see the blocks tightly packed in a repeating pattern, like the atoms in a solid. Now imagine dumping the blocks out of the box, and then trying to pour them back into the original tight-packing pattern. The jumbled blocks take up more space, like the atoms in a liquid (Figure 12.6).

Water is an exception

Water is an exception to this rule. The density of solid water, or ice, is *less* than the density of liquid water.

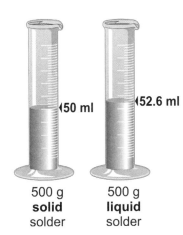

500 g **solid** solder

500 g **liquid** solder

Steel density

Steel cube
Volume: 10.0 cm³
Mass: 78 g
Density: 7.8 g/cm³

Nail
Volume: 1.6 cm³
Mass: 12.5 g
Density: 7.8 g/cm³

Figure 12.5: *The density of a steel nail is the same as the density of a solid cube of steel.*

Figure 12.6: *The same number (or mass) of blocks arranged in a tight, repeating pattern take up less space than when they are jumbled up.*

Determining density

Measuring density To find the density of a material, you need to know the mass and volume of a sample of the material. You can calculate the density from the formula below.

DENSITY

$$Density \longrightarrow D = \frac{m}{V} \begin{array}{l} \longleftarrow Mass \ (\text{kg or g}) \\ \longleftarrow Volume \ (\text{m}^3 \text{ or cm}^3) \end{array}$$

$(\text{kg/m}^3 \text{ or g/cm}^3)$

Calculating volume For simple shapes you can calculate the volume. The volume of spheres, cylinders, and rectangular solids is given in Figure 12.7. When calculating volume, all of the units of length involved in the calculation must be the same. For example, if you want volume in cubic centimeters, all of the measurements in the calculation must be in centimeters.

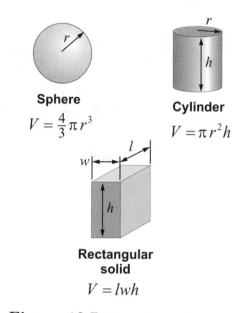

Sphere
$$V = \frac{4}{3}\pi r^3$$

Cylinder
$$V = \pi r^2 h$$

Rectangular solid
$$V = lwh$$

Figure 12.7: *The volume of some simple geometric shapes.*

Calculate density from mass and volume

Look at Figure 12.8. A student measures the mass of five steel nuts to be 96.2 g. The nuts displace 13 mL of water. Calculate the density of the steel in the nuts.

1. Looking for: Density

2. Given: Mass (96.2 g) and volume (13 mL)

3. Relationships: Density = mass ÷ volume

4. Solution: D = 96.2g ÷ 13 mL = 7.4 g/mL

Your turn...

a. A solid brass block measures 2 cm × 2 cm × 3 cm and has a mass of 48 g. What is its density? **Answer:** 4 g/cm³

Figure 12.8: *Use a scale to find the mass. Use the displacement method to find the volume of irregular objects.*

12.1 **Section Review**

1. List three physical properties of a piece of wood.
2. One cubic centimeter is the same volume as one _____.
3. Explain two ways to find the volume of a plastic cube.
4. A certain material has a density of 0.2 g/mL. Is this material better for building a bridge or for making cushions for a couch?
5. The density of a gas is lower than the density of a liquid because
    a. gas atoms are smaller than liquid atoms.
    b. gas atoms are larger than liquid atoms.
    c. atoms in a gas are farther apart than atoms in a liquid.
    d. atoms in a gas are closer together than atoms in a liquid.
6. Density is a _____ property of matter.
7. Density is the _____ per unit volume of a substance.
8. What measurements must be known in order to find the density of a substance?

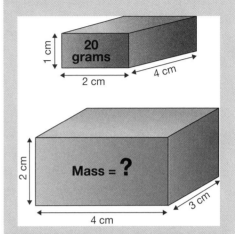

Two toy blocks are made of the same type of material. One has a mass of 20 grams and its dimensions are 2 cm × 4 cm × 1 cm. The second block measures 4 cm × 3 cm × 2 cm. Calculate the mass of the second block.

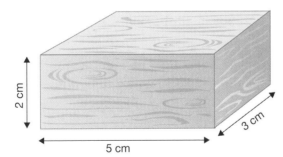

9. The piece of wood shown above has a mass of 18 grams. Calculate its volume and density. Then, use Table 12.1 on page 300 to determine which type of wood it is. What are the two factors that determine a material's density?

12.2 Buoyancy

If you drop a steel marble into a glass of water, it sinks to the bottom. The steel does not float because it has a greater density than the water. And yet many ships are made of steel. How does a steel ship float when a steel marble sinks? The answer has to do with gravity and weight.

VOCABULARY

buoyancy - the measure of the upward force that a fluid exerts on an object that is submerged.

Weight and buoyancy

Weight and mass are not the same We all tend to use the terms *weight* and *mass* interchangeably. In science however, *weight and mass are not the same thing*. Mass is a fundamental property of matter. Weight is a force caused by Earth's gravity. It is easy to confuse mass and weight because heavy objects (more weight) have lots of mass and light objects (less weight) have little mass.

Buoyancy is a force It is much easier to lift yourself in a swimming pool than to lift yourself on land. That is because the water in the pool exerts an upward force on you that acts in a direction opposite to your weight (Figure 12.9). We call this force **buoyancy**. Buoyancy is a measure of the upward force that a fluid exerts on an object that is submerged.

Figure 12.9: *The water in the pool exerts an upward force on your body, so the net force on you is lessened.*

Pushing a ball underwater

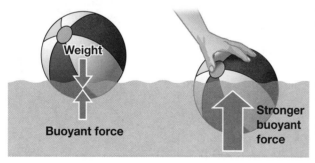

The strength of the buoyant force on an object in water depends on the volume of the object that is underwater. Suppose you have a large beach ball you want to submerge in a pool. As you keep pushing downward on the ball, you notice the buoyant force getting stronger and stronger. The greater the part of the ball you manage to push underwater, the stronger the force trying to push it back up. The strength of the buoyant force is proportional to the volume of the part of the ball that is submerged.

Archimedes' principle

What is Archimedes' principle? In the third century BCE, a Greek mathematician named Archimedes realized that buoyant force is equal to the weight of the fluid displaced by an object. We call this relationship **Archimedes' principle**. For example, suppose a rock with a volume of 1,000 cubic centimeters is dropped into water (Figure 12.10). The rock displaces 1,000 cm^3 of water, which has a mass of 1 kilogram. The buoyant force on the rock is the weight of 1 kilogram of water, which is 9.8 newtons.

VOCABULARY

Archimedes' principle - states that the buoyant force is equal to the weight of the fluid displaced by an object.

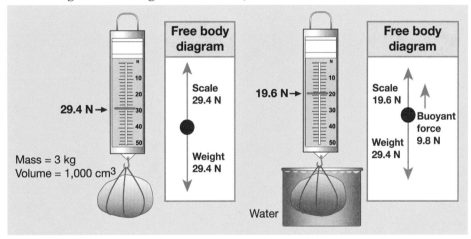

A simple buoyancy experiment Look at the illustration above. A simple experiment can be done to measure the buoyant force on a rock (or any object) using a spring scale. Suppose you have a rock with a volume of 1,000 cubic centimeters and a mass of 3 kilograms. In air, the scale shows the rock's weight as 29.4 newtons. The rock is then gradually immersed in a container of water, but not allowed to touch the bottom or sides of the container. As the rock enters the water, the reading on the scale decreases. When the rock is completely submerged, the scale reads 19.6 newtons.

Calculating the buoyant force Subtracting the two scale readings, 29.4 newtons and 19.6 newtons, results in a difference of 9.8 newtons. This is the buoyant force exerted on the rock, and it is the same as the weight of the 1,000 cubic centimeters of water the rock displaced.

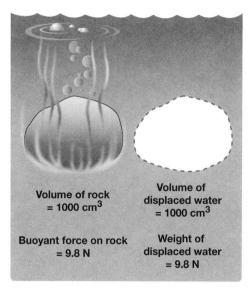

Figure 12.10: *A rock with a volume of 1,000 cm^3 experiences a buoyant force of 9.8 newtons.*

Sinking and floating

Comparing buoyant force and weight   Buoyancy explains why some objects sink and others float. A submerged object floats to the surface if the buoyant force is greater than its weight (Figure 12.11). If the buoyant force is less than its weight, then the object sinks.

Equilibrium   Suppose you place a block of foam in a tub of water. The block sinks partially below the surface. Then it floats without sinking any farther. The upward buoyant force perfectly balances the downward force of gravity (the block's weight). But how does the buoyant force "know" how strong it needs to be to balance the weight?

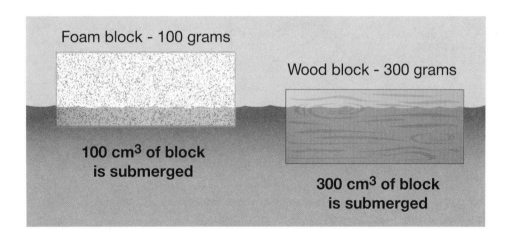

Foam block - 100 grams

Wood block - 300 grams

100 cm³ of block is submerged

300 cm³ of block is submerged

Denser objects float lower in the water   You can see the answer to this question in the illustration above. If a foam block and a wood block of the same size are both floating, the wood block sinks farther into the water. Wood has a greater density, so the wood block weighs more. A greater buoyant force is needed to balance the wood block's weight, *so the wood block displaces more water*. The foam block has to sink only slightly to displace water with a weight equal to the block's weight. A floating object displaces just enough water to make the buoyant force equal to the object's weight.

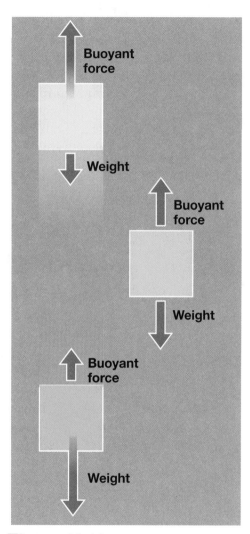

Buoyant force

Weight

Buoyant force

Weight

Buoyant force

Weight

Figure 12.11: *Whether an object sinks or floats depends on how the buoyant force compares with the weight.*

Density and buoyancy

Comparing densities

If you know an object's density, you can immediately predict whether it will sink or float—without measuring its weight. An object sinks if its density is greater than that of the liquid it is submerged into. It floats if its density is less than that of the liquid.

Two balls with the same volume but different densities

To see why, picture dropping two balls into a pool of water. The balls have the same size and volume but have different densities. The steel ball has a density of 7.8 g/mL which is greater than the density of water (1.0 g/mL). The wood ball has a density of 0.75 g/mL, which is less than the density of water.

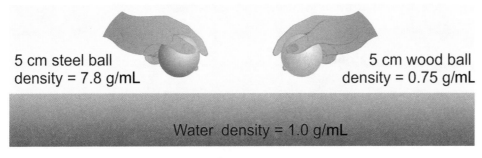

5 cm steel ball
density = 7.8 g/mL

5 cm wood ball
density = 0.75 g/mL

Water density = 1.0 g/mL

Why one sinks and the other floats

When they are completely underwater, both balls have the same buoyant force because they displace the same volume of water. However, the steel ball has more weight since it has a higher density. The steel ball sinks because steel's higher density makes the ball heavier than the same volume of water. The wood ball floats because wood's lower density makes the wood ball lighter than the same volume of displaced water.

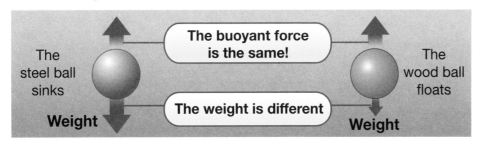

The steel ball sinks

The buoyant force is the same!

The weight is different

Weight

The wood ball floats

Weight

An object with an average density GREATER than the density of water will sink.

An object with an average density LESS than the density of water will float.

> **Average density**
> Average density is the total mass divided by the total volume.

Solid steel ball
volume = 25 mL
mass = 195 g

Hollow steel ball
volume = 25 mL
mass = 20 g

Avg. density = $\dfrac{195\ g}{25\ mL}$

Avg. density = $\dfrac{20\ g}{25\ mL}$

Avg. Density = 7.8 g/mL **SINKS!**	Avg. Density = 0.8 g/mL **FLOATS!**

Figure 12.12: *The meaning of* average density.

Boats and average density

How do steel boats float? If you place a solid chunk of steel in water, it immediately sinks because the density of steel (7.8 g/cm^3) is much greater than the density of water (1.0 g/cm^3). So how is it that thousands of huge ships made of steel are floating around the world? The answer is that *average density* determines whether an object sinks or floats.

Solid steel sinks because it is denser than water To make steel float, you have to reduce the *average* density somehow. Making the steel hollow does exactly that. Making a boat hollow expands its volume a tremendous amount without changing its mass. Steel is so strong that it is quite easy to reduce the average density of a boat to 10 percent of the density of water by making the shell of the boat relatively thin.

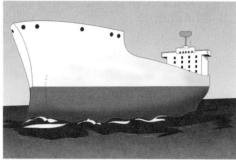

Empty cargo ship - less displaced water

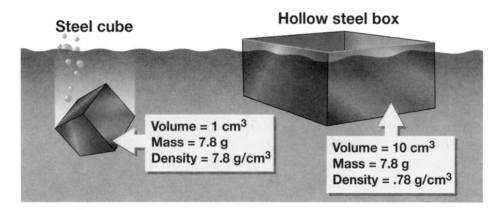

Steel cube

Volume = 1 cm^3
Mass = 7.8 g
Density = 7.8 g/cm^3

Hollow steel box

Volume = 10 cm^3
Mass = 7.8 g
Density = .78 g/cm^3

Full cargo ship - more displaced water

Figure 12.13: *By taking into account the density of materials and how they are shaped, a ship can be designed to carry an enormous amount of cargo. A full ship has more mass than an empty ship. This means a full ship must displace more water (sink deeper) to make the buoyant force large enough to balance the ship's weight.*

Increasing volume decreases density Ah, you say, but that is an empty ship. True, so the density of a new ship must be designed to be under 1.0 g/cm^3 to allow for cargo. When objects are placed in a boat, the boat's average density increases. The boat must sink deeper to displace more water and increase the buoyant force (Figure 12.13). If you have seen a loaded cargo ship, you might have noticed that it sat lower in the water than an unloaded ship nearby. In fact, the limit to how much a ship can carry is set by how low in the water the ship can get before rough seas cause waves to break over the sides of the ship.

12.2 **Section Review**

1. The buoyant force on an object depends on the _____ of the object that is underwater.
2. What happens to the buoyant force on an object as it is lowered into water? Why?
3. The buoyant force on an object is equal to the weight of the water it _____.
4. When the buoyant force on an object is greater than its weight, the object _____.

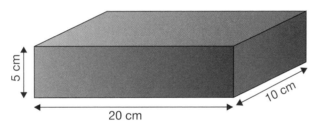

5. A rectangular object is 10 centimeters long, 5 centimeters high, and 20 centimeters wide. Its mass is 800 grams.
   a. Calculate the object's volume in cubic centimeters.
   b. Calculate the object's density in g/cm^3.
   c. Will the object float or sink in water? Explain.
6. Solid iron has a density of 7.9 g/cm^3. Liquid mercury has a density of 13.5 g/cm^3. Will iron float or sink in mercury? Explain.
7. Why is it incorrect to say that heavy objects sink in water?
8. Steel is denser than water and yet steel ships float. Explain.
9. A rock sinks in water, but suppose a rock was placed in a pool of mercury. Mercury is a liquid metal with a density of 13,500 kg/m^3. The density of rock is 2,600 kg/m^3. Will the rock sink or not? Explain how you got your answer.

Legend has it that Archimedes added to his fame by using the concepts of volume and density to figure out whether a goldsmith had cheated Hiero II, the king of Syracuse. The goldsmith had been given a piece of gold of a known weight to make a crown. Hiero suspected the goldsmith had kept some of the gold for himself and replaced it with an equal weight of another metal. Explain the steps you could follow to determine whether or not the crown was pure gold.

12.3 Properties of Materials

 VOCABULARY

We choose materials to have the properties we need. We use concrete and steel for buildings and bridges because these materials are strong. We use foam for sofa cushions because foam is soft. This section is about the properties of materials.

fluid - a form of matter that flows when a force is applied.

pressure - a force applied to a fluid. Pressure acts in all directions.

Pressure

Liquid and gas are fluids A **fluid** is a form of matter that flows when any force is applied, no matter how small. Liquids are one kind of fluid, gases are another. You have seen water flow from a faucet (or overflow a sink) and felt cool air flow through an open window.

Forces in fluids Think about what happens when you push down on an inflated balloon. The downward force you apply creates forces that act sideways as well as down. This is very different from what happens when you push down on a bowling ball. Because fluids change shape, forces in fluids are more complicated than forces in solids.

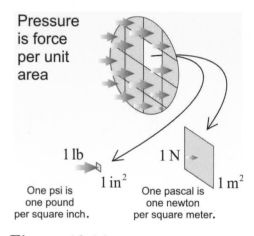

Pressure is force per unit area

One psi is one pound per square inch.

One pascal is one newton per square meter.

Figure 12.14: *The units of pressure.*

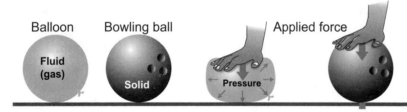

Pressure A force applied to a fluid creates **pressure**. Pressure acts in all directions, not just the direction of the applied force. When you inflate a car tire, you are increasing the pressure in the tire. This force acts up, down, and sideways in all directions inside the tire.

Units of pressure The units of pressure are force divided by area (Figure 12.14). If your car tires are inflated to 35 pounds per square inch (35 psi), then a force of 35 pounds acts on every square inch of area inside the tire. The pressure on the bottom of the tire is what holds up the car (Figure 12.15)! The metric unit of pressure is the Pascal (Pa). One pascal is one newton of force per square meter of area (N/m^2).

Figure 12.15: *The pressure inside your tire is what holds your car up.*

Pressure, energy, and force

The atomic level explanation What causes pressure? On the atomic level, pressure comes from collisions between atoms and molecules. Look at Figure 12.16. Molecules move around and bounce off each other and off the walls of a jar. It takes force to make a molecule reverse its direction and bounce the other way. The bouncing force is applied *to* the molecule *by* the inside surface of the jar. According to Newton's third law, an equal and opposite reaction force is exerted *by* the molecule *on* the jar. The reaction force is what creates the pressure acting on the inside surface of the jar. Trillions of molecules per second are constantly bouncing against every square millimeter of the inner surface of the jar. Pressure comes from the collisions of those many, many atoms.

Pressure is potential energy Differences in pressure create potential energy in fluids just like differences in height create potential energy from gravity. A pressure difference of one newton per m^2 is equivalent to a potential energy of one joule per m^3. We get useful work when we let a fluid under pressure expand. In a car engine high pressure is created by an exploding gasoline-air mixture. This pressure pushes the cylinders of the engine down, doing work that moves the car.

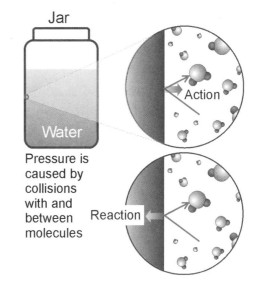

Figure 12.16: *Pressure comes from constant collisions of trillions of atoms.*

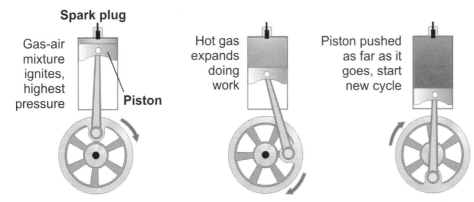

An engine uses pressure in an expanding gas to do work.

Car tires are usually inflated to a pressure of 32–40 pounds per square inch (psi). Racing bicycle tires are inflated to much higher pressure, 100–110 psi. A bicycle and rider are much lighter than a car! Why is the pressure in a bicycle tire higher than the pressure in a car tire?

Energy conservation and Bernoulli's principle

Bernoulli's principle   Everything obeys the law of energy conservation. It just gets trickier when talking about a fluid (liquid or gas)! You still have potential and kinetic energy, but you also have pressure energy. If friction is neglected, the total energy stays constant for any particular sample of fluid. This relationship is known as **Bernoulli's principle**.

Streamlines   *Streamlines* are imaginary lines drawn to show the flow of fluid. We draw streamlines so that they are always parallel to the direction of flow. If water is coming out of a hole in a bucket, the streamlines look like Figure 12.17. Bernoulli's principle tells us that the energy of any sample of fluid moving along a streamline is constant.

Bernoulli's principle

Form of energy	Potential energy	+	Kinetic energy	+	Pressure energy	= Constant
						Along any streamline in a fluid
Variable	*height*		*speed*		*pressure*	

The three variables   Bernoulli's principle says the three variables of height, pressure, and speed are related by energy conservation. Height is associated with potential energy, speed with kinetic energy, and pressure with pressure energy. If one variable increases along a streamline, *at least one of the other two must decrease*. For example, if speed goes up, pressure goes down.

The airfoil   One of the most important applications of Bernoulli's principle is the airfoil shape of wings on a plane (Figure 12.18). The shape of an airfoil causes air flowing along the top (A) to move faster than air flowing along the bottom (B). According to Bernoulli's principle, if the speed goes up, the pressure goes down. When a plane is moving, the pressure on the top surface of the wings is lower than the pressure beneath the wings. The difference in pressure is what creates the lift force that supports the plane in the air.

Bernoulli's principle - a relationship that describes energy conservation in a fluid.

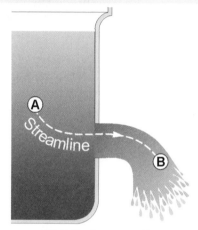

Figure 12.17: *A streamline is an imaginary line tracing the flow of a single particle of fluid.*

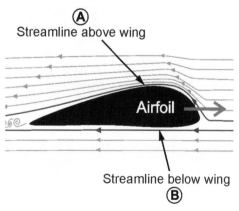

Figure 12.18: *Streamlines showing air moving around an airfoil (wing) that is moving from left to right.*

Mechanical properties

The meaning of "strength"

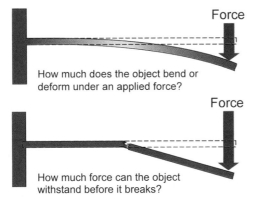

How much does the object bend or deform under an applied force?

How much force can the object withstand before it breaks?

When you apply a force to an object, the object may change its size, shape, or both. The concept of **strength** describes the ability of a solid object to maintain its shape even when force is applied. The strength of an object depends on the answers to the two questions in the illustration at the left.

Elasticity If you pull on a rubber band, its shape changes. If you let it go, the rubber band returns to its original shape. Rubber bands can stretch many times their original length before breaking, a property called elasticity. **Elasticity** describes a solid's ability to be stretched and then return to its original size. This property also gives objects the ability to bounce and to withstand impact without breaking.

Brittleness **Brittleness** is defined as the tendency of a solid to crack or break before stretching very much (Figure 12.19). Glass is a good example of a brittle material. You cannot stretch glass even one-tenth of a percent (0.001) before it breaks. To stretch or shape glass you need to heat the glass until it is almost melted. Heating causes molecules to move faster, temporarily breaking the forces that hold them together.

Ductility One of the most useful properties of metals is that they are ductile. A ductile material can be bent a relatively large amount without breaking. For example, a steel fork can be bent in half and the steel does not break. A plastic fork cracks when it is bent only a small amount. Steel's high **ductility** means steel can be formed into useful shapes by pounding, rolling, and bending. These processes would destroy a brittle material like glass.

strength - the ability to maintain shape under the application of force.

elasticity - the ability to be stretched or compressed and then return to original size.

brittleness - the tendency to crack or break; the opposite of elasticity.

ductility - the ability to bend without breaking.

BRITTLENESS

Figure 12.19: *Brittleness is the tendency of a solid to crack when force is applied.*

The arrangement of atoms and molecules in solids

Crystalline and amorphous solids

The atoms or molecules in a solid are arranged in two ways. If there is an orderly, repeating pattern, the solid is called **crystalline**. Examples of crystalline solids include salts, minerals, and metals. If the particles are arranged in a random way, the solid is **amorphous**. Examples of amorphous solids include rubber, wax, and glass.

Crystalline solids

Most solids on Earth are crystalline. Some materials, like salt, exist as single crystals and you can see the arrangement of atoms reflected in the shape of the crystal. If you look at a crystal of table salt under a microscope, you see that it is cubic in shape. If you could examine the arrangement of atoms, you would see that the shape of the crystal comes from the cubic arrangement of sodium and chlorine atoms (Figure 12.20). Metals are also crystalline. They don't look like "crystals" because solid metal is made from very tiny crystals fused together in a jumble of different orientations (Figure 12.21).

Amorphous solids

The atoms or molecules of amorphous solids are randomly arranged. While amorphous solids also hold their shape, they are often softer and more elastic than crystalline solids. This is because a molecule in an amorphous solid is not tightly connected to as many neighboring molecules as it would be in a crystalline solid. Glass is a common amorphous solid. Glass is hard and brittle because it is made from molten silica crystals that are cooled quickly, before they have time to re-crystallize. The rapid cooling leaves the silica molecules in a random arrangement. Plastic is another useful amorphous solid.

VOCABULARY

crystalline - solid with a regular, orderly arrangement of atoms.

amorphous - solid with a random, jumbled arrangement of atoms.

Salt Crystal

Sodium atom   Chlorine atom

Figure 12.20: *The shape of a salt crystal is due to the arrangement of atoms.*

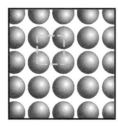

Cubic crystal

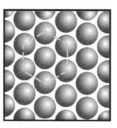

Hexagonal crystal

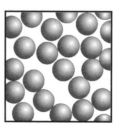

Amorphous

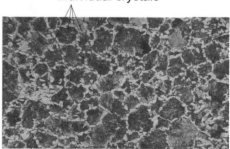

Individual crystals

Figure 12.21: *Metallic crystals in steel (high magnification).*

12.3 Section Review

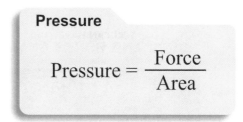

1. The pressure at the bottom of the Earth's atmosphere is about 100,000 N/m². That means there is a force of 100,000 N acting on every square meter of area! Your body has about 1.5 square meters of surface. Why aren't you crushed by the atmosphere?

2. The pressure at the bottom of the ocean is great enough to crush submarines with steel walls that are 10 centimeters thick. Suppose a submarine is at a depth of 1,000 meters. The weight of water above each square meter of the submarine is 9,800,000 newtons (Figure 12.22).
    a. What is the pressure? (*Hint*: Pressure is force divided by area.)
    b. How does this pressure compare with the air pressure we are immersed in every day (100,000 N/m²)?

3. What does pressure have to do with how a car engine works?

4. Bernoulli's principle relates the speed, height, and pressure in a fluid. Suppose speed goes up and height stays the same. What happens to the pressure?

5. Name one example of a material for each set of properties.
    a. crystalline and high strength
    b. crystalline and brittle
    c. amorphous and brittle
    d. amorphous and elastic

6. The strength of a material determines
    a. how dense the materials is.
    b. how much force it can withstand before breaking.
    c. how good a thermal or electrical conductor it is.

7. Latex is a soft, stretchy, rubber-like material. Would you expect latex to be crystalline or amorphous?

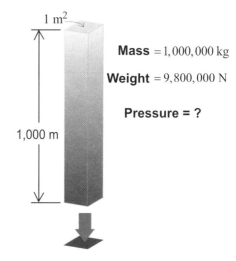

Figure 12.22: *Question 2.*

Silly Putty®: Solid or Liquid?

Silly Putty*—it's been a popular party favor for more than 50 years. Your parents probably played with it when they were kids. Some people call it America's longest-lasting fad.

It's easy to understand why people like Silly Putty. Roll it into a ball, and you can bounce it around the room. Pull on it slowly and it will stretch out like a long lazy snake. Give it a quick yank and it will break with a satisfying *snap*.

Have you ever tried to smash a ball of Silly Putty with a hammer? It keeps its shape every time. However, if you gently press on it with your thumb, you can flatten it easily. If you leave a ball of Silly Putty on your dresser overnight, in the morning you'll see that it flattened out by itself while you were sleeping.

What's going on here?

Silly Putty isn't easy to categorize. It holds its shape when hammered, yet flows into a puddle when left alone overnight. No wonder the people who make Silly Putty call it "a real solid liquid."

Rheologists (scientists who study how matter flows and/or deforms) have another term for Silly Putty: it's a *viscoelastic* liquid.

Viscoelastic is a compound word (like *snowman*). The *visco-* part comes from the word *viscous*, which means "resistant to flow." Thick, gooey, slow-flowing liquids like hot fudge sauce are *viscous*. Silly Putty is like that.

You're probably already familiar with the second half of the word. *Elastic*, in physics terms, describes a material that returns to its original shape when deformed.

So, rheologists describe Silly Putty as a slow-flowing, elastic liquid.

How did it get that way?

It's not too surprising that Silly Putty bounces, because it was accidentally invented by a chemist looking for a substitute for rubber. In 1943, James Wright, a researcher for General Electric, dropped some boric acid into silicone oil, creating a gooey compound.

This compound, first called "nutty putty," was sent to engineers around the world—but no practical uses were found. In 1949, a man named Peter Hodgson decided to sell it as a toy. He borrowed $147 to buy a batch from General Electric, divided the batch into one-ounce lumps, and placed each lump into a plastic egg. He renamed the compound "Silly Putty" after the main ingredient, silicone.

A *New Yorker* magazine reporter wrote an article about Silly Putty in 1950, and afterward Hodgson received 250,000 orders in three days. Silly Putty was a hit!

Inside Silly Putty

The silicone oil used to make Silly Putty is known to chemists as polydimethylsiloxane, or PDMS. PDMS is a polymer, which means each molecule is made up of long chain of identical smaller molecules.

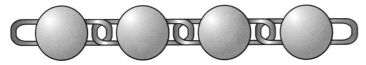

When boric acid is added to the long chains of PDMS, boron crosslinks begin to form. This means that the boron hooks chains of PDMS molecules together like this:

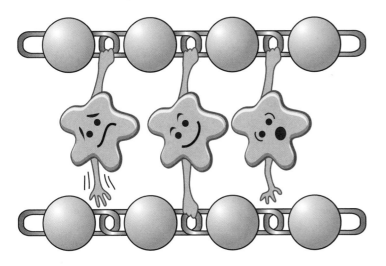

These boron crosslinks are not very strong. Remember that molecules in solids and liquids are always in motion. This motion breaks boron crosslinks, but over time new crosslinks form. This action is called *dynamic* (changing) *crosslinking*.

Because of this dynamic crosslinking, Silly Putty reacts one way to quick forces and another way to long-acting forces.

When you strike Silly Putty with a hammer, the Silly Putty reacts like an elastic solid: it bounces back. That's because most of the boron crosslinks remain in place during the split second of the hammer's strike.

When you leave a ball of Silly Putty untouched overnight, the boron crosslinks that help Silly Putty hold its shape have about eight hours to break down. Over that time, molecular motion breaks many of the original crosslinks. Gravitational force constantly pulls the PDMS molecules downward, and in the morning you're left with a Silly Putty puddle.

10:00 P.M.

6:00 A.M.

QUESTIONS

1. Silly Putty does have some practical uses, despite the fact that engineers in the 1940s couldn't think of any. Find out about these using the Internet, or come up with one on your own.

2. Use the Internet to find out about a man named Earl Warrick. What was his role in the invention of Silly Putty?

3. The crew of Apollo 8 took some Silly Putty to the moon. Use the Internet to find out how the astronauts used it.

*Permission granted by Binney and Smith to publish trademark named Silly Putty.

Make Your Own Viscoelastic Liquid

The exact recipe for Silly Putty is kept secret, but you can make your own viscoelastic liquid with ingredients you may have around the house. The homemade compound uses different molecules to form the polymer chains, but the boron crosslinks work the same way.

What you will need

white glue and water solution made in a 1:1 ratio; Borax and water solution: mix 5 mL of Borax in 60 mL of water (Borax powder is found in supermarket laundry detergent aisles); 8-ounce paper cup; stirring stick (a tongue depressor works well)

What you will do

1. Pour 60 mL of the white glue solution into the cup.

2. Add 30 mL of the borax solution.

3. Stir the mixture for 2–3 minutes.

4. Remove the mixture from the cup and knead it with your hands. It will be sticky at first. Keep kneading until it is easy to pull the putty away from your hands in a single lump.

Applying your knowledge

a. Develop a class procedure for measuring the putty's bounciness and stretchiness. Compare your results with your classmates'. Was every batch of putty the same? If not, can you suggest reasons for the differences?

b. There are lots of experiments you could do with your home-made putty. Here are a few examples:
   1. How does temperature affect bounciness?
   2. Does stretchiness change over time?
   Choose one of these questions or make up your own question to answer about your putty.

c. State your hypothesis.

d. Develop a procedure for testing your hypothesis. Remember, only one variable can be changed!

e. Create a data table to record your results. Here's a sample:

Temperature	Bounce height when dropped 50 cm
−10°C	
5°C	
20°C	
35°C	
50°C	

f. Carry out your experiment and record your results. What conclusion(s) can you draw?

g. Share your results with your classmates.

Chapter 12 Assessment

Vocabulary

Select the correct term to complete the sentences.

brittleness	amorphous	Archimedes' principle
density	buoyancy	Bernoulli's principle
fluid	ductility	crystalline
pressure	strength	elasticity

Section 12.1

1. The mass of matter per unit of volume is called ____.

Section 12.2

2. "An object will be buoyed up by a force equal to the weight of the fluid displaced" is a statement of ____.

3. The upward force exerted by a fluid on an object submerged in the fluid is called ____.

Section 12.3

4. Force per unit area is ____.

5. The principle that states the sum of the potential energy, kinetic energy and pressure energy is constant in a fluid is ____.

6. A(n) ____ is matter that flows, and can be either gas or liquid.

7. The ability to bend without breaking is known as ____.

8. An object that is stretched and then returns to its original shape and size is displaying the property of ____.

9. A(n) ____ solid has a regular and orderly arrangement of atoms.

10. The ability of a material to maintain its shape under the application of force is called ____.

11. The tendency to crack or break when a stretching force is applied to a material is called ____.

12. A(n) ____ solid has a random, jumbled arrangement of atoms.

Concepts

Section 12.1

1. A wooden baseball bat and an aluminum bat have the exact same size, shape, and mass. Aluminum is much denser than wood. Explain how the two bats could be the same size, shape, and mass.

2. A cube of solid steel and a cube of solid aluminum are both covered with a thin plastic coating making it impossible to identify the cubes based upon their color. Referring to Table 12.1, tell how you could determine which cube is steel and which is aluminum.

3. In general, how do the densities of a material in solid, liquid, and gas phases compare? Name a common exception to the general rule.

4. Describe how you would find the volume of a small, irregular stone using the displacement method.

5. Write the formulas for finding the volume of the following regular shapes if their dimensions are known.
   a. rectangular solid
   b. sphere
   c. cylinder

6. What is a meniscus?

7. When measuring the volume of a liquid using a graduated cylinder, what two rules should you follow to be sure of a correct reading?

8. Write the formula for calculating the density of an object if the mass and volume of the object are known.

9. Which makes a better packing material, a high-density or a low-density material? Why?

10. A 1,000-gram box made of yellow pine contains 36 blocks made of yellow pine. How does the density of each block compare to the density of the box?

11. Based upon the diagram to the right, arrange the three materials—cork, water, and lead—in order from most to least dense.

Section 12.2

12. Why does a glass marble sink in water?

13. What happens to the weight of a rock when it is placed under water? Why?

14. Compare the buoyant force to the weight of a floating block of foam.

15. A block of cork (density = 0.12 g/cm^3) and a wooden block (density = 0.60 g/cm^3) are placed in water. Which object will have a greater portion submerged in the water?

16. Explain why a solid steel ball sinks in water but a steel ship floats in water.

17. A solid steel ball and a hollow steel ball of the same size are dropped into a bucket of water. Both sink. Compare the buoyant force on each.

18. What is the maximum density that a fully-loaded cargo ship may have?

19. Why does ice float in a glass of water? Explain in terms of density and buoyancy.

Section 12.3

20. Compare the terms *liquid* and *fluid*.

21. Iliana pushed on a bicycle pump with a force of 20 newtons per square meter. How many joules of energy were added per cubic meter of air?

22. Describe how Newton's third law is related to fluid pressure.

23. While pumping up the tire of her bicycle, Kortney feels the tire and finds it warm to the touch. What is the most likely cause for the increase in the temperature of the tire?

24. Explain how Bernoulli's principle helps to explain the lift that airplane wings experience.

25. Tamara sprays a garden hose at her brother who is 20 feet off the ground in a tree. How would the speed of the water as it comes from the faucet compare to the speed of the water as it hits her brother? Explain.

26. Match the materials below with the mechanical property associated with the material.

    a. ____ gold   1. brittleness
    b. ____ rubber   2. ductility
    c. ____ glass   3. elasticity

27. Use the words *amorphous* or *crystalline* to describe each of the materials listed below.

    a. metal   e. taffy candy
    b. glass   f. plastic
    c. rubber   g. sugar
    d. diamond   h. ice

28. Compare the arrangement of atoms in an amorphous solid to the arrangement of atoms in a crystalline solid.

Problems

Section 12.1

1. The density of ice is 0.92 g/cm^3. What is the volume of 1 kg of ice? If that 1 kg of ice completely melted, what would the volume of water be? The density of water is 1 g/cm^3.

2. Convert the following to densities expressed in g/mL.
   a. 32 g/cm^3
   b. 5,100 kg/m^3

3. Calculate the volume of a cylinder 4 cm high if the base is a circle with a radius of 2 cm.

4. What is the volume of the liquid in the graduated cylinder pictured in the diagram?

5. Calculate the volume of a ball 30 centimeters in diameter.

6. What is the volume of a 25-gram pine block? The density of pine is 0.44 g/cm^3.

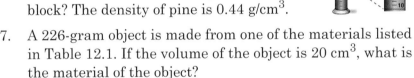

7. A 226-gram object is made from one of the materials listed in Table 12.1. If the volume of the object is 20 cm^3, what is the material of the object?

8. A piece of granite has a mass of 26 grams. The granite is placed in a graduated cylinder containing 10 mL of water. What is the reading of the water level in the graduated cylinder after the granite is fully submerged? Granite has a density of 2.6 g/cm^3.

Section 12.2

9. What buoyant force is exerted on a 6,000-mL toy balloon by the air surrounding the balloon? The density of air is 0.0009 g/mL.

10. An object weighing 45 newtons in air is suspended from a spring scale. The spring scale reads 22 newtons when the object is fully submerged. Calculate the buoyant force on the object.

11. A bucket of water is filled to the top with water and set into a large pan. When a 200-gram wooden block is carefully lowered into the water it floats, but some water overflows into the pan. What is the weight of the water that spills into the pan?

12. A stone that weighs 6.5 newtons in air weighs only 5.0 newtons when submerged in water. What is the buoyant force exerted on the rock by the water?

13. A 100-mL oak object is placed in water. What volume of water is displaced by the oak object? The density of oak is 0.60 g/cm^3.

14. The cube in the diagram has a mass of 7.8 grams and measures 1.2 centimeters on an edge.

    a. Find the density of the cube. Show your work, including an equation.
    b. Will the cube float in water? Explain.

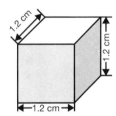

Section 12.3

15. Convert the pressure of 45 N/m^2 to pascals.

16. What is the pressure if 810 newtons of force are applied on an area of 9 m^2?

17. If the air pressure is 100,000 N/m^2, how much force is acting on a dog with a surface area of 0.5 meters?

18. A 4,000-pound car's tires are inflated to 35 pounds per square inch (psi). How much tire area must be in contact with the road to support the car?

UNIT 6

ATOMS, ELEMENTS, AND COMPOUNDS

CHAPTER 13
The Atom

CHAPTER 14
Elements and the Periodic Table

CHAPTER 15
Molecules and Compounds

Exploring on Your Own

Nuclear engineers use the energy within atoms to create new technologies. Describe three beneficial uses of nuclear energy. What are some of the risks? Which energy company provides power to your home? Invite a company representative to speak to your class about current and future uses for nuclear energy and career opportunities for nuclear scientists.

Chapter 13

The Atom

There is something more to wintergreen-flavored candy (the kind with the hole in the middle) than its refreshing taste. When you crush one of these candies with your teeth, blue sparks jump out of your mouth! You can only see the sparks if you hold a mirror up to your mouth in a very dark place, like a closet. You will be able to see the light even better if you crush one of the candies with a pair of pliers (no mirror required). In order to understand why the blue sparks appear, you must know what an atom is and what it is made of. After reading this chapter on atoms, you can do an Internet search on the term triboluminescence to find out why this candy sparks when you crush it.

Key Questions:

1. In the past, how did scientists learn about atoms if they couldn't see them?

2. What makes the atoms of various elements different?

3. What are atoms made of?

13.1 Fundamental Particles and Forces

Scientists once believed atoms were the smallest particles of matter. With the advancement of technology, it became clear that atoms themselves are made of simpler particles. Today, we believe atoms are made of three basic particles: the proton, electron, and neutron. It's amazing that the incredible variety of matter around us can be built from just three subatomic particles!

elementary charge - the smallest unit of electric charge that is possible in ordinary matter; represented by the lowercase letter *e*.

Electric charge

Electric charge is a property of matter   In Chapter 8 you were introduced to *electric charge*. In that chapter, we were interested mostly in electric current, which is moving charge. In order to understand atoms, we need to understand just where electric charge comes from. One of the two forces that hold atoms together comes from the attraction between positive and negative charge.

Electric charge only appears in multiples of the elementary charge, e.

Positive and negative

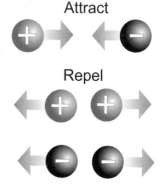

There are two different kinds of electric charge—*positive* and *negative*. Because there are two kinds of charge, the force between electric charges can be either attractive or repulsive. A positive and a negative charge will attract each other. Two positive charges will repel each other. Two negative charges will also repel each other.

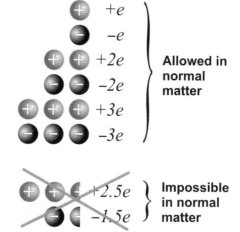

The elementary charge   We use the letter *e* to represent the **elementary charge**. At the size of atoms, electric charge always comes in units of +e or –e. It is *only* possible to have charges that are multiples of e, such as +e, +2e, –e, –2e, –3e, and so on. Scientists believe it is *impossible* for ordinary matter to have charges that are fractions of e. For example, a charge of +0.5e is impossible in ordinary matter. Electric charge only appears in whole units of the elementary charge (Figure 13.1).

Figure 13.1: *Just as normal matter is divided into atoms, electric charge appears only in whole units of the elementary charge, e.*

Inside an atom: Solving the puzzle

VOCABULARY

electron - a particle with an electric charge (–e) found inside of atoms but outside the nucleus.

nucleus - the tiny core at the center of an atom containing most of the atom's mass and all of its positive charge.

The electron identified   The first strong evidence that something smaller than an atom existed came in 1897. English physicist J. J. Thomson discovered that electricity passing through a gas caused the gas to give off particles that were too small to be atoms. The new particles had negative electric charge. Atoms have zero charge. Thomson's particles are now known as **electrons**. Electrons were the first particles discovered that are smaller than atoms.

An early model of an atom

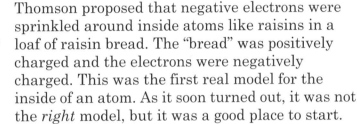

Thomson's original (incorrect) model
Electrons
Atom

Thomson proposed that negative electrons were sprinkled around inside atoms like raisins in a loaf of raisin bread. The "bread" was positively charged and the electrons were negatively charged. This was the first real model for the inside of an atom. As it soon turned out, it was not the *right* model, but it was a good place to start.

Testing the model with an experiment   In 1911, Ernest Rutherford, Hans Geiger, and Ernest Marsden did an experiment to test Thomson's model of the atom. They launched positively-charged helium ions (a charged atom is an *ion*) at a very thin gold foil (Figure 13.2). They expected most of the helium ions to be deflected a little as they plowed through the gold atoms.

An unexpected result!   They found something quite unexpected. Most of the helium ions passed right through with no deflection at all. Even more surprising, a few bounced back in the direction they came! This unexpected result prompted Rutherford to remark, *"It was as if you fired a five- inch (artillery) shell at a piece of tissue paper and it came back and hit you!"*

The nuclear model of the atom   The best way to explain the pass-through result was if a gold atom was mostly empty space. If most of the helium ions hit nothing, they wouldn't be deflected. The best way to explain the bounce-back result was if nearly all the mass of a gold atom were concentrated in a tiny, hard core at the center. Further experiments confirmed Rutherford's idea about this hard core. We now know that every atom has a tiny **nucleus**, which contains more than 99 percent of the atom's mass.

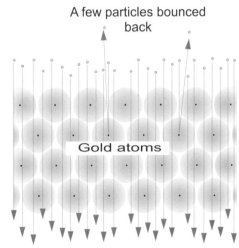

A few particles bounced back

Gold atoms

Almost all particles passed straight through without any deflection

Figure 13.2: *Rutherford's famous experiment led to the discovery of the nucleus.*

Three particles make up all atoms

Protons and neutrons
Today we know that the nucleus contains *protons* and *neutrons*. **Protons** have positive charge, opposite of electrons. The charge on a proton (+e) and an electron (–e) are exactly equal and opposite. **Neutrons** have zero electric charge.

VOCABULARY

proton - a particle found in the nucleus with a positive charge exactly equal and opposite to the electron.

neutron - a particle found in the nucleus with mass similar to the proton but with zero electric charge.

The nucleus contains most of the mass

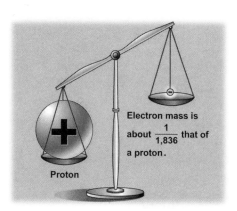

Electron mass is about $\frac{1}{1,836}$ that of a proton.

Proton

Protons and neutrons are *much* more massive than electrons. A proton has 1,836 times as much mass as an electron. A neutron has about the same mass as a proton. The chart below compares electrons, protons, and neutrons in terms of charge and mass. Because protons and neutrons have so much more mass, more than 99 percent of an atom's mass is in the nucleus.

	Occurrence	Charge	Mass (g)	Relative Mass
⊖ **Electron**	found outside of nucleus	-1	9.109×10^{-28}	1
⊕ **Proton**	found in all nuclei	+1	1.673×10^{-24}	1,836
⊙ **Neutron**	found in almost all nuclei (exception: most H nuclei)	0	1.675×10^{-24}	1,839

Electrons define the volume of an atom
Electrons take up the region *outside* the nucleus in a region called the *electron cloud*. The diameter of an atom is really the diameter of the electron cloud (Figure 13.3). Compared to the tiny nucleus, the electron cloud is enormous, more than 10,000 times larger than the nucleus. As a comparison, if an atom were the size of a football stadium, the nucleus would be the size of a pea, and the electrons would be equivalent to a small swarm of gnats buzzing around the stadium at extremely high speed. Can you imagine how much empty space there would be in the stadium? An atom is mostly empty space!

Size and Structure of the Atom

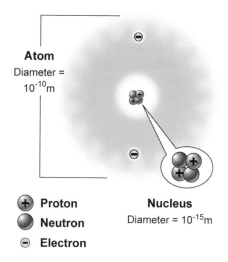

Atom
Diameter =
10^{-10} m

⊕ Proton
⊙ Neutron
⊖ Electron

Nucleus
Diameter = 10^{-15} m

Figure 13.3: *The overall size of an atom is the size of its electron cloud. The nucleus is much, much smaller.*

Forces inside atoms

Electromagnetic forces

Electrons are bound to the nucleus by the attractive force between electrons (−) and protons (+). The electrons don't fall into the nucleus because they have kinetic energy, or momentum. The energy of an electron causes it to move around the nucleus instead of falling in (Figure 13.4). A good analogy is Earth orbiting the Sun. Gravity creates a force that pulls the Earth toward the Sun. Earth's kinetic energy causes it to orbit the Sun rather than fall straight in. While electrons don't really move in orbits, the energy analogy is approximately right.

Strong nuclear force

Because of electric force, all the positively-charged protons in the nucleus *repel* each other. So, what holds the nucleus together? There is another force that is even stronger than the electric force. We call it the *strong nuclear force*. The strong nuclear force is the strongest force known to science (Figure 13.5). This force attracts neutrons and protons to each other and works only at the extremely small distances inside the nucleus. If there are enough neutrons, the attraction from the strong nuclear force wins out over repulsion from the electromagnetic force and the nucleus stays together. In every atom heavier than helium, there is at least one neutron for every proton in the nucleus.

Weak force

There is another nuclear force called the *weak force*. The weak force is weaker than both the electric force and the strong nuclear force. If you leave a single neutron outside the nucleus, the weak force eventually causes it to break down into a proton and an electron. The weak force does not play an important role in a stable atom, but comes into action in certain special cases when atoms break apart.

Gravity

The force of gravity inside the atom is much weaker even than the weak force. It takes a relatively large mass to create enough gravity to make a significant force. We know that particles inside an atom do not have enough mass for gravity to be an important force on the scale of atoms. But there are many unanswered questions. Understanding how gravity works inside atoms is an unsolved mystery in science.

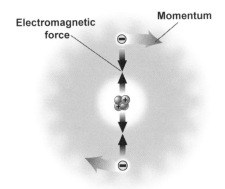

Figure 13.4: *The negative electrons are attracted to the positive protons in the nucleus, but their momentum keeps them from falling in.*

Figure 13.5: *When enough neutrons are present, the strong nuclear force wins out over the repulsion between positively charged protons and pulls the nucleus together tightly. The strong nuclear force is the strongest force in the universe that we know of.*

How atoms of various elements are different

The atomic number is the number of protons

How is an atom of one element different from an atom of another element? The atoms of different elements contain varying numbers of protons in the nucleus. For example, all atoms of carbon have six protons in the nucleus and all atoms of hydrogen have one proton in the nucleus (Figure 13.6). Because the number of protons is so important, it is called the **atomic number.** The atomic number of an element is the number of protons in the nucleus of every atom of that element.

Atoms of the same element always have the same number of protons in the nucleus.

Elements have unique atomic numbers

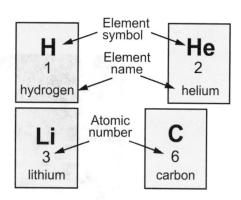

Each element has a unique atomic number. On a periodic table of elements, the atomic number is usually written above or below the atomic symbol. An atom with only one proton in its nucleus is the element hydrogen, atomic number 1. An atom with six protons is the element carbon, atomic number 6. Atoms with seven protons are nitrogen, atoms with eight protons are oxygen, and so on.

Complete atoms are electrically neutral

Because protons and electrons attract each other with very large forces, the number of protons and electrons in a complete atom is always equal. For example, hydrogen has one proton in its nucleus and one electron outside the nucleus. The total electric charge of a hydrogen atom is zero because the negative charge of the electron cancels the positive charge of the proton. Each carbon atom has six electrons, one for each of carbon's six protons. Like hydrogen, a complete carbon atom is electrically neutral.

VOCABULARY

atomic number - the number of protons in the nucleus of an atom. The atomic number determines what element the atom represents.

All carbon atoms have 6 protons

All hydrogen atoms have 1 proton

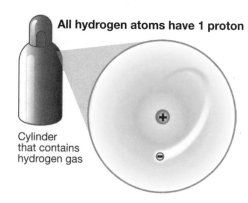

Cylinder that contains hydrogen gas

Figure 13.6: *Atoms of the same element always have the same number of protons in the nucleus.*

Isotopes

Isotopes All atoms of the same element have the same number of protons in the nucleus. However, atoms of the same element may have different numbers of neutrons in the nucleus. **Isotopes** are atoms of the *same* element that have different numbers of neutrons.

The isotopes of carbon Figure 13.7 shows three isotopes of carbon that exist in nature. Most carbon atoms have six protons and six neutrons in the nucleus. However, some carbon atoms have seven or eight neutrons. They are all carbon atoms because they all contain six protons, but they are different *isotopes* of carbon. The isotopes of carbon are called carbon-12, carbon-13, and carbon-14. The number after the name is called the mass number. The **mass number** of an isotope tells you the number of protons plus the number of neutrons.

VOCABULARY

isotopes - atoms of the same element that have different numbers of neutrons in the nucleus.

mass number - the number of protons plus the number of neutrons in the nucleus.

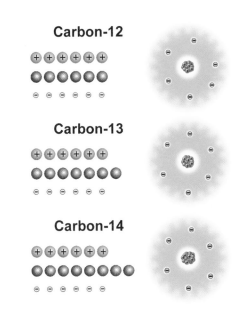

Carbon-12

Carbon-13

Carbon-14

Figure 13.7: *The isotopes of carbon.*

Calculating the number of neutrons in a nucleus

How many neutrons are present in an aluminum atom that has an atomic number of 13 and a mass number of 27?

1. Looking for: You are asked to find the number of neutrons.

2. Given: You are given the atomic number and the mass number.

3. Relationships: Use the relationship: protons + neutrons = mass number.

4. Solution: Plug in and solve: neutrons = 27 − 13 = 14
The aluminum atom has 14 neutrons.

Your turn...

a. How many neutrons are present in a magnesium atom with a mass number of 24? **Answer:** 12

b. Find the number of neutrons in a calcium atom that has a mass number of 40. **Answer:** 20

Radioactivity

What if there are too many neutrons?

Almost all elements have one or more isotopes that are **stable**. *Stable* means the nucleus stays together. For complex reasons, the nucleus of an atom becomes unstable if it contains too many or too few neutrons relative to the number of protons. If the nucleus is unstable, it breaks apart. Carbon has two stable isotopes, carbon-12 and carbon-13. Carbon-14 is **radioactive** because it has an unstable nucleus. An atom of carbon-14 eventually changes into an atom of nitrogen-14.

Radioactivity

If an atomic nucleus is unstable for any reason, the atom eventually changes into a more stable form. Radioactivity is a process in which the nucleus spontaneously emits particles or energy as it changes into a more stable isotope. Radioactivity can change one element into a completely different element. For example, carbon-14 is radioactive and eventually becomes nitrogen-14.

Alpha decay

In *alpha decay*, the nucleus ejects two protons and two neutrons (Figure 13.8). Check the periodic table and you can quickly find that two protons and two neutrons are the nucleus of a helium-4 (He-4) atom. Alpha radiation is actually fast-moving He-4 nuclei. When alpha decay occurs, the atomic number is reduced by two because two protons are removed. The atomic mass is reduced by four because two neutrons go along with the two protons. For example, uranium-238 undergoes alpha decay to become thorium-234.

Beta decay

Beta decay occurs when a neutron in the nucleus splits into a proton and an electron. The proton stays in the nucleus, but the high energy electron is ejected and is called beta radiation. During beta decay, the atomic number increases by one because one new proton is created. The mass number stays the same because the atom lost a neutron but gained a proton.

Gamma decay

Gamma decay is how the nucleus gets rid of excess energy. In gamma decay, the nucleus emits pure energy in the form of gamma rays. The number of protons and neutrons stays the same.

VOCABULARY

stable - a nucleus is stable if it stays together.

radioactive - a nucleus is radioactive if it spontaneously breaks up, emitting particles or energy in the process.

Alpha decay

Nucleus ejects a helium-4 nucleus

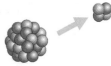

Protons	Decrease by 2
Neutrons	Decrease by 2
Atomic number	Decrease by 2
Mass number	Decrease by 4

Beta decay

Nucleus converts a neutron to a proton and electron, ejecting the electron.

Protons	Increase by 1
Neutrons	Decrease by 1
Atomic number	Increase by 1
Mass number	Stays the same

Figure 13.8: *Two common radioactive decay reactions.*

13.1 Section Review

1. Which of the following statements regarding electric charge is *true*?
   a. A positive charge repels a negative charge and attracts other positive charges.
   b. A positive charge attracts a negative charge and repels other positive charges.
2. Is electric charge a property of just electricity or is charge a property of all atoms?
3. Which of the drawings in Figure 13.9 is the most accurate model of the interior of an atom?
4. There are four forces in nature. Name the four forces and rank them from strongest to weakest.
5. There are three particles inside an atom. One of them has zero electric charge. Which one is it?
6. All atoms of the same element have (choose one)
   a. the same number of neutrons.
   b. the same number of protons.
   c. the same mass.
7. The atomic number is
   a. the number of protons in the nucleus.
   b. the number of neutrons in the nucleus.
   c. the number of neutrons plus protons.
8. The diagram in Figure 13.10 shows three isotopes of the element carbon. Which one is radioactive?
9. *Radioactive* means
   a. an atom gives off radio waves.
   b. the nucleus of an atom is unstable and will eventually change.
   c. the electrons in an atom have too much energy.

● Proton   ● Neutron   ○ Electron

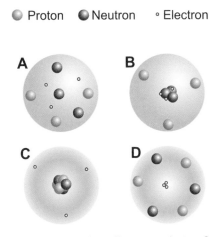

Which best describes a real atom?

Figure 13.9: *Question 3.*

● Proton   ● Neutron   ○ Electron

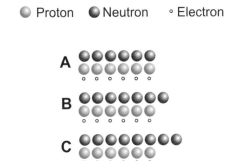

Which one of these shows the particles in a radioactive isotope of carbon?

Figure 13.10: *Question 8.*

13.2 Electrons in the Atom

Atoms interact with each other through their electrons. This is why almost all the properties of the elements (except mass) are due to electrons. Chemical bonds involve only electrons, so electrons determine how atoms combine into compounds. We find a rich variety of matter because electrons inside atoms are organized in unusual and complex patterns. Exactly how electrons create the properties of matter was a puzzle that took bright scientists a long time to figure out!

The spectrum

The spectrum is a pattern of colors
Almost all the light you see comes from atoms. For example, light is given off when electricity passes through the gas in a fluorescent bulb or a neon sign. When scientists look carefully at the light given off by a pure element, they find that the light does not include all colors. Instead, they see a few very specific colors, and the colors are different for different elements (Figure 13.11). Hydrogen has a red line, a green line, a blue line, and a violet line in a characteristic pattern. Helium and lithium have different colors and patterns. Each different element has its own characteristic pattern of colors called a **spectrum**. The colors of clothes, paint, and everything else around you come from this property of elements that allows them to emit or absorb light of only certain colors.

Spectroscopes and spectral lines
Each individual color in a spectrum is called a **spectral line** because each color appears as a line in a **spectroscope**. A spectroscope is a device that spreads light into its different colors. The illustration below shows a spectroscope made with a prism. The spectral lines appear on the screen at the far right.

VOCABULARY

spectrum - the characteristic colors of light given off or absorbed by an element.

spectral line - a bright-colored line in a spectroscope.

spectroscope - an instrument that separates light into a spectrum.

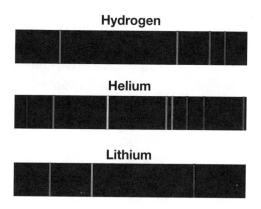

Hydrogen

Helium

Lithium

Figure 13.11: *When light from energized atoms is directed through a prism, spectral lines are observed. Each element has its own distinct pattern of spectral lines.*

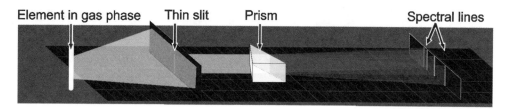

The Bohr model of the atom

Energy and color   In Chapter 10, you learned that light is a form of pure energy that comes in tiny bundles called *photons*. The amount of energy in a photon determines the color of the light. Red light has lower energy and blue light has higher energy. Green and yellow light have energy between red and blue. The fact that atoms only emit certain colors of light tells us that something inside an atom can only have certain values of energy.

Neils Bohr   Danish physicist Neils Bohr proposed the concept of **energy levels** to explain the spectrum of hydrogen. In Bohr's model, the electron in a hydrogen atom must be in a specific energy level. You can think of energy levels like steps on a staircase. You can be on one step or another, but you cannot be between steps except in passing. Electrons must be in one energy level or another and cannot remain in between energy levels. Electrons change energy levels by absorbing or emitting light (Figure 13.12).

Explaining the spectrum   When an electron moves from a higher energy level to a lower one, the atom gives up the energy difference between the two levels. The energy comes out as different colors of light. The specific colors of the spectral lines correspond to the differences in energy between the energy levels. The diagram below shows how the spectral lines of hydrogen come from electrons falling from the third, fourth, fifth, and sixth energy levels down to the second energy level.

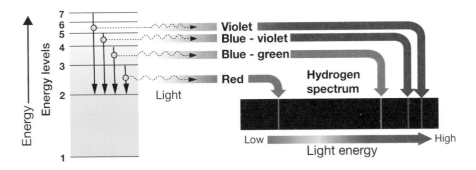

energy level - one of the discrete allowed energies for electrons in an atom.

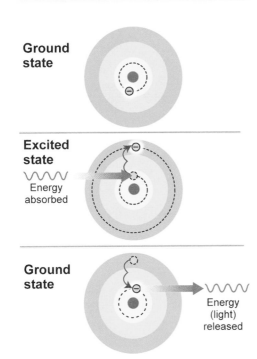

Figure 13.12: *When the right amount of energy is absorbed, an electron in a hydrogen atom jumps to a higher energy level. When the electron falls back to the lower energy, the atom releases the same amount of energy it absorbed. The energy comes out as light of a specific color.*

The quantum theory

Quantum versus classical

Quantum theory says that when things get very small, like the size of an atom, matter and energy do *not* obey Newton's laws or other laws of *classical* physics. That is, the classical laws are not obeyed in the same way as with a larger object, like a baseball. According to the quantum theory, when a particle (such as an electron) is confined to a small space (inside an atom) then the energy, momentum, and other variables of the particle become restricted to certain specific values.

Everything is fuzzy in the quantum world

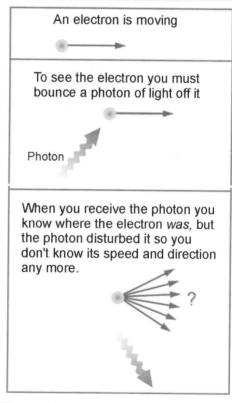

A grain of sand has a definite shape and position

On a much smaller size, an electron has no definite shape

Electron

You are used to thinking of a "particle" like a grain of sand. A sand grain is small but you can easily imagine it has a definite shape, size, position, and speed. According to quantum theory, particles the size of electrons are fundamentally different. Instead, when you look closely, an electron is "smeared out" into a wave-like "cloud." There is no exact position where the entire electron is.

The uncertainty principle

If an electron is spread out into a cloud, how can you locate its exact position in an atom? You can't! The work of German physicist Werner Heisenberg (1901–1976) led to Heisenberg's **uncertainty principle.** According to the uncertainty principle, a particle's position, momentum, energy, and time can never be precisely known.

Understanding the uncertainty principle

The uncertainty principle arises because the quantum world is so small. To "see" an electron you have to bounce a photon of light off it, or interact with the electron in some way (Figure 13.13). Because the electron is so small, even a single photon moves it and changes its motion. That means the moment you use a photon to locate an electron, you push it, so you no longer know precisely how fast it was going. In fact, any process of observing in the quantum world changes the very system you are trying to observe. The uncertainty principle exists because measuring any variable disturbs the others in an unpredictable way.

VOCABULARY

quantum theory - the theory that describes matter and energy at very small (atomic) sizes.

uncertainty principle - it is impossible to know variables exactly in the quantum world.

An electron is moving

To see the electron you must bounce a photon of light off it

Photon

When you receive the photon you know where the electron *was*, but the photon disturbed it so you don't know its speed and direction any more.

?

Figure 13.13: *The act of observing anything in the quantum world means disturbing in unpredictable ways the very thing you are trying to observe.*

Electrons and energy levels

The energy levels are at different distances from the nucleus

The positive nucleus attracts negative electrons like gravity attracts a ball down a hill. The farther down the "hill" an electron slides, the less energy it has. Conversely, electrons have more energy farther up the hill, and away from the nucleus. The higher energy levels are farther from the nucleus and the lower energy levels are closer.

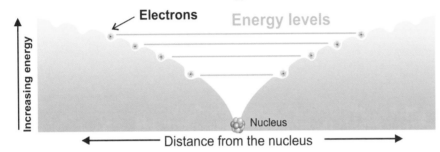

The electron cloud

Bohr's model of electron energy levels was incomplete. Electrons are so fast and light that their exact position within an atom cannot be defined. Remember, in the current model of the atom, we think of the electrons in an atom as moving around the nucleus in an area called an electron cloud. The energy levels occur because electrons in the cloud are at different average distances from the nucleus.

Rules for energy levels

Inside an atom, electrons always obey these rules:

- The energy of an electron must match one of the energy levels in the atom.
- Each energy level can hold only a certain number of electrons, and no more.
- As electrons are added to an atom, they settle into the lowest unfilled energy level.

Quantum mechanics

Energy levels are predicted by *quantum mechanics*, the branch of physics that deals with the microscopic world of atoms. While quantum mechanics is outside the scope of this book, you should know that it is a very accurate theory and it explains energy levels.

Orbitals

The energy levels in an atom are grouped into different shapes called *orbitals*.

The s-orbital

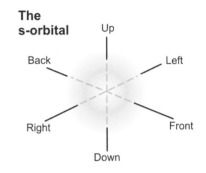

The s-orbital is spherical and holds two electrons. The first two electrons in each energy level are in the s-orbital.

The p-orbitals

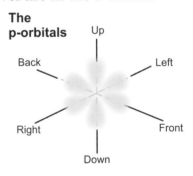

The p-orbitals hold six electrons and are aligned along the three directions on a 3-D graph.

The energy levels in an atom

How electrons fill in the energy levels

The first energy level can accept up to two electrons. The second and third energy levels hold up to eight electrons each. The fourth and fifth energy levels hold 18 electrons (Figure 13.14). A good analogy is to think of the electron cloud like a parking garage in a crowded city. The first level of the garage only has spaces for two cars, just as the first energy level only has spaces for two electrons. The second level of the garage can hold eight cars just as the second energy level can hold eight electrons. Each new car that enters the garage parks in the lowest unfilled space, just as each additional electron occupies the lowest unfilled energy level.

How the energy levels fill

The number of electrons in an atom depends on the atomic number because the number of electrons equals the number of protons. That means each element has a different number of electrons and therefore fills the energy levels to a different point. For example, a helium atom (He) has two electrons (Figure 13.15). The two electrons completely fill up the first energy level (diagram below). The next element is lithium (Li) with three electrons. Since the first energy level only holds two electrons, the third electron must go into the second energy level. The diagram shows the first 10 elements which fill the first and second energy levels.

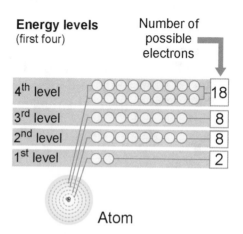

Figure 13.14: *Electrons occupy energy levels around the nucleus. The farther away an electron is from the nucleus, the higher the energy it possesses.*

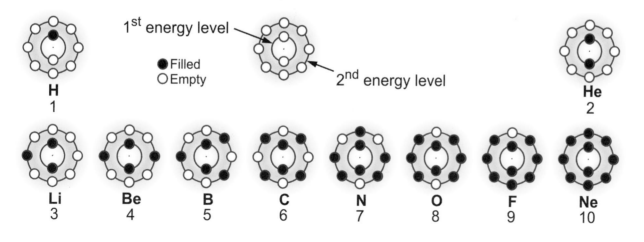

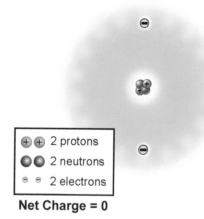

Figure 13.15: *A helium atom has two protons in its nucleus and two electrons.*

13.2 Section Review

1. The pattern of colors given off by a particular atom is called
   a. an orbital.
   b. an energy level.
   c. a spectrum.
2. Which of the diagrams in Figure 13.16 corresponds to the element lithium?
3. When an electron moves from a lower energy level to a higher energy level, the atom
   a. absorbs energy.
   b. gives off light.
   c. becomes a new isotope.
4. Two of the energy levels can hold eight electrons each. Which energy levels are these?
5. How many electrons can fit in the fourth energy level?
6. The element beryllium has four electrons. Which diagram in Figure 13.17 shows how beryllium's electrons are arranged in the first four energy levels?
7. Which two elements have electrons only in the first energy level?
   a. hydrogen and lithium
   b. helium and neon
   c. hydrogen and helium
   d. carbon and oxygen
8. On average, electrons in the fourth energy level are
   a. farther away from the nucleus than electrons in the second energy level.
   b. closer to the nucleus than electrons in the second energy level.
   c. about the same distance from the nucleus as electrons in the second energy level.

Which belongs to lithium?

Figure 13.16: *Question 2.*

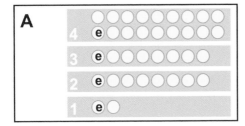

Which is correct for normal beryllium?

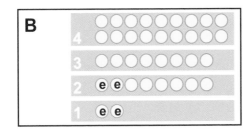

Figure 13.17: *Question 6.*

Aim For the Stars: Dr. Shirley Ann Jackson

What is it like to study something you cannot see, like atoms? What sort of scientist studies atoms? Dr. Shirley Ann Jackson is a well-known scientist. She has studied atoms and the particles inside atoms for several decades. How did Dr. Jackson become an atomic physicist? She's been curious about the way things work for as long as she can remember.

Photo courtesy of Gloria Joseph

Speeding sisters

Brushing sweaty curls back from their faces, 12-year-old Shirley Jackson and her younger sister Gloria steered their homemade go-cart between two others, lining up the front wheels with a chalk line drawn across the alley. A small crowd of kids gathered to watch the three carts race down a steep hill in their Washington, D.C., neighborhood.

The Jackson girls had built their go-cart from old wheels, axles, bicycle handlebars, and other junk parts. Their father provided wood for the base and lessons on using his workshop tools. They had spent hours figuring out ways to make their "hot rod" go faster.

Now Gloria climbed into the cart. Shirley crouched behind, hands on the smaller girl's back. A neighbor kid yelled, "On your mark, get set . . . GO!" and Shirley pushed with all her might, propelling Gloria and the go-cart down the steep hill.

Faster and faster Gloria sped down the hill, cruising across the finish line well ahead of her two competitors. Shirley raced down hill on foot to congratulate her.

But just before she reached her sister, Shirley was stopped in her tracks. A boy in one of the other carts, furious with jealousy, jumped on the Jacksons' hot rod, breaking it in two.

The girls stared at him in disbelief. Gloria blinked back tears. Shirley wanted to smack him. But she took a deep breath, and head held high, she grabbed Gloria's hand.

"We'll be back," she glared. The two of them dragged their broken cart home. With their father's encouragement, they rebuilt it and returned to race again.

It was the summer of 1958. Shirley was about to enter seventh grade. Her high test scores placed her in an honors program with a challenging curriculum. Shirley was one of the school's first African American students to participate.

Directing her path

As she looks back at this time, Dr. Shirley Ann Jackson says four significant factors shaped the direction her life would take. The first two were inherited traits: her father's interest in science and technology and her mother's love of reading.

The other two were national events. In 1954, the supreme court decision, *Brown v. the Board of Education of Topeka, Kansas*, ended the practice of racial segregation in schools, giving Shirley the opportunity for a high-quality education.

In October 1957, the Soviet Union launched a satellite into space. People in the United States were stunned. As Shirley entered high school, an intense interest in attracting young people into math and science careers emerged. Across the country, school boards put money into better science labs. Government and corporations provided college scholarships to talented students. There was a great sense of urgency about doing science.

Shirley enjoyed all her classes, but math was her favorite. She loved the way math could describe patterns and bring to light hidden connections. So when it was time to apply to college, a teacher suggested Massachusetts Institute of Technology—a school known for its excellent math, science, and engineering programs.

It was difficult to get into MIT, but Shirley's father advised her to "Aim for the stars so that you can reach the treetops, and at any rate you will get off the ground."

She did far more than get off the ground. She was accepted to MIT, receiving corporate and community scholarships!

University Life

Shirley was one of 43 women in her freshman class of 900 students, and one of 10 African Americans out of 4,000 undergraduates. Sometimes she felt isolated and lonely. She volunteered in a hospital pediatric ward and tutored children at a local YMCA. This, she says, helped her keep perspective.

At first, Shirley thought she might choose math as her major at MIT. But her favorite freshman class turned out to be Physics: A New Introductory Course (which the students called "PANIC" for short). In PANIC, she discovered the fascinating world of subatomic particles—the tiniest things in the universe.

Shirley enjoyed conducting experiments in the huge physics labs at MIT, which reminded her of the time she had spent in her father's workshop. But what really captured her interest was using mathematics to predict the behavior of subatomic particles. She decided to stay at MIT and pursue a Ph.D. in theoretical high energy particle physics.

In 1973, Shirley Ann Jackson became the first African American woman to receive a Ph.D. from MIT, and one of the first two African American women in the United States to receive a doctorate in physics.

Working in Research, Government, and Education

Dr. Jackson's career in physics has taken many interesting turns. First, she researched subatomic particles at Fermilab near Chicago and CERN in Geneva, Switzerland. Both labs have huge machines called particle accelerators which send particles zooming around at nearly the speed of light and then smash them into each other. By studying the energy released by the collisions, scientists can deduce properties of the subatomic particles, such as their mass and charge.

Next, Dr. Jackson turned her attention to condensed matter physics, working on semiconductors and other material systems at AT&T Bell laboratories.

In 1995, Dr. Jackson was appointed the Chairman of the U.S. Nuclear Regulatory Commission by President Bill Clinton. She worked to increase nuclear plant safety in the United States and with international organizations to enhance worldwide nuclear safety.

Photo courtesy of
Rensselaer Polytechnic Institute

Dr. Jackson became president of Rensselaer Polytechnic Institute in 1999. She was awarded the 2014 National Medal of Science, the highest award for scientific achievement given by the United States.

QUESTIONS

1. Think about the physics involved in Shirley's go-cart races. What force caused the motion? What force resisted motion? What changes do you think the girls made to increase the go-cart's speed?

2. *Resilience* is defined as the ability to bounce back after a painful experience. How did Shirley demonstrate this character trait?

3. Find out more about the particle accelerators at Fermilab or CERN. How large are they? How are they shaped?

To find out more about Dr. Jackson, check out this book: O'Connell, Diane. (2005). *Strong Force: The Story of Physicist Shirley Ann Jackson.* New York: Scholastic, Inc.

Half-Life

Radioactivity is how we describe any process where the nucleus of an atom emits particles or energy. All radioactive elements have a half-life. This means that there is a certain length of time after which half of the radioactive element has decayed. Radioactive elements have an unstable nucleus, which decays into an different type of atom with a more stable nucleus. As it decays, it releases radiation.

Materials:

can of pennies; graph paper

What you will do

Your teacher has given you a can of pennies to represent the atoms of a sample of a newly discovered, radioactive element. You will use the pennies to simulate the process of radioactive decay. Upon completion of the simulation, you will construct a graph of your data.

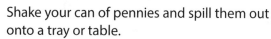

Shake your can of pennies and spill them out onto a tray or table.

1. Remove all pennies that are "heads" up and count them.

2. Record these as decayed atoms in a table like the one shown at right.

3. Put the rest of the pennies back into the can and shake them again.

4. Spill them out onto the tray or table, and again, remove and count the "heads."

5. Repeat this process until there are no pennies left.

Trial	Sample number	Number of decayed atoms
1		
2		
3		
4		
5		
6		
7		
8		
9		
10		

Applying your knowledge

a. Graph your data. The sample number will be on the *x*-axis and the number of decayed atoms per sample will be on the *y*-axis. Label the axes clearly and provide a title for the graph.

b. Describe what your graph looks like.

c. How many trials did it take for half of your original number of pennies to decay to "heads up"?

d. How many trials did it take for all your pennies to decay?

e. Would it make a difference if you graphed the number of "tails" up instead?

f. If you were to put a sticker on one of the pennies and repeat the activity, could you predict in which trial the marked penny would decay?

g. Another student did this activity, and on the third shake 12 pennies decayed. Can you tell how many pennies the other student started with?

Chapter 13 Assessment

Vocabulary

Select the correct term to complete the sentences.

atomic number	electron	elementary charge
energy level	isotopes	mass number
neutron	nucleus	spectral line
quantum theory	radioactive	spectroscope

Section 13.1

1. The sum of protons plus neutrons in the nucleus of an atom is known as the ____.

2. The negatively charged particle found outside the nucleus of an atom is called a(n) ____.

3. The core of the atom containing most of the atom's mass and all of its positive charge is called a(n) ____.

4. The smallest unit of electric charge that is possible in ordinary matter is called a(n) ____.

5. A neutral particle with nearly the same mass as the proton is the ____.

6. The number of protons in an atom, unique to each element is known as the ____.

7. A nucleus that spontaneously breaks apart, emitting particles or energy is referred to as ____.

8. Atoms of the same element containing different numbers of neutrons are called ____.

Section 13.2

9. One of the allowed energies for electrons in an atom is known as a(n) ____.

10. The theory that describes matter and energy at atomic sizes is the ____.

11. A bright colored line produced by a spectroscope is a(n) ____.

12. An instrument that is used to separate light into spectral lines is a(n) ____.

Concepts

Section 13.1

1. Explain why Rutherford assumed most of the atom to be empty space.

2. Explain how Rutherford concluded that positive charge was concentrated in a small area.

3. How did Rutherford's model of the atom differ from Thomson's model?

4. Summarize the characteristics of the electron, proton, and neutron, comparing their relative mass, charge, and location within the atom by completing the table below.

Particle	Place in Atom	Charge	Relative Mass
electron	?	?	1
proton	?	+1	?
neutron	?	?	?

5. Name the four forces of nature and compare their relative strengths.

6. Explain the effect of the electromagnetic and strong forces on the structure of the atom.

7. What do the atomic number and mass number tell you about an atom?

8. Compare the number of protons and electrons in a neutral atom.

9. Compare the mass number and atomic number for isotopes of an element. Explain your answer.

10. Describe the radioactive disintegrations known as alpha, beta, and gamma decay.

Section 13.2

11. Which particle in an atom is most responsible for its chemical properties?

12. What is the source of the light you see?

13. How can a spectroscope be used to identify an element heated to incandescence?

14. Cite evidence that atoms are restricted to have only certain amounts of energy.

15. How did Neils Bohr explain spectral lines?

16. What is the difference between an electron in ground state and one in an excited state?

17. What would occur if electrons were to move from a certain energy level to a lower energy level?

18. Summarize the uncertainty principle.

19. Why can't the position of an electron be determined with certainty?

20. How is the location of an electron described?

Problems

Section 13.1

1. Which of the following charges do *not* appear in normal matter?

    a. +2e   d. −5.4e
    b. +1/4e   e. +3/4e
    c. −4e   f. −1e

2. What charge would an atom have if it lost one electron?

3. A neutral atom has seven protons and eight neutrons. Determine its

    a. mass number.
    b. atomic number.
    c. number of electrons.

4. A carbon atom contains 6 protons in the nucleus. If an atom of carbon-14 were to undergo alpha decay, determine each of the following for the new element.

    a. mass number
    b. atomic number
    c. number of protons
    d. number of neutrons

5. A uranium atom contains 92 protons in the nucleus. If an atom of uranium-238 were to undergo alpha decay, determine each of the following for the new element.

    a. mass number
    b. atomic number
    c. number of protons
    d. number of neutrons

Section 13.2

6. If electrons in the hydrogen atom become excited and then fall back to the second energy level from levels 3, 4, 5, and 6, four colors of light are emitted: violet, red, blue-violet and blue-green.

    a. Which transition is responsible for the blue-violet light: 6 to 2, 5 to 2, 4 to 2, or 3 to 2?

    b. If an electron on the second level were struck by a photon, then it could be excited to the sixth energy level. What color photon would be absorbed by the electron?

7. An atom has an atomic number of 6. Sketch a diagram that correctly represents the electron arrangement in energy levels around the nucleus.

Elements and the Periodic Table

What are metals like? Think of things that are made with metals like aluminum, copper, iron, and gold. What do they have in common? They are usually shiny, and they can often be bent into different shapes without breaking. Did you know there is a metal that is shiny, but is so soft it can be cut with a knife? This metal is very reactive. If you place a piece of this metal in water, it will race around the surface, and the heat given off is often enough to melt the metal and ignite the hydrogen gas that is produced! This strange metal is called sodium. You can look at the periodic table of elements to find other metals that behave like sodium. In this chapter, you will become familiar with how you can predict the properties of different elements by their location on the periodic table.

Key Questions:

1. How are the elements arranged in the periodic table?

2. What sort of information can the periodic table of elements give you?

3. Why does the periodic table have the shape that it does?

14.1 **The Periodic Table of the Elements**

Long before scientists understood atoms, they grouped elements by their chemical properties. In this section, you will learn how the *periodic table* gives us a way to organize all the known elements. The periodic table also shows how chemical properties are related to the arrangement of electrons inside the atom.

Physical and chemical properties

Physical properties
Properties that you can measure or see through direct observation are called **physical properties**. For example, water is a colorless, odorless substance that exists as a liquid at room temperature. Gold is shiny, exists as a solid at room temperature, and can be hammered into very thin sheets. Physical properties include color, texture, density, brittleness, and state (solid, liquid, or gas). Melting point, boiling point, and specific heat are also physical properties.

Physical changes are reversible
Physical changes, such as melting, boiling, or bending, are usually *reversible*. When water freezes, it undergoes a physical change from a liquid to a solid. This does not change the water into a new substance. It is still water, only in solid form. The change can easily be reversed by melting the water. Bending a steel bar is another physical change. Bending changes the shape of the bar, but it is still steel.

Chemical properties
Properties that can only be observed when one substance changes into a different substance are called **chemical properties**. For example, if you leave an iron nail outside, it will eventually rust (Figure 14.1). A chemical property of iron is that it reacts with oxygen in the air to form iron oxide (rust).

Chemical changes are hard to reverse
Any change that transforms one substance into a different substance is called a *chemical change*. The transformation of iron into rust is a chemical change. Chemical changes are not easily reversible. Rusted iron will not turn shiny again even if you remove it from the oxygen in the air.

VOCABULARY

physical properties - characteristics of matter that can be seen through direct observation such as density, melting point, and boiling point.

chemical properties - characteristics of matter that can only be observed when one substance changes into a different substance, such as iron into rust.

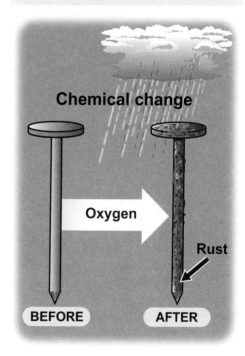

Figure 14.1: *Rusting is an example of a chemical change.*

The periodic table

How many elements are there? Humans have long wondered how many elements make up our universe. The only way to tell if a substance is an element is to try and break it down into other substances by any possible means. A substance that can be chemically broken apart cannot be an element. As of this writing, scientists have identified 118 different elements, and five more are expected to be confirmed in the near future. Only about 90 of these elements occur naturally. The others are made in laboratories.

The modern periodic table As chemists worked on finding the true elements, they noticed that some elements acted like other elements. For example, the soft metals lithium, sodium, and potassium always combine with oxygen in a ratio of two atoms of metal per atom of oxygen (Figure 14.2). By keeping track of how each element combined with other elements, scientists began to recognize repeating patterns. From this data, they developed the first periodic table of the elements. The **periodic table** organizes the elements according to how they combine with other elements (chemical properties).

Organization of the periodic table

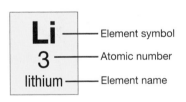

The periodic table is organized in order of increasing atomic number. The lightest element (hydrogen) is at the upper left. The heaviest (No. 118) is on the lower right. Each element corresponds to one box in the periodic table, identified with the element symbol.

The periodic table is further divided into *periods* and *groups*. Each horizontal row is called a **period**. Across any period, the properties of the elements gradually change. Each vertical column is called a **group**. Groups of elements have similar properties. The *main group elements* are Groups 1–2 and 13–18 (the tall columns of the periodic table). Elements in Groups 3 through 12 are called the *transition elements*. The inner transition elements, called lanthanides and actinides, are usually put below to fit on a page.

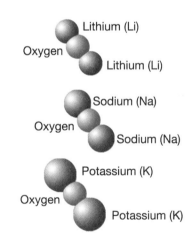

Figure 14.2: *The metals lithium, sodium, and potassium all form compounds with a ratio of 2 atoms of the metal to 1 atom of oxygen. All the elements in Group 1 of the periodic table form similar compounds.*

Reading the periodic table

Metals, nonmetals, and metalloids

Most of the elements are metals. A **metal** is typically shiny, opaque, and a good conductor of heat and electricity as a pure element. Metals are also ductile, which means they can be bent into different shapes without breaking. With the exception of hydrogen, the nonmetals are on the right side of the periodic table. **Nonmetals** are poor conductors of heat and electricity. Solid nonmetals are brittle and appear dull. The elements on the border between metals and nonmetals are called *Metalloids*. Silicon is an example of a metalloid element with properties in between those of metals and nonmetals.

VOCABULARY

metal - elements that are typically shiny and good conductors of heat and electricity.

nonmetal - elements that are poor conductors of heat and electricity.

Periodic Table of the Elements

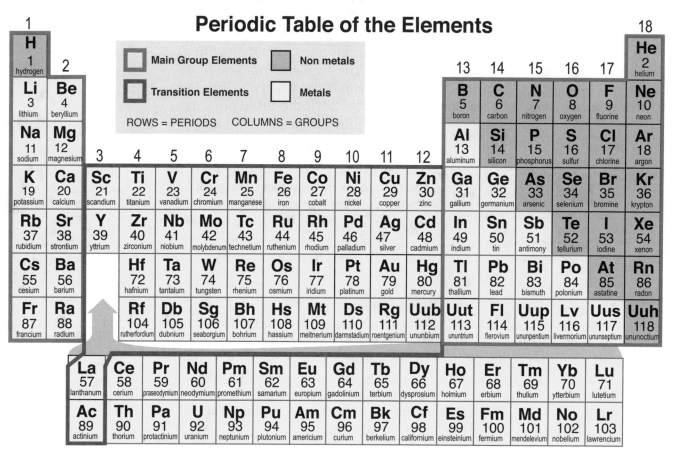

Atomic mass

Atomic mass units   The mass of individual atoms is so small that the numbers are difficult to work with. To make calculations easier, scientists came up with the **atomic mass unit** (amu). One atomic mass unit is about the mass of a single proton (or a neutron). In laboratory units, 1 amu is 1.66×10^{-24} grams. That's 0.00000000000000000000000166 grams!

Atomic mass and isotopes   The **atomic mass** is the *average* mass (in amu) of an atom of each element. Atomic masses differ from mass numbers because most elements in nature contain more than one isotope (see chart below). For example, the atomic mass of lithium is 6.94 amu. That does *not* mean there are 3 protons and 3.94 neutrons in a lithium atom! On average, out of every 100 g of lithium, 94 grams are Li-7 and 6 grams are Li-6 (Figure 14.3). The *average* atomic mass of lithium is 6.94, because of the mixture of isotopes.

atomic mass unit - a unit of mass equal to 1.66×10^{-24} grams, which is one twelfth the mass of the isotope carbon-12.

atomic mass - the average mass of all the known isotopes of an element, expressed in amu.

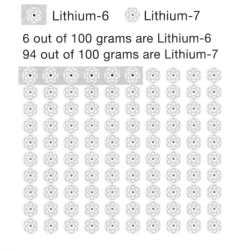

Lithium-6   Lithium-7

6 out of 100 grams are Lithium-6
94 out of 100 grams are Lithium-7

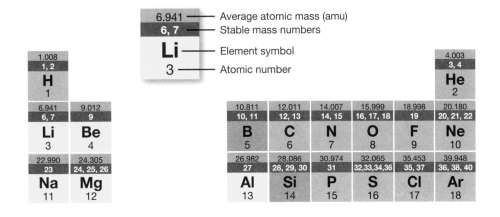

Figure 14.3: *Naturally occurring elements have a mixture of isotopes.*

Groups of the periodic table

Alkali metals

The different groups of the periodic table have similar chemical properties. For example the first group is known as the **alkali metals**. This group includes the elements lithium (Li), sodium (Na), and potassium (K). The alkali metals are soft and silvery in their pure form and are highly reactive. Each of them combines in a ratio of two to one with oxygen. For example, lithium oxide has two atoms of lithium per atom of oxygen.

Group 2 metals

The group two metals include beryllium (Be), magnesium (Mg), and calcium (Ca). These metals also form oxides however they combine one-to-one with oxygen. For example, beryllium oxide has one beryllium atom per oxygen atom.

Halogens

The **halogens** are on the opposite side of the periodic table. These elements tend to be toxic gases or liquids in their pure form. Some examples are fluorine (F), chlorine (Cl), and bromine (Br). The halogens are also very reactive and are rarely found in pure form. When combined with alkali metals, they form salts such as sodium chloride (NaCl) and potassium chloride (KCl).

Noble gases

On the far right of the periodic table are the **noble gases**, including the elements helium (He), neon (Ne), and argon (Ar). These elements do not naturally form chemical bonds with other atoms and are almost always found in their pure state. They are sometimes called *inert gases* for this reason.

Transition metals

In the middle of the periodic table are the transition metals, including titanium (Ti), iron (Fe), and copper (Cu). These elements are usually good conductors of heat and electricity. For example, the wires that carry electricity in your school are made of copper.

VOCABULARY

alkali metals - elements in the first group of the periodic table.

halogens - elements in the group containing fluorine, chlorine, and bromine, among others.

noble gases - elements in the group containing helium, neon, and argon, among others.

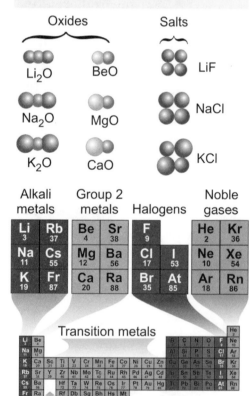

Energy levels and the periodic table

Row 1 is the first energy level
The periods (rows) of the periodic table correspond to the energy levels in the atom (Figure 14.4). The first energy level can accept up to two electrons. Hydrogen has one electron and helium has two. These two elements complete the first period.

Row 2 is the second energy level
The next element, lithium (Li), has three electrons. Lithium begins the second period because the third electron goes into the second energy level. The second energy level can hold eight electrons so there are eight elements in the second row of the periodic table, ending with neon. Neon (Ne) has 10 electrons, which completely fills the second energy level.

Row 3 is the third energy level
Sodium (Na) has 11 electrons, and starts the third period because the 11th electron goes into the third energy level. We know of elements with up to 118 electrons. These elements have their outermost electrons in the seventh energy level.

Outer electrons
As we will see in the next chapter, the outermost electrons in an atom are the ones that interact with other atoms. The outer electrons are the ones in the highest energy level. Electrons in the completely filled inner energy levels do not participate in forming chemical bonds.

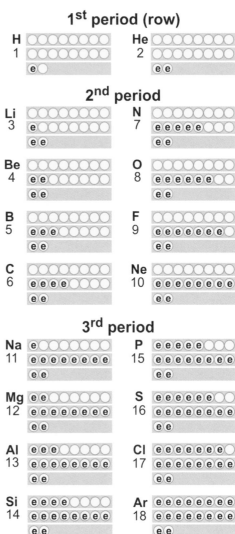

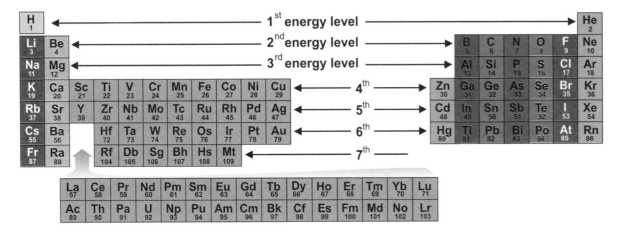

Figure 14.4: *The rows (periods) of the periodic table correspond to the energy levels for the electrons in an atom.*

14.1 Section Review

1. Which of the following (pick 2) are physical properties of matter and *not* chemical properties?
   a. melts at 650°C
   b. density of 1.0 g/mL
   c. forms molecules with two oxygen atoms
2. Groups of the periodic table correspond to elements with
   a. the same color.
   b. the same atomic number.
   c. similar chemical properties.
   d. similar numbers of neutrons.
3. Which element is the atom in Figure 14.5?
4. Name three elements that have similar chemical properties to oxygen.
5. The atomic mass unit (amu) is
   a. the mass of a single atom of carbon.
   b. one millionth of a gram.
   c. approximately the mass of a proton.
   d. approximately the mass of electron.
6. Which element belongs in the empty space in Figure 14.6?
7. The outermost electrons of the element vanadium (atomic No. 23) are in which energy level of the atom? How do you know?
8. The elements fluorine, chlorine, and, bromine are in which group of the periodic table?
   a. the alkali metals
   b. the oxygen-like elements
   c. the halogens
   d. the noble gases
9. Which three metals are in the third period (row) of the periodic table?

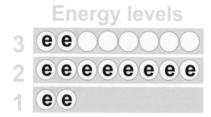

Energy levels

What element is this?

Figure 14.5: *Question 3.*

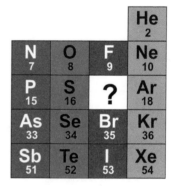

Figure 14.6: *Question 6.*

14.2 Properties of the Elements

The elements have a wide variety of chemical and physical properties. Some are solid at room temperature, like copper. Others are liquid (like bromine) or gas (like oxygen). Some solid elements (like zinc) melt at very low temperatures and some melt at very high temperatures (like titanium). Chemically, there is an equally wide variety of properties. Some elements, like sodium, form salts that dissolve easily in water. Other elements, like neon, do not form compounds with any other elements.

Room temperature appearance

Most elements are solid at room temperature

Most of the pure elements are solid at room temperature. Only 11 of the 92 naturally occurring elements are a gas, and 10 of the 11 are found on the far right of the periodic table. Only two elements (Br and Hg) are liquid at room temperature.

What this tells us about intermolecular forces

An element is solid when intermolecular forces are strong enough to overcome the thermal motion of atoms. At room temperature, this is true for most of the elements. The noble gases and elements to the far right of the periodic table are the exception. *These elements have completely filled or nearly filled energy levels* (Figure 14.7). When an energy level is completely filled the electrons do not interact strongly with electrons in other atoms, reducing the forces that hold atoms together.

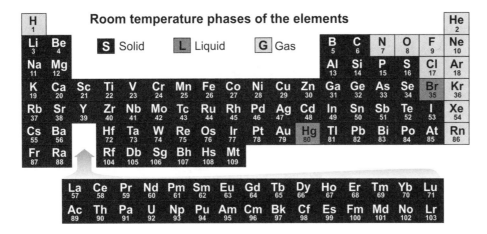

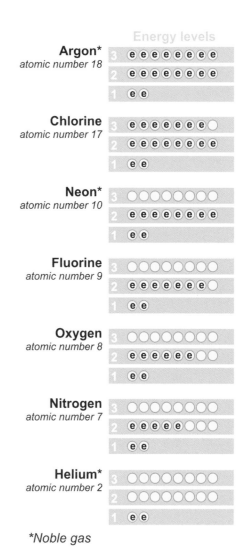

Figure 14.7: *The noble gases have completely filled energy levels. All of the elements that are gas at room temperature have filled or nearly filled energy levels.*

Periodic properties of the elements

The pattern in melting and boiling points
We said earlier that the periodic table arranges elements with common properties in groups (columns). The diagram below shows the melting and boiling points for the first 36 elements. The first element in each row always has a low melting point (Li, Na, K). The melting (and boiling) points rise toward the center of each row and then decrease again.

Periodicity
The pattern of melting and boiling points is an example of **periodicity**. Periodicity means properties repeat each period (row) of the periodic table (Figure 14.8). Periodicity tells us a property is strongly related to the filling of electron energy levels. Melting points reflect the strength of forces between molecules. The diagram shows that these forces are strongest when energy levels are about half full (or half empty). Elements with half filled energy levels have the greatest number of electrons that can participate in bonding.

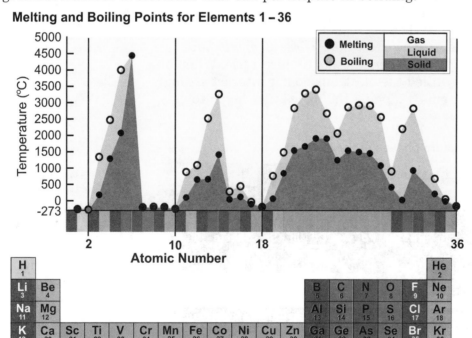

Melting and Boiling Points for Elements 1–36

periodicity - the repeating pattern of chemical and physical properties of the elements.

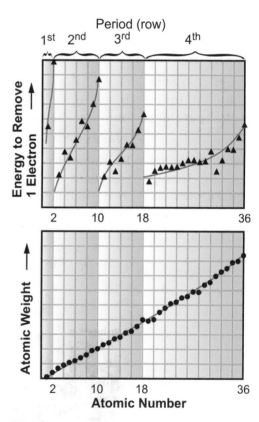

Figure 14.8: *One of these graphs shows periodicity and the other does not. Can you tell which one is periodic? The top graph shows the energy it takes to remove an electron. The bottom graph shows the atomic weight.*

Thermal and electrical conductivity

Metals are good electrical conductors

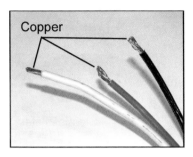

Electricity is something we often take for granted because we use it every day. Fundamentally, electricity is the movement of electric charge, usually electrons. Some materials allow electrons to flow easily through them. If you connected a battery and a bulb through one of these materials, the bulb would light. We call these materials **electrical conductors**. Copper and aluminum are excellent electrical conductors. Both belong to the family of metals, which are elements in the center and left-hand side of the periodic table (Figure 14.9). Copper and aluminum are used for almost all electrical wiring.

Metals are good conductors of heat

If you hold one end of a copper pipe with your hand and heat the other end with a torch, your hand will quickly get hot. That is because copper is a good conductor of heat as well as electricity. Like copper, most metals are good **thermal conductors**. That is one reason pots and pans are made of metal. Heat from a stove can pass easily through the metal walls of a pot to transfer energy to the food inside.

Nonmetals are typically insulators

Elements to the far right of the periodic table are not good conductors of electricity or heat, especially since many are gases. Because they are so different from metals, these elements are called *nonmetals*. Nonmetals make good *insulators*. An insulator is a material that slows down or stops the flow of either heat or electricity. Air is a good insulator. Air is made of oxygen, nitrogen, and argon.

VOCABULARY

electrical conductor - a material that allows electricity to flow through easily.

thermal conductor - a material that allows heat to flow easily.

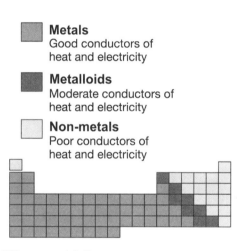

Metals
Good conductors of heat and electricity

Metalloids
Moderate conductors of heat and electricity

Non-metals
Poor conductors of heat and electricity

Figure 14.9: *Dividing the periodic table into metals, metalloids, and nonmetals.*

Metals and metal alloys

Steel is an alloy of iron and carbon
When asked for an example of a metal, many people immediately think of **steel**. Steel is made from iron, which is the fourth most abundant element in the Earth's crust. However, steel is not pure iron. Steel is an *alloy*. An alloy is a solid mixture of one or more elements. Most metals are used as alloys and not in their pure elemental form. Common steel contains mostly iron with a small percentage of carbon. Stainless steel and high-strength steel alloys also contain small percentages of other elements such as chromium, manganese, and vanadium. More that 500 different types of steel are in everyday use (Figure 14.10).

Aluminum is light
Aluminum is a metal widely used for structural applications. Aluminum alloys are not quite as strong as steel, but aluminum has one third the density of steel. Aluminum alloys are used when weight is a factor, such as for airplane construction. The frames and skins of airplanes are built of aluminum alloys (Figure 14.11).

Titanium is both strong and light

Titanium combines the strength and hardness of steel with the light weight of aluminum. Titanium alloys are used for military aircraft, racing bicycles, and other high performance machines. Titanium is expensive because it is somewhat rare and difficult to work with.

Brass

Brass is a hard, gold-colored metal alloy. Ordinary (yellow) brass is an alloy of 72 percent copper, 24 percent zinc, 3 percent lead, and 1 percent tin. Hinges, door knobs, keys, and decorative objects are made of brass because brass is easy to work with. Because it contains lead, however, you should never eat or drink from anything made of ordinary (yellow) brass.

VOCABULARY

steel - an alloy of iron and carbon.

Stainless steel kitchen knife (does not rust)

Ordinary steel nails (will rust)

Figure 14.10: *Nails are made of steel that contains 95 percent iron and 5 percent carbon. Kitchen knives are made of stainless steel that is an alloy containing vanadium and other metals.*

Figure 14.11: *This aircraft is made mostly from aluminum alloys. Aluminum combines high strength and light weight.*

Carbon and carbon-like elements

Carbon is an important element for life

Carbon represents less than 1/100th of a percent of the Earth's crust by mass, yet it is the element most essential for life on our planet. Virtually all the molecules that make up plants and animals are constructed around carbon. The chemistry of carbon is so important it has its own name, organic chemistry (Figure 14.12), which is the subject of Chapter 18.

Diamond and graphite

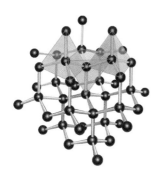

Pure carbon is found in nature in two very different forms. Graphite is a black solid made of carbon that becomes a slippery powder when ground up. Graphite is used for lubricating locks and keys. Diamond is also pure carbon. Diamond is the hardest natural substance known and also has the highest thermal conductivity of any material. Diamond is so strong because every carbon atom in diamond is bonded to four neighboring atoms in a tetrahedral crystal.

Silicon

Directly under carbon on the periodic table is the element silicon. Silicon is the second most abundant element in the Earth's crust, second only to oxygen. Like carbon, silicon has four electrons in its outermost energy level. This means silicon can also make bonds with four other atoms. Sand, rocks, and minerals are predominantly made from silicon and oxygen (Figure 14.13). Most gemstones, such as rubies and emeralds, are compounds of silicon and oxygen with traces of other elements. In fact, when you see a glass window, you are looking at (or through) pure silica (SiO_2).

Silicon and semiconductors

Perhaps silicon's most famous application today is for making semiconductors. Virtually every computer chip and electronic device uses crystals of very pure silicon (Figure 14.14). The area around San Jose, California, is known as Silicon Valley because of the electronics companies located there. Germanium, the element just below silicon on the periodic table, is also used to make semiconductors.

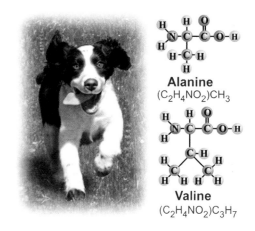

Alanine
($C_2H_4NO_2$)CH_3

Valine
($C_2H_4NO_2$)C_3H_7

Figure 14.12: *Organic chemistry is the chemistry of living organisms and is based on the element carbon.*

Glass

Examples of silica (SiO_2)

Sand

Figure 14.13: *Sand and glass are two common materials based on silicon.*

Figure 14.14: *Microelectronics are constructed on crystals of pure silicon.*

Nitrogen, oxygen, and phosphorus

Nitrogen and oxygen make up most of the atmosphere

Nitrogen is a colorless, tasteless, and odorless gas that makes up 77 percent of Earth's atmosphere. Oxygen makes up another 21 percent of the atmosphere (Figure 14.15). Both oxygen and nitrogen gas consist of molecules with two atoms (N_2, O_2).

Oxygen in rocks and minerals

Oxygen is only 21 percent of the atmosphere, however oxygen is by far the most abundant element in Earth's crust. Almost 46 percent of the Earth's crust is oxygen (Figure 14.16). Because it is so reactive, all of this oxygen is bonded to other elements in rocks and minerals in the form of oxides. Silicon dioxide (SiO_2), calcium oxide (CaO), aluminum oxide (Al_2O_3), and magnesium oxide (MgO) are common mineral compounds. Hematite, an oxide of iron (Fe_2O_3), is a common ore from which iron is extracted.

Liquid nitrogen

With a boiling point of –196°C, liquid nitrogen is used for rapid freezing in medical and industrial applications. A common treatment for skin warts is to freeze them with liquid nitrogen.

Oxygen and nitrogen in living organisms

Oxygen and nitrogen are crucial to living animals and plants. For example, proteins and DNA both contain nitrogen. Nitrogen is part of a key ecological cycle. Bacteria in soil convert nitrogen dioxide (NO_2) in the soil into complex proteins and amino acids. These nutrients are taken up by the roots of plants, and later eaten by animals. Waste and dead tissue from animals is recycled by the soil bacteria that return the nitrogen to begin a new cycle.

Phosphorus

Directly below nitrogen in the periodic table is phosphorus. Phosphorus is a key ingredient of DNA, the molecule responsible for carrying the genetic code in all living creatures. Like nitrogen and oxygen, phosphorus is vital to plant nutrition, and its primary use by industry is in agricultural fertilizer.

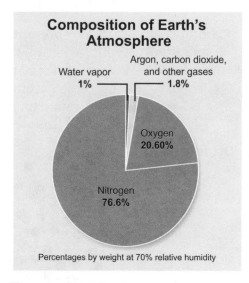

Figure 14.15: *The Earth's atmosphere is predominantly nitrogen and oxygen.*

Figure 14.16: *Oxygen makes up 46 percent of the mass of Earth's crust. This enormous quantity of oxygen is bound up in rocks and minerals.*

14.2 Section Review

1. Name two elements that are liquid at room temperature.
2. Which of the following is *not* true about the noble gases?
   a. They have completely filled energy levels.
   b. They have weak intermolecular forces.
   c. They do not bond with other elements in nature.
   d. They have boiling points above room temperature.
3. Describe what it means if a chemical or physical property is periodic.
4. Name three elements that are good conductors of electricity.
5. Name three elements that are good conductors of heat.
6. A metalloid is an element that
   a. has properties between those of a metal and a nonmetal.
   b. is a good thermal conductor but a poor electrical conductor.
   c. is a good electrical conductor but a poor thermal conductor.
   d. belongs to the same group as carbon in the periodic table.
7. Steel is a metallic-like material but is not a pure element. What is steel?
8. Almost all of the oxygen on the planet Earth is found in the atmosphere. Is this statement true or false?
9. This element is abundant in Earth's crust and combines with oxygen to form rocks and minerals. Which element is it?
10. An element that has strong intermolecular forces is most likely to have
    a. a boiling point below room temperature.
    b. a melting point below room temperature.
    c. a boiling point very close to its melting point.
    d. a very high melting point.
11. Which element in Figure 14.17 is likely to be a good conductor of electricity?
12. Which element in Figure 14.17 is likely to be a good insulator?

One of the elements with atomic number less than 54 does not exist in nature. It was created in the laboratory. Which element is this and how was it discovered?

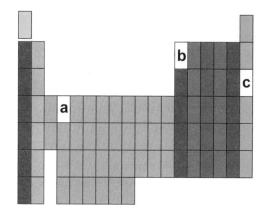

Figure 14.17: *Questions 11 and 12.*

Digging for Gold

Look around the room you're in. Can you find any objects containing gold?

Most people, when asked this question, look for jewelry. Necklaces and rings are easy places to find gold. But if you pointed to a computer, a telephone jack, or a wheelchair, you would also be correct. The physical properties of gold make it useful in surprising ways. You can find gold in astronaut gear, airplane windshields, and even in some people's eyelids!

Soft gold

If you had a lump of pure gold in your hand, you would be able to squish it easily with pliers. Scientists call this property malleability. Because it is so malleable, gold is useless for jewelry unless it is combined with other metals—usually silver and copper. Have you heard of "14 karat gold"? This means that the "gold" is 14/24ths gold and 10/24ths something else. Pure gold is 24 karat.

The malleability of pure gold is useful in other ways. Pure gold can be hammered into thin sheets only 1,000 atoms thick! One cubic centimeter of gold can be pounded into a sheet stretching out over three square meters.

Typically, a thicker one-square meter sheet of gold foil is formed. This thickness is easier to handle and more durable. Pure gold foil, also known as gold leaf, covers the domes of important public buildings like the New York Metropolitan Opera House. Prized for its beauty, gold leaf also lasts a lot longer than paint.

You can also take a lump of gold and draw it out into a thin wire. Scientists call this property ductility. An ounce of gold can be shaped into a wire five miles long!

A great conductor

Gold is a great conductor of both heat and electricity. This means that very small currents can travel along thin gold wires at a wide range of temperatures. Why should you care about this? For one thing, there's a gold plated membrane in the mouthpiece of your cell phone that helps turn the sound of your voice into an electrical current. Without it, your cell phone might fail you in very hot or cold weather.

There are two metals that have similar thermal and electrical conductivity to gold: silver and copper. They are less expensive than gold, so why aren't they used in your cell phone instead?

Here's the reason: silver turns black and copper turns green when exposed to air for awhile. This process is called tarnishing. It happens because these metals undergo a chemical reaction with substances in the air. The tarnish disrupts the flow of electrons and also acts as an insulator, holding in heat.

Gold is non-reactive in air

Gold, on the other hand, doesn't react with substances in air. As a result, it's often used for electrical contacts in items that are frequently unplugged and plugged back in, like telephone jacks and computer connectors.

Gold wire is used to connect the microprocessor to the controls of an electric wheelchair. Wheelchairs have to survive exposure to rain, salt water, high and low temperatures, and constant use. Gold holds up under these conditions better than any other metal.

Eye doctors have found another use for gold. Accidents or diseases sometimes prevent an eyelid from fully closing. If the cornea dries out, infection or blindness can result. Eye doctors can solve this problem by implanting a thin strip of gold into the upper eyelid. Tiny muscles contract to open the eyelid. When those muscles relax, the weight of the gold causes the eyelid to drop fully closed.

Gold is used for two reasons: its high density and malleability mean that just a small thin strip is needed, and gold does not react with body substances like blood or tears, so it won't break down over time.

However, doctors are now searching for a new material to use. The reason? People with metal implanted in their bodies can't have MRI scans. If doctors could find a non-metal alternative to gold, people with eyelid implants would still have access to this valuable diagnostic tool.

Gold reflectors

There is no metal that reflects infrared energy better than gold. Gold is used to coat the face shield on an astronaut's helmet, providing protection from the sun's strong rays. It's also used to coat the windows of airplane cockpits. The coating keeps the crew cooler when the plane is sitting on hot tarmac. An electric current runs through the gold coating during cold weather to melt frost and prevent fogging.

QUESTIONS

1. Now that you have read this Connection, look around the room again. Can you name two more objects that contain gold?

2. List four important physical properties of gold. Compare/contrast these with another common natural product, rubber.

3. You have learned about how gold is used in everyday objects. It also has some interesting high-tech uses. Find out how gold is used in the world's largest telescope at the Keck observatory in Hawaii, or why gold-coated mylar sheets are wrapped around satellites.

Astronaut photo courtesy of NASA.

Name That Element

Each element on the periodic table has a chemical symbol that is an abbreviation of the element's name. Unlike the abbreviations for a U.S. state, these symbol-abbreviations are not always obvious. Many are derived from the element's name in a language such as Latin or German. The chemical symbol for silver is Ag. Note that the first letter in the symbol is upper case and the second is lower case. Writing symbols this way allows us to represent all of the elements without getting confused. There is a big difference between the element cobalt, with its symbol Co, and the compound carbon monoxide, written as CO. In this activity, you'll make a set of flashcards for 30 elements and then play a game to see who in your class knows their elements.

Materials:

30 blank 8 × 10 cards and markers

What you will do

1. Each person in the class writes the symbol of one of the elements from the list on one of the large cards. Make sure you write the chemical symbol large enough so you can see it all the way across the classroom. The elements suggested below are some of the most common elements.

C	Cu	O	N	He
H	Cl	Mg	Na	K
S	Ca	Mn	Fe	Br
B	Cs	Ag	Au	Pb
I	Si	Al	F	Ne
Ba	Be	Cr	Ni	Hg

2. The teacher collects all the cards and stands in front of the class.

3. The first two players stand next to each other. The teacher holds up a chemical symbol card and the first player to correctly give the name of the element moves on to the next player. The player who didn't answer sits down.

4. The game goes all the way around the classroom, with the player who names the element moving on and the other player sitting down.

5. The player who is left standing at the end of the game is the winner.

Applying your knowledge

a. Find the element whose chemical symbol comes from the Latin word *aurum* which means "shining dawn."

b. What word does the chemical symbol for lead, Pb, come from?

c. Find the element whose chemical symbol comes from the Latin word *natrium*.

d. Which element comes from the Latin word for coal?

e. Another game to play is to see who can come up with the longest word spelled completely with chemical symbols. Some examples are *life*, from lithium (Li) and iron (Fe), and *brook*, from bromine (Br), oxygen (O), and potassium (K).

Chapter 14 Assessment

Vocabulary

Select the correct term to complete the sentences.

group	chemical properties	insulator
period	periodicity	nonmetals
physical properties	steel	periodic table
atomic mass	electrical conductor	thermal conductor

Section 14.1

1. A chart that organizes elements by their chemical properties and increasing atomic number is the ____.

2. Characteristics of matter that can be seen through direct observation are called ____.

3. A row of the periodic table is referred to as a(n) ____.

4. Characteristics of matter that can be observed only as one substance changes to another are called ____.

5. A column of the periodic table is known as a(n) ____.

6. The average mass of all known isotopes of an element, expressed in amu, is the ____.

7. Elements that are generally poor conductors, are in a solid form, and are generally dull and brittle are called ____.

Section 14.2

8. A repeating pattern of chemical and physical properties of the elements is called ____.

9. A material that allows heat to flow easily is called ____.

10. A material that slows or stops the flow of heat or electricity is called a(n) ____.

11. An alloy of iron and carbon is called ____.

12. A material that allows electricity to flow easily is a(n) ____.

Concepts

Section 14.1

1. Label each of the following changes or properties as being a physical (*P*) or chemical (*C*) property.
   a. One cm^3 of water has a mass of one gram.
   b. Burning hydrogen in the presence of oxygen produces water.
   c. Candle wax will melt when heated gently.
   d. An iron nail left outside for a year will rust.
   e. To raise the temperature of 1 kg of lead 1°C requires 130 joules of energy.
   f. If ice is heated enough, the ice will change to steam.

2. Melting, boiling, and bending are considered physical changes, but burning is a chemical change. Explain why this is so.

3. How may a substance be tested to determine whether or not it is an element?

4. Supply the missing number for each of the following.
   a. The number of naturally occurring elements.
   b. The atomic number of the heaviest element.
   c. The atomic number of the lightest element.
   d. The total number of elements identified (as of the publication of this book).

5. Describe the difference between a period and a group on the periodic table.

6. What property of elements was used to organize the periodic table?

7. Describe the difference between the mass number and the atomic mass of an element.

8. Identify each of the following as a metal (*M*), nonmetal (*N*), or metalloid (*T*).
   a. includes most of the elements
   b. as solid they are dull, poor conductors, and brittle
   c. generally located on the right side of the periodic table
   d. ductile
   e. share properties in between metals and nonmetals

9. Briefly describe each group below and give an example of one element in each group.
   a. alkali metals
   b. halogens
   c. noble gases

10. How does the energy level of an element on the periodic table compare to its period number?

Section 14.2

11. Most elements occur as solids at room temperature.
    a. Name the two elements found as liquids at room temperature.
    b. Name 5 elements (out of 11) found as gases at room temperature.

12. Explain why the elements in group 18 are all gases.

13. Name two properties that display periodicity across the periodic table.

14. Name three elements that are good conductors of both heat and electricity.

15. Name three elements that are poor conductors that are good insulators of both heat and electricity.

16. Carbon is not an exceptionally abundant element but is the most essential element for life on our planet. Why?

17. Name two reasons why silicon is an important element economically.

18. Name the following.
    a. the two most abundant gases and their approximate percentage of occurrence in our atmosphere
    b. the most abundant element in Earth's crust and its percentage of occurrence

Problems

Section 14.1

1. How many electrons can be held in energy level one? In energy level two?

2. Aluminum has 13 electrons. Which is its outermost energy level and how many electrons are found in it?

3. Name the elements found at the following positions.
   a. group 1, period 2
   b. period 4, group 9

4. Give the symbol, name, and atomic number of the two elements in period 4 most similar to cobalt (Co).

Section 14.2

5. Using the diagram of the periodic table below, state one property for each element indicated on the table.

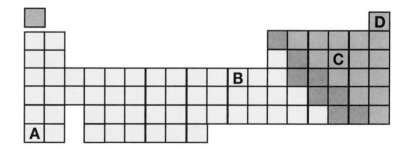

Chapter 15

Molecules and Compounds

What do aspirin, plastic wrap, and vinegar have in common? Give up? They are all compounds made from different combinations of the same three atoms: carbon, hydrogen, and oxygen. By themselves, these atoms cannot reduce pain, keep food fresh, or season food. But when they are chemically combined in certain ways to form compounds, they can be useful in many ways. Study this chapter to learn how millions upon millions of compounds and molecules are made from combinations of less than 100 basic elements.

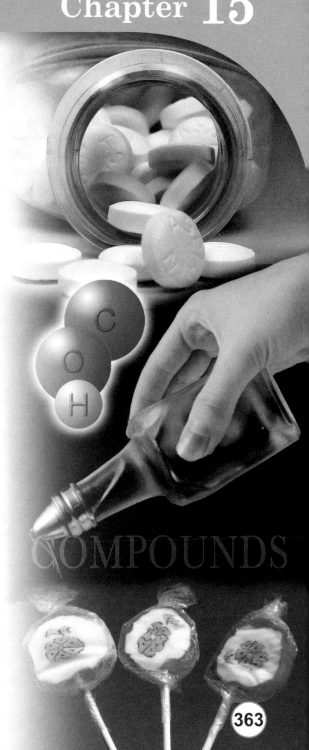

Key Questions:

1. What does the chemical formula H_2O mean?

2. What are chemical bonds, and how do they form?

3. How do scientists show the shape of a molecule?

15.1 Compounds and Chemical Bonds

Sometimes elements are found in their pure forms, but usually they are found within compounds. That's because most pure elements are more stable when they are bonded to other atoms. For example, water (H_2O) is a compound of hydrogen and oxygen that has different properties than either of its elements. This chapter is about how and why elements combine into compounds.

Most matter is in the form of compounds and mixtures

Compounds and mixtures

A **compound** contains two or more elements that are chemically combined. In Figure 15.1, we can see that sugar is a compound of carbon, hydrogen, and oxygen atoms. Different types of sugar contain different numbers and combinations of these three elements. A **mixture** contains two or more elements and/or compounds that are *not* chemically bonded together. The atmosphere is a gaseous mixture of oxygen and nitrogen, but it is *not* a compound. Nitrous oxide (N_2O) *is* a compound because oxygen and nitrogen atoms are chemically bonded together.

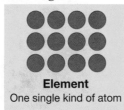 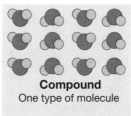 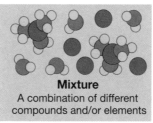

Element One single kind of atom	**Compound** One type of molecule	**Mixture** A combination of different compounds and/or elements

Homogeneous and heterogeneous mixtures

A **homogeneous mixture** is the same throughout and maintains the properties of its components. A can of cola is a homogeneous mixture. Each sip you take from the can tastes and looks the same. Brass is a homogeneous mixture made up of zinc and copper. Brass can be separated into its two components, but when combined they give brass uniform properties throughout. A **heterogeneous mixture** is one that has several components, each with its own set of properties. One example is chicken noodle soup. One spoonful of the soup might contain broth, noodles, and chicken while another might contain carrots, noodles, and broth. The properties of the soup change depending on which components are found in the sample.

VOCABULARY

compound - a substance whose smallest particles include more than one element chemically bonded together.

mixture - a substance that includes more than one type of element and/or compound that are not bonded together and can be separated by physical means.

homogeneous mixture - has the same composition and maintains the properties of its components.

heterogeneous mixture - may have several parts, each with its own set of properties.

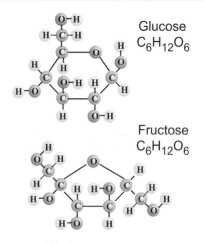

Glucose $C_6H_{12}O_6$

Fructose $C_6H_{12}O_6$

Figure 15.1: *"Pure" sugar is a compound made up of two chemically bonded simple sugars: glucose and fructose.*

Covalent bonds and molecules

Electrons form chemical bonds   A **chemical bond** forms when atoms transfer or share electrons. Two atoms that are sharing one or more electrons are chemically bonded and move together. In a water molecule, each hydrogen atom shares its single electron with the oxygen atom at the center. Almost all the elements form chemical bonds easily. This is why most of the matter you experience is in the form of compounds.

A chemical bond forms when atoms transfer or share electrons.

Covalent bonds   A **covalent bond** is formed when atoms share electrons. The bonds between oxygen and hydrogen in a water molecule are covalent bonds (Figure 15.2). There are two covalent bonds in a water molecule, between the oxygen and each of the hydrogen atoms. Each bond represents one electron. In a covalent bond, electrons are *shared* between atoms, not transferred.

Four examples of molecules held together by covalent bonds

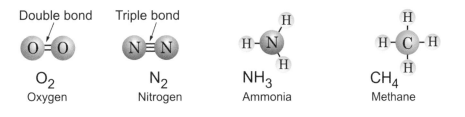

Molecules   A group of atoms held together by covalent bonds is called a **molecule**. Water is a molecule, and so are the two different sugar molecules shown on the previous page. Other examples of molecules are methane (CH_4), ammonia (NH_3), oxygen (O_2), and nitrogen (N_2).

chemical bond - a bond formed between atoms through the sharing or transferring of electrons.

covalent bond - a type of chemical bond formed by shared electrons.

molecule - a group of atoms held together by covalent bonds.

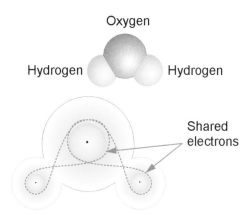

Figure 15.2: *In a covalent bond, the shared electrons act like ties that hold a molecule together.*

Chemical formulas and diagrams

The chemical formula Molecules are represented by a **chemical formula**. The chemical formula tells you how many of each kind of atom are in the molecule. For example, the chemical formula for water is H_2O. The subscript 2 indicates there are two hydrogen atoms in a water molecule. The chemical formula also tells you that water always contains twice as many hydrogen atoms as oxygen atoms. This is important to know if you wish to make water from the elements oxygen and hydrogen.

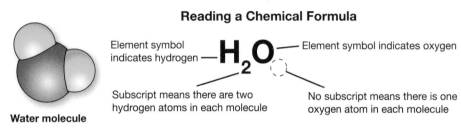

Reading a Chemical Formula

Element symbol indicates hydrogen — H_2O — Element symbol indicates oxygen

Subscript means there are two hydrogen atoms in each molecule

No subscript means there is one oxygen atom in each molecule

Water molecule

Ratio of two hydrogen atoms to one oxygen atom in the compound

The shape of a molecule is also important to its function and properties. For this reason, molecules are represented by structural diagrams that show the shape and arrangement of atoms. Single bonds between atoms are shown with solid lines connecting the element symbols. Double and triple bonds are shown with double and triple lines. Both the chemical formulas and structural diagrams are shown in Figure 15.3.

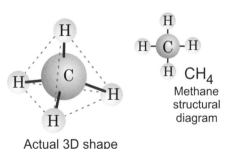

Actual 3D shape

CH_4
Methane structural diagram

Of course, real molecules are three-dimensional, not flat as shown in the structural diagram. For example, a methane molecule has the shape of a four-sided pyramid called a *tetrahedron*. Each hydrogen atom is at a corner of the tetrahedron and the carbon atom is at the center.

VOCABULARY

chemical formula - identifies the number and element of each type of atom in a compound. For example, the chemical formula Fe_2O_3 is for a compound with iron (Fe) and oxygen (O) in a ratio of two iron atoms for every three oxygen atoms.

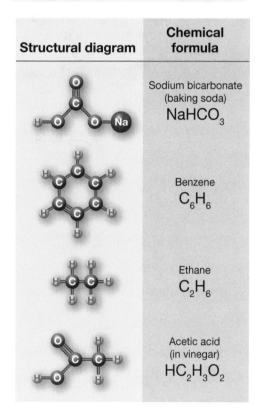

Structural diagram	Chemical formula
	Sodium bicarbonate (baking soda) $NaHCO_3$
	Benzene C_6H_6
	Ethane C_2H_6
	Acetic acid (in vinegar) $HC_2H_3O_2$

Figure 15.3: *Chemical formulas and structural diagrams.*

Structure and function

Properties come from the molecule

The properties of a compound depend *much* more on the exact structure of its molecule than on the individual elements of which it is made. As a good example, aspirin is a molecule made from carbon, hydrogen, and oxygen according to the chemical formula $C_9H_8O_4$ (Figure 15.4). Aspirin relieves swelling and reduces pain in humans.

Properties depend on the exact chemical formula

By themselves, the elements (H, C, O) do not have the property of reducing pain. In fact, other molecules formed from the same elements have very different properties than aspirin. For example, polyethylene plastic wrap and formaldehyde (a toxic preservative) are also made from carbon, oxygen, and hydrogen. The beneficial properties of aspirin come from the specific combination of exactly eight hydrogen, nine carbon, and four oxygen atoms in a particular structure. If the ratio of elements was changed, for example removing even one hydrogen, the resulting molecule would not have the properties of aspirin.

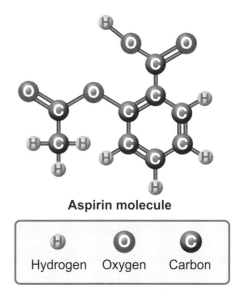

Aspirin molecule

H	O	C
Hydrogen	Oxygen	Carbon

Figure 15.4: *An aspirin molecule (acetylsalicylic acid).*

Three Different Molecules, Same Chemical Formula

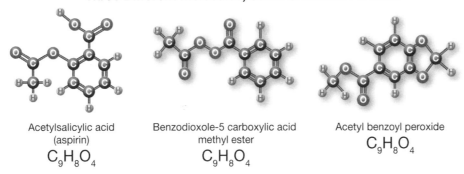

| Acetylsalicylic acid (aspirin) $C_9H_8O_4$ | Benzodioxole-5 carboxylic acid methyl ester $C_9H_8O_4$ | Acetyl benzoyl peroxide $C_9H_8O_4$ |

Like many modern medicines, the active ingredient in aspirin was first discovered in nature. In fact, aspirin's pain-relieving properties were known and used in its natural form long before scientists learned of it. Research the discovery of aspirin to find out the intriguing story of this widely used medicine.

Properties also depend on molecular structure

The structure of a molecule is very important to the properties of a compound. The same 21 atoms in aspirin can be combined in other structures with the same chemical formula! The resulting molecules are something completely different (see diagram above) and do not have the beneficial properties of aspirin. *Both chemical formula and the structure of the molecules determine the properties of a compound.*

Ionic compounds

An ion is a charged atom

Not all compounds are made of molecules. For example, sodium chloride (NaCl) is a compound of sodium (Na) and chlorine (Cl) in a ratio of one sodium atom per chlorine atom. The difference is that in sodium chloride, the electron is essentially transferred from the sodium atom to the chlorine atom. When atoms gain or lose an electron they become **ions**. An ion is a charged atom. By losing an electron, the sodium atom becomes a sodium ion with a charge of +1. By gaining an electron, the chlorine atom becomes a chloride ion with a charge of −1 (note that when chlorine becomes an ion, the name changes to chlor*ide*).

Ionic bonds

Sodium and chlorine form an **ionic bond** because the positive sodium ion is attracted to the negative chloride ion. Ionic bonds are bonds in which electrons are transferred from one atom to another.

Ionic compounds do not form molecules

Ionic bonds are not limited to a single pair of atoms, like covalent bonds. In sodium chloride, each positive sodium ion is attracted to all of the neighboring chloride ions (Figure 15.5). Likewise, each chloride ion is attracted to all the neighboring sodium atoms. Because the bonds are not just between pairs of atoms, *ionic compounds do not form molecules*! In an ionic compound, each atom bonds with *all* of its neighbors through attraction between positive and negative charge.

The chemical formula for ionic compounds

Like molecular compounds, ionic compounds also have fixed ratios of elements. For example, there is one sodium ion per chloride ion in sodium chloride. This means we can use the same type of chemical formula for ionic compounds and molecular compounds.

Ions may be multiply charged

Sodium chloride involves the transfer of one electron. However, ionic compounds may also be formed by the transfer of two or more electrons. A good example is magnesium chloride ($MgCl_2$). The magnesium atom gives up two electrons to become a magnesium ion with a charge of +2 (Mg^{2+}). Each chlorine atom gains one electron to become a chloride ion with a charge of −1 (Cl^-). The ion charge is written as a superscript after the element (Mg^{2+}, Fe^{3+}, Cl^-, etc.).

VOCABULARY

ion - an atom that has an electric charge different from zero. Ions are created when atoms gain or lose electrons.

ionic bond - a bond that transfers an electron from one atom to another resulting in attraction between oppositely charged ions.

Sodium and chlorine form an ionic crystal

 Sodium ion
 Chlorine ion

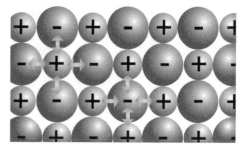

Figure 15.5: *Sodium chloride is an ionic compound in which each positive sodium ion is attracted to all of its negative chloride neighbors and vice versa.*

Why chemical bonds form

Atoms form bonds to reach a lower energy state

Imagine pulling tape off a surface. It takes energy to pull the tape off. It also takes energy to separate atoms that are bonded together. If it takes energy to separate bonded atoms, then the same energy must be released when the bond is formed. *Energy is released when chemical bonds form.* Energy is released because atoms bonded together have less total energy than the same atoms separately. Like a ball rolling downhill, atoms form compounds because the atoms have lower energy when they are together in compounds. For example, one carbon atom and four hydrogen atoms have more total energy apart than they do when combined in a methane molecule (Figure 15.6).

Chemical reactivity

All elements, except the noble gases, form chemical bonds. However, some elements are much more reactive than others. In chemistry, *reactive* means an element readily forms chemical bonds, often releasing energy. For example, sodium is a highly-reactive metal. Chlorine is a highly reactive gas. If pure sodium and pure chlorine are placed together, a violent explosion occurs as the sodium and chlorine combine and form ionic bonds. The energy of the explosion is the energy given off by the formation of the chemical bonds.

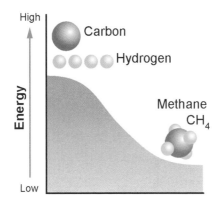

Figure 15.6: *The methane (CH_4) molecule has lower total energy than four separate hydrogen atoms and one separate carbon atom.*

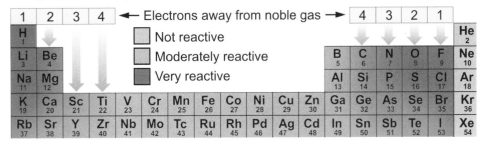

Some elements are more reactive than others

The closer an element is to having the same number of electrons as a noble gas, the more reactive the element is. The alkali metals are very reactive because they are just one electron away from the noble gases. The halogens are also very reactive because they are also one electron away from the noble gases. The beryllium group and the oxygen group are less reactive because each element in these groups is two electrons away from a noble gas.

CHALLENGE

The noble gases (He, Ne, Ar, etc.) are called *inert* because they do not ordinarily react with anything. You can put sodium in an atmosphere of pure helium and nothing will happen. However, scientists have found that a few noble gases *do* form compounds, in very special circumstances. Research this topic and see if you can find a compound involving a noble gas.

15.1 Section Review

1. What is the difference between a compound and a mixture?
2. Give one example of a compound and one example of a mixture.
3. How many atoms of chlorine (Cl) are in the carbon tetrachloride molecule (CCl_4)?
4. Which of the diagrams in Figure 15.7 is the correct structural diagram for carbon tetrachloride (CCl_4)?
5. Write a chemical formula for a compound that has two atoms of oxygen (O) and three atoms of iron (Fe).
6. What is the chemical formula for the molecule in Figure 15.8?
7. How many atoms of hydrogen are in a molecule of acetic acid ($HC_2H_3O_2$)?

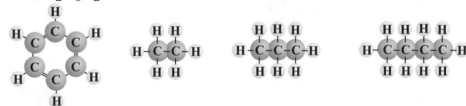

8. Which of the molecules above has the chemical formula C_3H_8?
9. Which of the following statements is *false*?
   a. The properties of a compound depend more on which elements are present and less on the structure of the molecule.
   b. The properties of a compound depend more on the structure of the molecule and less on which elements are present.
10. Chemical bonds form because:
    a. the atoms have more energy bonded together than separated.
    b. the atoms have less energy bonded together than separated.

Which is the correct CCl_4?

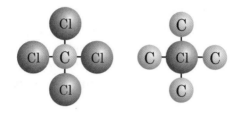

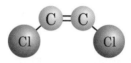

Figure 15.7: *Question 4.*

What is the chemical formula for this molecule?

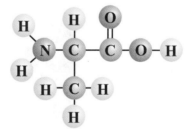

Figure 15.8: *Question 6.*

15.2 Electrons and Chemical Bonds

The discovery of energy levels in the atom solved a 2,000-year-old mystery. The mystery was why elements combined with other elements only in particular ratios (or not at all). For example, why do two hydrogen atoms bond with one oxygen atom to make water? Why isn't there a molecule with three (H_3O) or even four (H_4O) hydrogen atoms? Why does sodium chloride have a precise ratio of one sodium ion to one chloride ion? Why don't helium, neon, and argon form compounds with any other element? The answer has to do with energy levels and electrons.

Valence electrons

What are valence electrons? Chemical bonds are formed only between the electrons in the highest unfilled energy level. These electrons are called **valence electrons**. You can think of valence electrons as the outer "skin" of an atom. Electrons in the inner (filled) energy levels do not "see" other atoms because they are shielded by the valence electrons. For example, chlorine has seven valence electrons. The first 10 of chlorine's 17 electrons are in the inner (filled) energy levels (Figure 15.9).

Most elements bond to reach 8 valence electrons It turns out that *eight is a magic number for chemical bonding.* All the elements heavier than boron form chemical bonds to try and get to a configuration with eight valence electrons (Figure 15.10). Eight is a preferred number because eight electrons are a complete (filled) energy level. The noble gases already have a magic number of eight valence electrons. They don't form chemical bonds because they don't need to!

Light elements bond to reach 2 valance electrons For elements with atomic number 5 (boron) or less, the magic number is two instead of eight. For these light elements, two valence electrons completely fills the *first* energy level. The elements H, He, Li, Be, and B form bonds to reach the magic number of two valence electrons.

Hydrogen is special Because of its single electron, hydrogen can also have zero valence electrons! Zero is a magic number for hydrogen, as well as two. This flexibility makes hydrogen a very "friendly" element; hydrogen can bond with almost any other element.

valence electrons - electrons in the highest unfilled energy level of an atom. These electrons participate in chemical bonds.

Chlorine
17 electrons

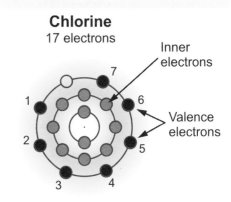

Chlorine has 7 valence electrons

Figure 15.9: *Chlorine has seven valence electrons. The other 10 electrons are in filled (inner) energy levels.*

Bond

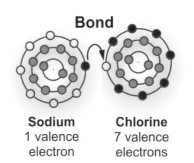

Sodium
1 valence
electron

Chlorine
7 valence
electrons

Figure 15.10: *Chlorine and sodium bond so each can reach a configuration with eight valence electrons.*

Valence electrons and the periodic table

Period 2 elements The illustration below shows how the electrons in the elements in the second period (lithium to neon) fill the energy levels. Two of lithium's three electrons go in the first energy level. Lithium has one valence electron because its third electron is the only one in the second energy level.

Each successive element has one more valence electron Going from left to right across a period, each successive element has one more valence electron. Beryllium has two valence electrons, boron has three, and carbon has four. Each element in the second period adds one more electron until all eight spots in the second energy level are full at atomic number 10, which is neon, a noble gas. Neon has eight valence electrons.

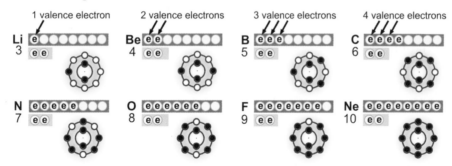

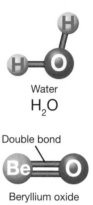

Water
H_2O

Double bond

Beryllium oxide
BeO

Figure 15.11: *Water (H_2O) and beryllium oxide (BeO).*

Bonding Oxygen has six valence electrons. To get to the magic number of 8, oxygen needs to add two electrons. *Oxygen forms chemical bonds that provide these two extra electrons.* For example, a single oxygen atom combines with two hydrogen atoms because each hydrogen can supply only one electron. Oxygen combines with one beryllium atom because beryllium can supply two valence electrons to give oxygen its preferred number of 8 (Figure 15.11).

Two atoms can have two bonds between them Each covalent bond between atoms shares two electrons. What happens if two atoms share four valence electrons? They make two covalent bonds together, called a double bond. A double bond shares twice as many electrons as a single bond. In carbon dioxide (CO_2), the carbon atom has four valence electrons and shares those electrons with two oxygen atoms (Figure 15.12).

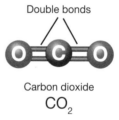

Double bonds

Carbon dioxide
CO_2

Figure 15.12: *Carbon forms two double bonds with oxygen to make carbon dioxide.*

Lewis dot diagrams

Dot diagrams of the elements A Lewis dot diagram shows the element symbol surrounded by one to eight dots representing the valence electrons. Each dot represents one electron. Lithium has one dot, beryllium has two, boron has three, etc. Figure 15.13 shows the dot diagrams for the first 10 elements.

Dot diagrams of molecules Each element forms bonds to reach one of the magic numbers of valence electrons: 2 or 8. In dot diagrams of a complete molecule, each element symbol has either two or eight dots around it. Both configurations correspond to completely filled (or empty) energy levels.

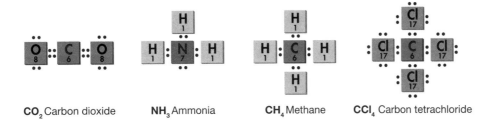

CO₂ Carbon dioxide   **NH₃** Ammonia   **CH₄** Methane   **CCl₄** Carbon tetrachloride

Example dot diagrams Carbon has four dots and hydrogen has one. One carbon atom bonds with four hydrogen atoms because this allows the carbon atom to have eight valence electrons (eight dots)—four of its own and four shared from the hydrogen atoms. The picture above shows dot diagrams for carbon dioxide (CO_2), ammonia (NH_3), methane (CH_4), and carbon tetrachloride (CCl_4), a flammable solvent.

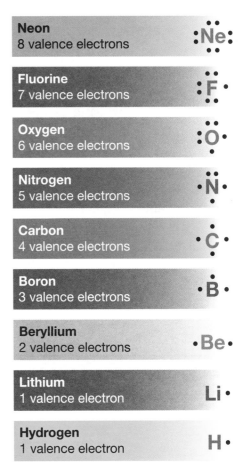

Neon 8 valence electrons	:Ne:
Fluorine 7 valence electrons	:F·
Oxygen 6 valence electrons	:O·
Nitrogen 5 valence electrons	·N·
Carbon 4 valence electrons	·C·
Boron 3 valence electrons	·B·
Beryllium 2 valence electrons	·Be·
Lithium 1 valence electron	Li·
Hydrogen 1 valence electron	H·

Dot diagrams Draw the dot diagram for water, H_2O.

1. Looking for: Dot diagram

2. Given: Chemical formula H_2O

3. Relationships:

4. Solution:

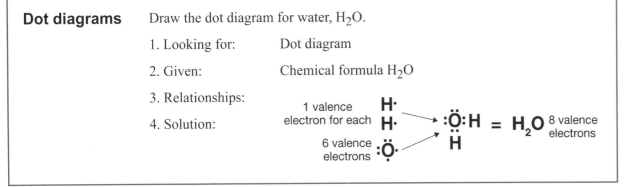

Figure 15.13: *Lewis dot diagrams show valence electrons as dots around the element symbol. Atoms form bonds to get eight valence electrons by sharing with other atoms.*

Oxidation numbers

Oxidation numbers
A sodium atom always ionizes to become Na+ (a charge of +1) when it combines with other atoms to make a compound. Therefore, we say that sodium has an **oxidation number** of 1+. An oxidation number indicates the charge on the remaining atom (ion) when electrons are lost, gained, or shared in chemical bonds. Table 15.1 shows the oxidation numbers for some elements. Notice that the convention for writing oxidation numbers is the opposite of the convention for writing the charge. When writing the oxidation number, the positive (or negative) symbol is written after the number, not before it.

Oxidation numbers and the periodic table
Oxidation numbers correspond closely to an element's group on the periodic table. All of the alkali metals have oxidation numbers of 1+ since these elements all prefer to lose one electron in chemical bonds. All of the halogens have an oxidation number of 1– because these elements prefer to gain an electron in chemical bonds. The diagram below shows the trend in oxidation numbers across the periodic table. Most transition metals have complicated oxidation numbers because they have many more electrons.

oxidation number - indicates the charge of an atom when an electron is lost, gained, or shared in a chemical bond. An oxidation number of 1+ means an electron is lost, 1– means an electron is gained.

Table 15.1: Some oxidation numbers

atom	electrons gained or lost	oxidation number
K	loses 1	1+
Mg	loses 2	2+
Al	loses 3	3+
P	gains 3	3–
Se	gains 2	2–
Br	gains 1	1–
Ar	loses 0	0

What is fluorine's (F) oxidation number? If you think it is 1–, you are right. Like the other halogens, fluorine gains one electron, one negative charge, when it bonds with other atoms.

| 1+ | 2+ | Most common oxidation number | 3+ | 4+ | 3- | 2- | 1- |

NOTE: Many elements have more than one possible oxidation number.

Li 3	Be 4											B 5	C 6	N 7	O 8	F 9	He 2
Na 11	Mg 12											Al 13	Si 14	P 15	S 16	Cl 17	Ne 10
K 19	Ca 20	Sc 21	Ti 22	V 23	Cr 24	Mn 25	Fe 26	Co 27	Ni 28	Cu 29	Zn 30	Ga 31	Ge 32	As 33	Se 34	Br 35	Ar 18
Rb 37	Sr 38	Y 39	Zr 40	Nb 41	Mo 42	Tc 43	Ru 44	Rh 45	Pd 46	Ag 47	Cd 48	In 49	Sn 50	Sb 51	Te 52	I 53	Kr 36
																	Xe 54

Predicting a chemical formula

Oxidation numbers in a compound add up to zero
When elements combine in molecules and ionic compounds, the total electric charge is always zero. This is because any electron donated by one atom is accepted by another. The rule of zero charge is easiest to apply using oxidation numbers. The total of all the oxidation numbers for all the atoms in a compound must be zero. This important rule allows you to predict many chemical formulas.

The oxidation numbers for all the atoms in a compound must add up to zero.

Example, carbon tetrachloride
To see how this works, consider the compound carbon tetrachloride (CCl_4). Carbon has an oxidation number of 4+. Chlorine has an oxidation number of 1–. It takes four chlorine atoms to cancel with carbon's 4+ oxidation number.

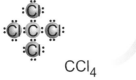

CCl_4
Carbon tetrachloride

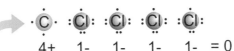

4+   1–   1–   1–   1–   = 0

The total of the oxidation numbers for each atom in the molecule must be zero.

Predict a chemical formula
Iron and oxygen combine to form a compound. Iron (Fe) has an oxidation number of 3+. Oxygen (O) has an oxidation number of 2–. Predict the chemical formula of this compound.

1. Looking for: Chemical formula

2. Given: Oxidation numbers Fe 3+ and O 2–

3. Relationships: The oxidation numbers for all the atoms in a compound must add up to zero.

4. Solution: Three oxygen atoms contribute the total oxidation number of 6–. It takes only two iron atoms to get a total oxidation number of 6+. Therefore, the chemical formula is Fe_2O_3.

Your turn...

a. Predict the chemical formula of the compound containing beryllium (2+) and fluorine (1–). **Answer:** BeF_2

Ionic and covalent bonds

Why bonds are ionic or covalent Whether or not a compound is ionic or covalently bonded depends on how much each element "needs" an electron to get to a magic number (two or eight). Elements that are very close to the noble gases tend to give or take electrons rather than share them. These elements often form ionic bonds rather than covalent bonds.

Sodium chloride is ionic As an example, sodium has one electron more than the noble gas neon. Sodium has a very strong tendency to give up that electron and become a positive ion. Chlorine has one electron less than argon. Therefore, chlorine has a very strong tendency to accept an electron and become a negative ion. Sodium chloride is an ionic compound because sodium has a strong tendency to give up an electron and chlorine has a strong tendency to accept an electron.

Widely separated elements form ionic compounds On the periodic table, strong electron donors are the left side (alkali metals). Strong electron acceptors are on the right side (halogens). The farther separated two elements are on the periodic table, the more likely they are to form an ionic compound.

Nearby elements form covalent compounds Covalent compounds form when elements have roughly equal tendency to accept electrons. Elements that are nonmetals and therefore close together on the periodic table tend to form covalent compounds with each other because they have approximately equal tendency to accept electrons. Compounds involving carbon, silicon, nitrogen, and oxygen are often covalent.

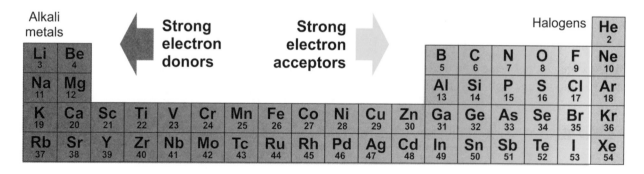

Predicting ionic or covalent bonds

Potassium (K) combines with bromine (Br) to make the salt, potassium bromide (KBr). Is this likely to be an ionic or covalently bonded compound?

1. Looking for: Ionic or covalent bond

2. Given: K and Br

3. Relationships: K is a strong electron donor. Br is a strong electron acceptor.

4. Solution: KBr is an ionic compound because K and Br are from opposite sides of the periodic table.

Your turn...

a. Is silica (SiO_2) likely to be an ionic or covalently bonded compound?
Answer: covalent

b. Is calcium fluoride (CaF_2) likely to be an ionic or covalently bonded compound?
Answer: ionic

15.2 Section Review

1. Atoms form chemical bonds using
   a. electrons in the innermost energy level.
   b. electrons in the outermost energy level.
   c. protons and electrons.
2. Which of the diagrams in Figure 15.14 shows an element with three valence electrons? What is the name of this element?
3. Which of the following elements will form a double bond with oxygen making a molecule with one atom of the element and one atom of oxygen?
   a. lithium
   b. boron
   c. beryllium
   d. nitrogen
4. Name two elements that have the Lewis dot diagram shown in Figure 15.15.
5. The oxidation number is
   a. the number of oxygen atoms an element bonds with.
   b. the positive or negative charge acquired by an atom in a chemical bond.
   c. the number of electrons involved in a chemical bond.
6. Name three elements that have an oxidation number of 3+.
7. What is the oxidation number for the elements shown in Figure 15.16?
8. When elements form a molecule, what is *true* about the oxidation numbers of the atoms in the molecule?
   a. The sum of the oxidation numbers must equal zero.
   b. All oxidation numbers from the same molecule must be positive.
   c. All oxidation numbers from the same molecule must be negative.

Which of these diagrams shows 3 valence electrons?

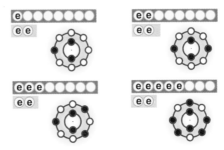

Figure 15.14: *Question 2.*

Name two elements that have this Lewis dot diagram.

Figure 15.15: *Question 4.*

What is the oxidation number for these elements?

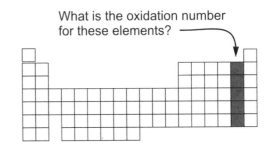

Figure 15.16: *Question 7*

Spiderman's Favorite Compound

What is your favorite compound? Maybe it's $C_6H_5(CH_2)_2NH_2$, phenylethylamine—that's one of the lively compounds in chocolate. Maybe your favorite compound is $C_{16}H_{10}N_2O_2$, indigo—that's the blue dye used for jeans. What do you think Spiderman's favorite compound is? You guessed it—the complex protein known as spider silk!

Amazing spider silk

Photo courtesy of Peter C. Neil, Jr.

Spiderman releases a super-strong thread of silk and swings from one towering skyscraper to another, as if suspended from a steel cable. Spiderman stops a runaway train with spider silk. These

super-spidey tricks are Hollywood gimmicks, but did you know that *real* spider silk is stronger by weight than steel? If you had a thread of steel and a thread of spider silk that were both the same diameter, the spider silk would be about five times

stronger! Spider silk is also incredibly elastic. The sticky silk a spider uses to capture its prey can stretch two to four times its original length before breaking. There are not many materials, manmade or natural, that have both *strength* and *toughness*. Spider silk is strong and tough. Spider silk is an amazing compound.

Spiders and silk

Most spiders are silk thread factories. They produce the fibers and spin them into all sorts of neat structures that may look delicate and filmy, but looks can be deceiving! You probably know that spider webs are used to capture prey. The unsuspecting fly becomes trapped in the sticky silk threads. Sometimes the prey *slams* into the web, and the silk threads absorb this energy without breaking. One of the only materials that can absorb energy like this is manmade Kevlar, which is used in bullet-proof vests.

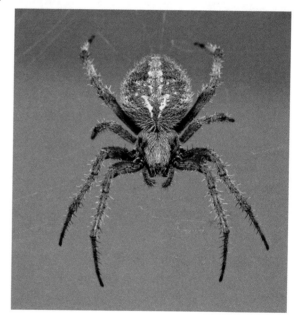

How spiders use silk

Webs	sticky silk is elastic, and prey can't rebound
Shelters	some spiders make burrows or nests from the silk threads
Egg-sacs	spider silk can form a protective case around eggs
Draglines	threads can connect the spider to its web, and non-sticky threads are used in the spokes of the web so the spider itself doesn't get trapped!
Parachuting	silk can be released and caught by the wind to transport young
Swathing	spiders can wrap their prey in silk threads to immobilize them

Chemical structure

Spider silk is a natural protein. Proteins are a huge group of compounds that are found in all living things. Spider silk protein belongs to a sub-group called scleroproteins. These include collagen (found in ligaments) and keratin (hair and nails). Each sub-unit of a protein is called an amino acid. One of the most common amino acids used by the spider to build its protein silk threads is alanine. This is a simple amino acid. Where does the spider get the amino acid units to make the long silk protein chains? Some of the amino acids come from the spider's high protein diet of insects. But there is another way. Many spiders eat their own webs to reuse the amino acids to make a new web. This is a natural recycling program!

Alanine $(C_2H_4NO_2)CH_3$

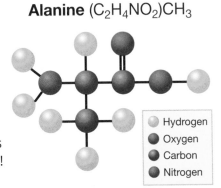

○	Hydrogen
●	Oxygen
●	Carbon
●	Nitrogen

Humans and spider silk

People have long benefited from the amazing properties of spider silk. Greeks of long ago used spider webs to cover bleeding wounds. Some cultures used spider silk to catch small fish, and some still use spider silk for small fish nets. Silk was used before World War II as the crosshairs in spotting scopes on guns and in some telescopes. What do we use spider silk for now? Well, there are not many commercial uses of spider silk, despite it's incredible strength and toughness. You can only imagine how difficult it would be to maintain "spider farms" to harvest spider silk. Spiders tend to eat one another when in close quarters. Spider silk is thinner than a human hair. It is difficult to work with. However, scientists are extremely interested in studying spider silk to learn how the proteins are structured, and how the spider spins the thread. The amazing strength and toughness of spider silk can be better understood (and perhaps copied) if more is known about the chemical makeup of silk proteins.

Man-made spider silk

Several companies around the world are marketing engineered spider silk fibers that can be produced on a commercial scale. By examining the DNA of spiders, scientists have developed ways to synthesize liquid silk proteins that are very similar to the spider's. An extrusion process is then used to spin the fibers. Maybe someday soon, Spiderman could be more than a comic book superhero!

QUESTIONS

1. What is an amino acid, and what does it have to do with spider silk?

2. How do spiders recycle the compounds they use to make spider silk?

3. Why would it be difficult to harvest spider silk directly from spiders?

Mystery Substances

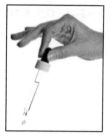

Imagine you reach into your kitchen cabinet and find a container of white powder. Should you smell it? Should you taste it? Is it safe to flush it down the drain? These are important questions for home safety. We should always identify substances before smelling, tasting, or disposing of them. Chemists observe both chemical and physical properties to help classify and identify unknown substances. In this activity, you and your classmates will act as chemists and try to identify six mystery powders.

Unknown Substances	Physical Properties			Chemical Properties	
	Color	Texture	Dissolves in Water	Reacts with Acid	Reacts to Heat
A.					
B.					
C.					
D.					
E.					
F.					

Materials

six squares laminated black paper or cardstock; water and acetic acid (vinegar) in small dropper bottles; white colored pencil, hand lens; toothpicks; six unidentified substances in labeled containers with spoons; safety goggles; wet paper towels or damp sponges for clean up

What you will do

1. Copy the data table (upper right) into your notebook or on a piece of paper. If you work in teams, assign each member a substance to test. Be sure to wear safety goggles during the tests. Share your results with your team members.

2. Use a spoon to add a small amount of sample A to the middle of one paper square. Use the white pencil to label the paper "A". Repeat this step for the remaining samples, B–F.

3. Examine each sample with a hand lens. Record the color and describe the texture as powdery or grainy.

4. When you finish observing, divide each substance into two equal piles and move them apart on the paper.

5. For each sample, add five drops of water onto one of the piles and stir with a toothpick. Write "yes" if the solid dissolves in water, or "no" if it does not.

6. Add five drops of acid from the second bottle to the other pile. Describe any evidence of color change or reaction with the acid.

7. Your teacher will perform a test to see if the samples react to heat. Record your observations as a class.

Applying your knowledge

a. You may already recognize some of the substances. Write the names of any substances you recognize next to the corresponding letter in your data table. Discuss as a class.

b. Forensic chemists use methods to decide what chemical reactions may have taken place at a crime. Their tests are very complex. What substances might a forensic chemist test in his or her laboratory to help solve a crime? Check your answers on-line or with your teacher.

Chapter 15 Assessment

Vocabulary

Select the correct term to complete the sentences.

compound	covalent	ion
mixture	chemical bond	molecule
chemical formula	ionic bond	oxidation number
valence electrons		

Section 15.1

1. When two atoms share or trade electrons a(n) ____ is formed.

2. An atom that has acquired a positive or negative charge is called a(n) ____.

3. To represent the number and type of each element in a molecule, chemists write a(n) ____.

4. A substance whose smallest particles include more than one element chemically bonded together is a(n) ____.

5. The type of chemical bond formed when atoms share electrons is the ____ bond.

6. A substance made of two or more elements or compounds not chemically bonded to each other is a(n) ____.

7. A bond formed when an electron is transferred from one atom to another is a(n) ____.

8. A group of atoms held together by covalent bonds in a specific ratio form a(n) ____.

Section 15.2

9. Electrons in the highest unfilled energy level of an atom that may participate in chemical bonds are called ____.

10. The number which indicates the charge on an atom when an electron is lost, gained, or shared is called the ____.

Concepts

Section 15.1

1. What is the chemical formula for water? What atoms make up this compound?

2. What is the difference between a compound and a mixture?

3. List three examples of a mixture and three examples of a compound.

4. Why do atoms form compounds instead of existing as single atoms?

5. What type of bond holds a water molecule together?

6. What do we call the particle that is a group of atoms held together by covalent bonds?

7. List four examples of a molecule.

8. What does the subscript 2 in H_2O mean?

9. What do the subscripts in the formula for ethane represent?

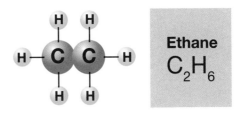

Ethane
C_2H_6

10. Name the two most important factors in determining the properties of a compound.

11. Summarize the differences between a covalent compound and an ionic compound.

12. What happens when chemical bonds form? Why?

13. Which group of elements usually don't form chemical bonds?

14. Name a very reactive group of metals and a very reactive group of nonmetals. Why do they behave this way?

Section 15.2

15. When atoms form chemical bonds, which of their electrons are involved in the bonds?

16. How many electrons represent a complete (filled) outermost energy level for elements heavier than Boron (atomic number greater than 5)?

17. Noble gases usually don't form chemical bonds. Why?

18. What is so special about hydrogen when it comes to forming bonds?

19. Each successive element on a period table going from left to right across a period has what?

20. In a Lewis dot diagram, what is represented by the dots surrounding the element symbol?

21. How many valence electrons does oxygen have? How many more electrons are needed to fill the outermost energy level?

22. How does the oxidation number indicate if an electron will be lost or gained by the bonding atom?

23. Using the periodic table, what is the oxidation number of
    a. calcium?
    b. aluminum?
    c. fluoride?

24. What is the total electric charge on molecules and compounds?

25. Elements close to the noble gases tend to form what type of bond?

26. Elements that are widely separated on the periodic table tend to form____ compounds.

27. Elements that are close together on the periodic table tend to form ____ compounds.

28. Strong electron donors are on the ____ side of the periodic table, while strong electron acceptors are on the ____ side.

Problems

Section 15.1

1. Label each of the diagrams below as a mixture, compound, or separate elements.

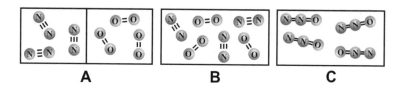

A   B   C

2. For each of the formulas for molecules listed below, name each element and how many of atoms of each element are in that molecule.
    a. $C_6H_{12}O_6$
    b. $CaCO_3$
    c. Al_2O_3

3. Predict the formula for a molecule containing carbon (C) with an oxidation number of 4+ and oxygen (O) with an oxidation number of 2–.

4. Which of the following would be a correct chemical formula for a molecule of N^{3-} and H^+?
    a. HNO_3
    b. H_3N_6
    c. NH_3

5. Referring to the diagram of the periodic table in Chapter 7, determine which element in each pair is more active.

    a. Li or Be

    b. Ca or Sc

    c. P or S

    d. O or Ne

Section 15.2

6. In order for nitrogen to form a compound with other elements, how many additional electrons are required to give nitrogen the required number of electrons in its outermost energy level?

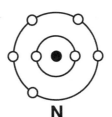

N

7. Draw Lewis dot diagrams for the following.

    a. an atom of hydrogen (one valence electron)

    b. an atom of oxygen (six valence electrons)

    c. a molecule of water, H_2O

    d. a molecule of carbon dioxide, CO_2

8. Using the periodic table,

    a. determine the oxidation number of Ca and Cl.

    b. write the chemical formula for calcium chloride.

9. Give the most common oxidation number and how many electrons are gained or lost for the following elements.

    a. oxygen (O)

    b. boron (B)

    c. lithium (Li)

    d. sodium (Na)

    e. magnesium (Mg)

    f. aluminum (Al)

    g. carbon (C)

    h. iodine (I)

10. Use the periodic table to determine the type of bond most likely formed between the elements

    a. carbon and oxygen.

    b. lithium and fluorine.

    c. carbon and carbon.

    d. carbon and nitrogen.

11. Carbon and oxygen combine to form a gas called carbon dioxide. Carbon (C) has an oxidation number of 4+ and oxygen (O) has an oxidation number of 2–.

    a. What is the total of the oxidation numbers for all the atoms in carbon dioxide?

    b. Predict the formula for carbon dioxide.

    c. Is carbon dioxide an ionic or covalently bonded compound?

12. Carbon and hydrogen combine to form a gas called methane. Carbon (C) has an oxidation number of 4+ and hydrogen has an oxidation number of 1–.

    a. What is the total of all the oxidation numbers for all the atoms in methane?

    b. Predict the formula for methane.

    c. Is methane an ionic or covalently bonded compound?

13. The chemical formula for a molecule of glucose is $C_6H_{12}O_6$.

    a. How many atoms of carbon are in a molecule of glucose?

    b. How many atoms of hydrogen are in a molecule of glucose?

    c. How many atoms of oxygen are in a molecule of glucose?

UNIT 7

CHANGES IN MATTER

CHAPTER 16
Acids, Bases, and Solutions

CHAPTER 17
Chemical Reactions

CHAPTER 18
The Chemistry of Living Systems

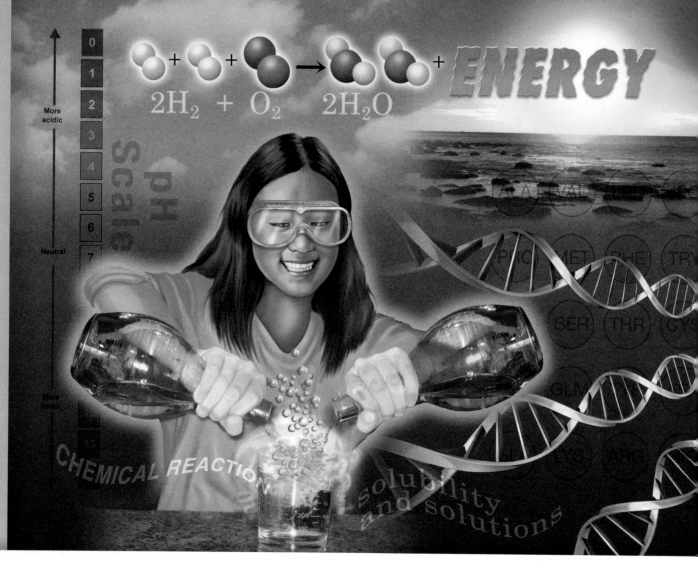

$$2H_2 + O_2 \rightarrow 2H_2O + ENERGY$$

Exploring on Your Own

Agricultural biotechnologists often use selective breeding to create foods with desirable qualities. In what ways are genetically-modified foods useful? What are some of the concerns raised by opponents of this technology? Describe the legal and ethical responsibilities of genetically-altered food manufacturers. What are your suggestions for meeting the nutrition needs of the world's population without using genetically-modified foods?

Chapter 16

Acids, Bases, and Solutions

Water is essential to all living things on Earth. Why is water such an important substance for living creatures? Consider your body for example—it is about 65 percent water by weight. For every hour of vigorous exercise, you may lose as much as a half-gallon of your body's water content through sweating and exhaling! You also lose small amounts of salts when you sweat. If the lost water and dissolved salts are not replaced, eventually your body will stop working. You can replace lost water by drinking fluids. To quickly replace salts, many athletes consume sports drinks.

Sweat and sports drinks are both examples of solutions—they are mostly water with dissolved substances. In this chapter, you will learn about solutions. You will also learn about some special solutions called acids and bases. Among other things, acids create the bitter taste in food and can dissolve many things, even rocks! Bases are slippery, like soap. Both acids and bases play a key role in maintaining your body's internal chemical balance.

Key Questions:

1. What is the difference between 10-, 14-, and 24-karat gold?

2. Why does salt dissolve in water but substances like chalk and sand do not?

3. What are acids and bases?

16.1 **Water and Solutions**

Water is one substance that makes our planet unique. All life on Earth depends on this useful combination of hydrogen and oxygen atoms. In our solar system, Earth is the only planet with so much warm, liquid water on its surface. Because we seem to have so much water, it is easy to take it for granted. Think about what you did yesterday. How often did you use water and how much? Now think about how yesterday would have been different if you didn't have water!

 **VOCABULARY**

solution - a mixture of two or more substances that is uniform at the molecular level.

alloy - a solution of two or more solids.

Solutions

A solution is homogeneous at the molecular level

A **solution** is a mixture of two or more substances that is uniform at the molecular level. *Uniform* means there are no clumps bigger than a molecule and the solution has the same ingredients everywhere. Grape soda is a solution you have probably consumed. All the particles in grape soda, from the flavor molecules to the color molecules, are evenly dispersed throughout the bottle (Figure 16.1).

An alloy is a solution of two or more solids

We often think of solutions as liquid. However, solutions exist in every phase: solid, liquid, and gas. Solutions of two or more solids are called **alloys**. Steel is an alloy (solution) of iron and carbon. Fourteen-karat gold is an alloy of silver and gold. "Fourteen-karat" means that 14 out of every 24 atoms in the alloy are gold atoms and the rest are silver atoms. The sweet smell of perfume is a solution of perfume molecules in air. This is an example of a solution of gases.

Muddy water is *NOT* a true solution

Muddy water is not a solution. Particles of soil are small, but each still contains thousands of atoms and molecules. A true solution contains only individual molecules that are not clumped together into larger particles.

Soda and seltzer water

Vinegar

Food color and water

Steel

Figure 16.1: *Examples of solutions.*

Solvents and solutes

What are solvents and solutes?

A solution is a mixture of at least two substances: a **solvent**, and a **solute**. The solvent is the substance that makes up the biggest percentage of the mixture. For example, the solvent in grape soda is water. The remaining parts of a solution (other than the solvent) are called solutes. Sugar, coloring dyes, flavoring chemicals, and carbon dioxide gas are solutes in grape soda.

Dissolving

When the solute particles are evenly distributed throughout the solvent, we say that the solute has **dissolved**. The illustration below shows a sugar and water solution being prepared. The solute (sugar) starts as a solid in the graduated cylinder on the left. Water is added and the mixture is carefully stirred until all the solid sugar has dissolved. Once the sugar has dissolved, the solution is clear again.

VOCABULARY

solvent - the component of a solution that is present in the greatest amount.

solute - any component of a solution other than the solvent.

dissolve - to separate and disperse a solid into individual particles in the presence of a solvent.

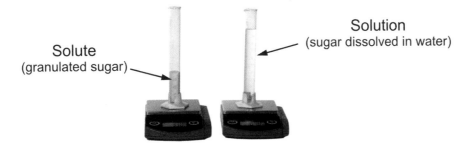

Solute
(granulated sugar)

Solution
(sugar dissolved in water)

The molecular explanation for dissolving

Dissolving of a solid (like sugar) occurs when molecules of solvent interact with and separate molecules of solute (Figure 16.2). Most substances dissolve faster at higher temperatures. You may have noticed that sugar dissolves much faster in hot water than in cold water. This is because higher temperature molecules have more energy and are more effective at knocking off molecules of solute.

Why solutes are ground up into powder

Dissolving can only occur where the solvent can touch the solute. Most things that are meant to be dissolved, like salt and sugar, are ground up to a powder to increase their surface areas. Increased surface area makes dissolving faster because more solute is exposed to the solvent.

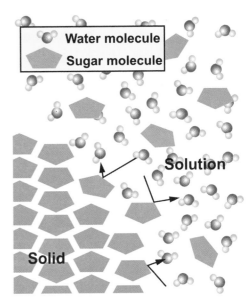

Figure 16.2: *The molecular explanation for a solid dissolving in a liquid. Molecules of solvent interact with and carry away molecules of solute.*

Solubility

What is solubility? The term **solubility** means the amount of solute (if any) that can be dissolved in a volume of solvent. Solubility is often listed in grams per 100 milliliters of solvent. Solubility is always given at a specific temperature since temperature strongly affects solubility. For example, Table 16.1 tells you that 200 grams of sugar can be dissolved in 100 milliliters of water at 25°C.

Insoluble substances do not dissolve Notice in Table 16.1 that chalk and talc do not have solubility values. These substances are **insoluble** in water because they do not dissolve in water. You can mix chalk dust and water and stir them all you want but you will still just have a mixture of chalk dust and water. The water will not separate the chalk dust into individual molecules because chalk does not dissolve in water.

Saturation Suppose you add 300 grams of sugar to 100 milliliters of water at 25°C? What happens? According to Table 16.1, 200 grams will dissolve in the water. *The rest will remain solid*. That means you will be left with 100 grams of solid sugar at the bottom of your solution. Any solute added in excess of the solubility does not dissolve. A solution is **saturated** if it contains as much solute as the solvent can dissolve. Dissolving 200 grams of sugar in 100 milliliters of water creates a saturated solution because no more sugar will dissolve.

 VOCABULARY

solubility - the amount of solute that can be dissolved in a specific volume of solvent under certain conditions.

insoluble - a substance is insoluble in a particular solvent if it does not dissolve in that solvent.

saturated - a solution is saturated if it contains as much solute as the solvent can dissolve.

Table 16.1: Solubility of some materials in water.

Common name	Solubility at 25°C (grams per 100 mL H$_2$O)
table salt (NaCl)	37.7
sugar (C$_{12}$H$_{22}$O$_{11}$)	200
baking soda (NaHCO$_3$)	approx. 10
chalk (CaCO$_3$)	insoluble
talc (Mg silicates)	insoluble

How much salt will dissolve in water?

Seawater is a solution of water, salt, and other minerals. How much salt can dissolve in 200 milliliters of water at 25°C?

1. Looking for: Grams of solute (salt)

2. Given: Volume (200 mL) and temperature of solvent

3. Relationships: 37.7 grams of salt dissolves in 100 milliliters of water at 2°C (Table 16.1).

4. Solution: If 37.7 grams dissolves in 100 milliliters, then twice as much, or 75.4 grams, will dissolve in 200 milliliters.

Concentration

How do you express solution concentration? In chemistry, it is important to know the exact **concentration** of a solution—that is, the exact amount of solute dissolved in a given amount of solvent. The mass-percent is an accurate way to describe concentration. The concentration of a solvent in mass-percent is the mass of the solute divided by the total mass of the solution.

$$\text{Concentration} = \frac{\text{mass of solute}}{\text{total mass of solution}} \times 100\%$$

Mass percent example Suppose you dissolve 10.0 grams of sugar in 90.0 grams of water (Figure 16.3). What is the mass percent of sugar in the solution?

$$\text{Concentration} = \frac{10\text{g sugar}}{(10\text{ g} + 90\text{ g})\text{ solution}} \times (100\%) = 10\%$$

Describing very low concentrations Parts per million (ppm), parts per billion (ppb), and parts per trillion (ppt) are commonly used to describe very small concentrations of pollutants in the environment. These terms are measures of the ratio (by mass) of one material in a much larger amount of another. For example, a pinch (gram) of salt in 10 tons of potato chips is about 1 gram of salt per billion grams of chips, or a concentration of 1 ppb.

10 g sugar

90 g water

+

Mix

100 g of solution that is 10% sugar

Figure 16.3: *Preparing a sugar solution with a concentration of 10 percent.*

Concentration	How many grams of salt do you need to make 500 grams of a solution with a concentration of 5 percent salt?
	1. Looking for: Mass of salt (solute)
	2. Given: Concentration (5%) and total mass of solution (500 g)
	3. Relationships: Concentration = mass of solute ÷ total mass of solution
	4. Solution: 0.05 = mass of salt ÷ 500 g mass of salt = 0.05 × 500 g = 25 g

 *CHALLENGE*

Lead is toxic to humans and therefore there are limits on the allowable concentration of lead in drinking water. What is the maximum concentration of lead in drinking water allowed by the Environmental Protection Agency (EPA)?

Equilibrium and supersaturation

Dissolving and undissolving

When a solute like sugar is mixed with a solvent like water, *two* processes are actually going on continuously:

- molecules of solute dissolve and go into solution; and
- molecules of solute come out of solution and become "undissolved."

When the concentration is lower than the solubility, the dissolving process puts molecules into solution faster than they come out. The concentration increases and the mass of undissolved solute decreases. However, dissolving and undissolving are still going on!

Equilibrium concentration

The more molecules that are in solution (higher concentration) the faster molecules come out of solution. As the concentration increases, the undissolving process also gets faster until the dissolving and undissolving rates are exactly equal. When the rate of dissolving equals the rate of coming out of solution, we say **equilibrium** has been reached. At equilibrium, a solution is *saturated* because the concentration is as high as it can go.

Supersaturation

According to the solubility table in Figure 16.4, at 80°C, 100 grams of water reaches equilibrium with 360 grams of dissolved sugar. At lower temperatures, less sugar can dissolve. What happens if we cool the saturated solution? As the temperature goes down, sugar's solubility also goes down and the solution becomes **supersaturated**. A supersaturated solution means there is more dissolved solute than the maximum solubility.

Growing crystals

Rock Candy

A supersaturated solution is unstable. The excess solute comes out of solution and returns to its undissolved state. This is how the large sugar crystals of rock candy are made. Sugar is added to boiling water until the solution is saturated. As the solution cools, it becomes supersaturated. Solid sugar crystals form as the sugar comes out of the supersaturated solution.

VOCABULARY

equilibrium - occurs when a solution has the maximum concentration of dissolved solute; the dissolving rate equals the rate at which molecules come out of solution (undissolve).

supersaturated - having a concentration greater than the maximum solubility.

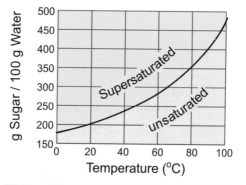

Temp (°C)	g Sugar / 100 g H₂O	Temp (°C)	g Sugar / 100 g H₂O
0	177	50	259
10	189	60	284
20	204	70	318
30	219	80	360
40	238	90	410

Figure 16.4: *The process for making rock candy uses a supersaturated solution of sugar in water.*

The solubility of gases and liquids

Gas dissolves in water

The bubbles in soda are dissolved CO_2

Gases can also dissolve in liquids. When you drink carbonated soda, the fizz comes from dissolved carbon dioxide gas (CO_2). Table 16.2 lists the solubility of CO_2 as 1.74 grams per kilogram of water at room temperature and atmospheric pressure (1 atm).

Solubility of gas increases with pressure

The solubility of gases in liquids increases with pressure. Soda is fizzy because the carbon dioxide was dissolved in the liquid at high pressure. When you pop the tab on a can of soda, you release the pressure. The solution immediately becomes supersaturated, causing the CO_2 to bubble out of the water and fizz.

Dissolved oxygen

Table 16.2 also shows that 0.04 grams of oxygen dissolves in 1 kilogram of water. Dissolved oxygen keeps fish and other underwater animals alive (Figure 16.5). Just like on land, oxygen is produced by underwater plants as a by-product of photosynthesis.

Solubility of gas decreases with temperature

When temperature goes up, the solubility of gases in liquid goes down (Figure 16.6). When the water temperature rises, the amount of dissolved oxygen decreases. Less dissolved oxygen means less oxygen for fish. When the weather is warm, fish stay near the bottom of ponds and rivers where there is cooler, more oxygenated water.

Solubility of liquids

Oil

Vinegar
(water solution)

Some liquids, such as alcohol, are soluble in water. Other liquids, such as corn oil, are not soluble in water. Oil and vinegar (water solution) salad dressing separates because oil is not soluble in water. Liquids that are not soluble in water may be soluble in other solvents. For example, vegetable oil is soluble in mineral spirits, a petroleum-based solvent used to thin paint.

Table 16.2: Solubility of gases in water at 21°C and 1 atm.

Gas	Solubility
Oxygen (O_2)	0.04 g/kg water
Nitrogen (N_2)	0.02 g/kg water
Carbon dioxide (CO_2)	1.74 g/kg water

Figure 16.5: *Fish and other aquatic life are sustained by dissolved oxygen in water.*

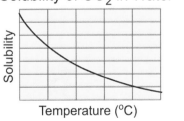

Solubility of CO_2 in Water

Solubility

Temperature (°C)

Figure 16.6: *The solubility of bases in water decreases as temperature increases.*

Water as a solvent

The universal solvent
Water is often called the "universal solvent." While water doesn't dissolve everything, it does dissolve many different types of substances such as salts and sugars. Water is a good solvent because of the way the H_2O molecule is shaped.

Water is a polar molecule
A water molecule has a negative end (pole) and a positive end. This is because electrons are shared unequally; pulled toward the oxygen atom and away from the two hydrogen atoms. The oxygen side of the molecule has a partially-negative charge and the hydrogen side of the molecule has a partially-positive charge. A molecule (like water) with a charge separation is called a **polar** molecule (Figure 16.7).

How water dissolves salt
The polar molecules of water dissolve many ionic compounds. Suppose a sodium chloride (table salt) crystal is mixed with water. The polar water molecules surround the sodium and chlorine atoms in the crystal. This causes the ions in the crystal to separate. Because opposites attract, the negative ends of the water molecules are attracted to the Na+ ions and the positive ends are attracted to the Cl– ions. Water molecules surround the Na+ and Cl– ions and make a solution (Figure 16.8).

Water dissolves many molecular compounds
When sucrose is mixed with water, the individual molecules of sucrose become separated from each other and are attracted to the opposite poles of the water molecules. Because sucrose is a covalent compound, the sucrose molecules do not dissociate into ions but remain as neutral molecules in the solution.

Water does not dissolve oils

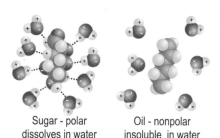

Sugar - polar
dissolves in water

Oil - nonpolar
insoluble in water

Oil does not dissolve in water because water is a polar molecule and oil molecules are nonpolar. In general, like dissolves like: water dissolves polar substances, and nonpolar solvents (like mineral spirits) dissolve nonpolar substances.

polar - describes a molecule that has charge separation, like water.

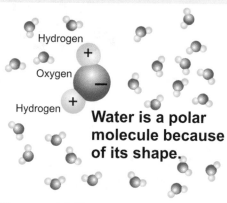

Hydrogen

Oxygen

Hydrogen

Water is a polar molecule because of its shape.

Figure 16.7: *Water is a polar molecule because it has a negative pole and a positive pole.*

⊕ Sodium ion   ⊖ Chlorine ion

Water molecule

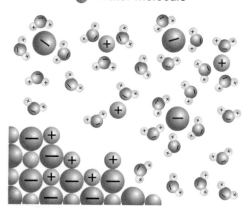

Figure 16.8: *Water dissolves sodium chloride to form a solution of sodium (+) and chlorine (–) ions.*

16.1 **Section Review**

1. One of the following is *not* a solution. Choose the one that is *not* a solution and explain why.
   a. steel
   b. ocean water
   c. 24-karat gold
   d. muddy water
   e. orange soda
2. For each of the following solutions, name the solvent and the solute.
   a. saltwater
   b. seltzer water (*Hint*: What causes the fizz?)
   c. lemonade made from powdered drink mix
3. Give an example of a solution in which the solute is *not* a solid and the solvent is *not* a liquid.
4. When can you say that a solute has dissolved?
5. Does sugar dissolve faster in cold water or hot water? Explain your answer.
6. Jackie likes to put sugar on her breakfast cereal. When she has eaten all of the cereal, there is some cold milk left in the bottom of the bowl. When she dips her spoon into the milk, she notices a lot of sugar is sitting at the bottom of the bowl. Explain what happened in terms of saturation.
7. Describe exactly how you would make 100 grams of a saltwater solution that is 20 percent salt. In your description, tell how many grams of salt and how many grams of water you would need.
8. Why is water often called the "universal solvent"?

Larry opens a new bottle of soda. He quickly stretches a balloon over the opening of the bottle. As he gently shakes the bottle, the balloon expands! Explain what is happening to cause the balloon to expand. Use at least three vocabulary words from this section. Draw a diagram to illustrate your explanation.

Dehumidifiers

A dehumidifier is a device that removes water vapor dissolved in air. A dehumidifier works by reducing the temperature of the air. The *dew point* is the temperature at which air with a given concentration of water vapor is saturated. Below the dew point, air becomes supersaturated. Dropping the temperature below the dew point causes the excess water to condense out as liquid water, which is then collected by the dehumidifier.

16.2 Acids, Bases, and pH

Acids and bases are among the most familiar of all chemical compounds. Some of the acids you may have encountered include acetic acid (found in vinegar), citric acid (found in orange juice), and malic acid (found in apples). You may be familiar with some bases including ammonia in cleaning solutions and magnesium hydroxide found in some antacids. The pH scale is used to describe whether a substance is an acid or a base. This section is about properties of acids and bases, and how the pH scale works.

What are acids?

Properties of acids An **acid** is a compound that dissolves in water to make a particular kind of solution. Some properties of acids are listed below and some common acids are shown in Figure 16.9. (*Note*: You should *never* taste a laboratory chemical!)

- Acids create the sour taste in food, like lemons.
- Acids react with metals to produce hydrogen gas (H_2).
- Acids change the color of blue litmus paper to red.
- Acids can be very corrosive, destroying metals and burning skin through chemical action.

Acids make hydronium ions Chemically, an acid is any substance that produces *hydronium ions* (H_3O^+) when dissolved in water. When hydrochloric acid (HCl) dissolves in water, it ionizes, splitting up into hydrogen (H+) and chlorine (Cl–) ions. Hydrogen ions (H+) are attracted to the negative oxygen end of a water molecule, combining to form hydronium ions.

What an acid does in water

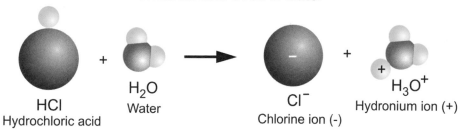

HCl
Hydrochloric acid

+

H_2O
Water

→

Cl^-
Chlorine ion (-)

+

H_3O^+
Hydronium ion (+)

acid - a substance that produces hydronium ions (H_3O^+) when dissolved in water.

Some common acids
(relatively weak)

Oranges and citrus fruits

Vinegar   Lemon juice

Figure 16.9: *Some weak acids you may have around your home.*

Bases

Properties of bases
A **base** is a compound that dissolves in water to make a different kind of solution, opposite in some ways to an acid. Some properties of bases are listed below and some common bases are shown in Figure 16.10.

- Bases create a bitter taste.
- Bases have a slippery feel, like soap
- Bases change the color of red litmus paper to blue.
- Bases can be very corrosive and can burn skin through chemical reaction.

Bases produce hydroxide ions
A base is any substance that dissolves in water and produces *hydroxide ions* (OH^-). A good example of a base is sodium hydroxide ($NaOH$), found in many commercial drain cleaners. This compound dissociates in water to form sodium (Na^+) and hydroxide (OH^-) ions:

What a base does in water

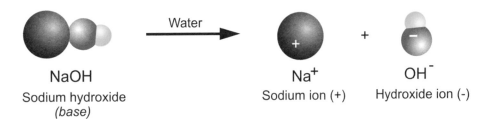

NaOH
Sodium hydroxide
(base)

Na⁺
Sodium ion (+)

OH⁻
Hydroxide ion (-)

Ammonia is a base
Ammonia (NH_3), found in cleaning solutions, is a base because it dissociates in water to form hydroxide ions. Notice that a hydroxide ion is formed when ammonia *accepts* H^+ ions from water molecules in solution as shown below. How is this different than $NaOH$?

What ammonia (base) does in water

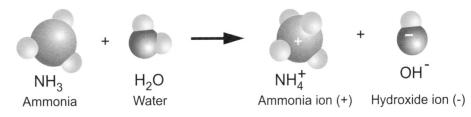

NH_3
Ammonia

H_2O
Water

NH_4^+
Ammonia ion (+)

OH⁻
Hydroxide ion (-)

base - a substance that produces hydroxide ions (OH^-) when dissolved in water.

Some common bases

Ammonia   Baking soda

Soap

Figure 16.10: *Some common bases.*

Strength of acids and bases

The strength of acids The strength of an acid depends on the concentration of hydronium ions (H_3O^+) the acid produces when dissolved in water. Hydrochloric acid (HCl) is a *strong acid* because HCl completely dissolves into H^+ and Cl^- ions in water. This means that every molecule of HCl that dissolves produces one hydronium ion.

Acetic acid is a weak acid Acetic acid ($HC_2H_3O_2$), in vinegar, is a *weak acid*. When dissolved in water, only a small percentage of acetic acid molecules ionize (break apart) and become H^+ and $C_2H_3O_2^-$ ions. This means that a small number of hydronium ions are produced compared to the number of acetic acid molecules dissolved (Figure 16.11).

The strength of bases The strength of a base depends on the relative amount of hydroxide ions (OH^-) produced when the base is mixed with water. Sodium hydroxide (NaOH) is considered a strong base because it dissociates completely in water to form Na^+ and OH^- ions. Every molecule of NaOH that dissolves creates one OH^- ion (Figure 16.12). Ammonia (NH_3) on the other hand, is a weak base because only a few molecules react with water to form NH_4^+ and OH^- ions.

Water can be a weak acid or a weak base One of the most important properties of water is its ability to act as both an acid and as a base. In the presence of an acid, water acts as a base. In the presence of a base, water acts as an acid. In pure water, the H_2O molecule ionizes to produce both hydronium and hydroxide ions. This reaction is called the *dissociation of water*.

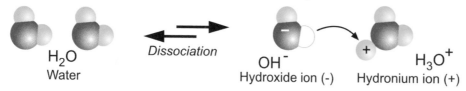

What does the double arrow mean? The double arrow in the equation means that the dissociation of water can occur in *both* directions. This means that water molecules can ionize and ions can also form water molecules. However, water ionizes so slightly that most water molecules exist whole, not as ions.

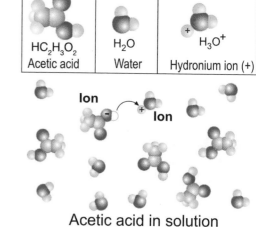

Acetic acid in solution

Figure 16.11: *Acetic acid dissolves in water, but only a few molecules ionize (break apart) to create hydronium ions.*

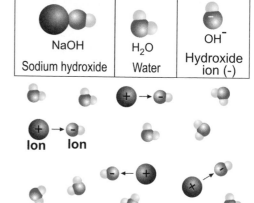

Sodium hydroxide in solution

Figure 16.12: *Sodium hydroxide (NaOH) is a strong base because every NaOH molecule contributes one hydroxide (OH^-) ion.*

pH and the pH scale

What is pH? pH measures the acidity of a solution. The **pH scale** describes the concentration of hydronium ions in a solution. The pH scale ranges from 0 to 14. A pH of 7 is *neutral*, neither acidic nor basic. Distilled water has a pH of 7. An acid has a pH less than 7. A concentrated solution of a *strong acid* has the *lowest* pH. Strong hydrochloric acid has a pH of 1. Seltzer water is a weak acid at a pH of 4. Weaker acids have a pH nearer to 7. A base has a pH greater than 7. A concentrated solution of a *strong base* has the *highest* pH. A strong sodium hydroxide solution can have a pH close to 14. Weak bases such as baking soda have pH closer to 7.

VOCABULARY

pH - pH measures the acidity of a solution.

pH scale - the pH scale goes from 1 to 14 with 1 being very acidic and 14 being very basic. Pure water is neutral with a pH of 7.

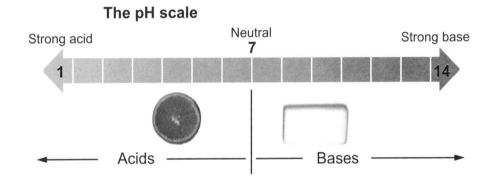

The pH scale

Strong acid　　　　Neutral 7　　　　Strong base

1 　　　　　　　14

← Acids ——　　—— Bases →

Table 16.3: The pH of some common chemicals.

Household chemical	Acid or base	pH
lemon juice	acid	2
vinegar	acid	3
soda water	acid	4
baking soda	base	8.5
bar soap	base	10
ammonia	base	11

The pH of common substances Table 16.3 lists the pH of some common substances. It turns out that many foods we eat and many ingredients we use for cooking are acidic. On the other hand, many of our household cleaning products are basic.

pH indicators Certain chemicals turn different colors when pH changes. These chemicals are called pH indicators and they are used to determine pH. The juice of boiled red cabbage is a pH indicator that is easy to prepare. Red cabbage juice is deep purple and turns various shades ranging from purple to yellow at different values of pH. Litmus paper is another pH indicator that changes color (Figure 16.13).

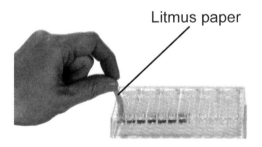
Litmus paper

Figure 16.13: *Red and blue litmus paper are pH indicators that test for acid or base.*

pH in the environment

The best pH for plants
The pH of soil directly affects nutrient availability for plants. Most plants prefer a slightly acidic soil with a pH between 6.5 and 7.0. Azaleas, blueberries, and conifers grow best in more acid soils with a pH of 4.5 to 5.5 (Figure 16.14). Vegetables, grasses, and most other shrubs do best in less acidic soils with a pH range of 6.5 to 7.0.

Effects of pH too high or low
In highly-acidic soils (pH below 4.5), too much aluminum, manganese, and other elements may leach out of soil minerals and reach concentrations that are toxic to plants. Also, at these low pH values, calcium, phosphorus, and magnesium are less available to plant roots. At more basic pH values of 6.5 and above, iron and manganese become less available.

pH and fish
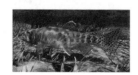
The pH of water directly affects aquatic life. Most freshwater lakes, streams, and ponds have a natural pH in the range of 6 to 8. Most freshwater fish can tolerate pH between 5 and 9 although some negative effects appear below pH of 6. Trout (like the California Golden shown above) are among the most pH tolerant fish and can live in water with a pH from 4 to 9.5.

pH and amphibians

Frogs and other amphibians are even more sensitive to pH than fish. This California tree frog, and other frogs, prefer a pH close to neutral and don't survive below a pH of 5.0. Frog eggs develop and hatch in water with no protection from environmental factors. Research shows that even a pH below 6 has a negative effect on frog hatching rates.

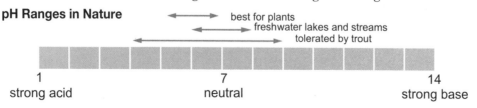

pH Ranges in Nature

best for plants
freshwater lakes and streams
tolerated by trout

1	7	14
strong acid	neutral	strong base

Figure 16.14: *Blueberries grow best in acid soils that have a pH between 4.5 and 5.5.*

Acids and bases in your body

Acids and bases play a role in digestion

Many reactions, such as the ones that occur in your body, work best at specific pH values. For example, acids and bases are very important in the reactions involved in digesting food. As you may know, the stomach secretes hydrochloric acid (HCl), a strong acid (pH 1.4). The level of acidity in our stomachs is necessary to break down the protein molecules in food so they can be absorbed. A mucus lining in the stomach protects it from the acid produced (Figure 16.15).

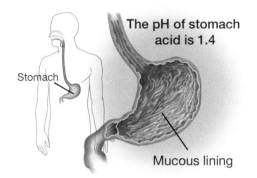

The pH of stomach acid is 1.4

Stomach

Mucous lining

Figure 16.15: *The stomach secretes a strong acid (HCl) to aid with food digestion. A mucus lining protects the stomach tissue from the acid.*

Ulcers and heartburn

Very spicy foods, stress, or poor diet can cause the stomach to produce too much acid, or allow stomach acid to escape from the stomach. An *ulcer* may occur when the mucus lining of the stomach is damaged. Stomach acid can then attack the more sensitive tissues of the stomach itself. Infections by the bacteria *h. pylori* can also damage the mucus lining of the stomach, leading to ulcers. The uncomfortable condition called *heartburn* is caused by excessive stomach acid backing up into the esophagus. The *esophagus* is the tube that carries food from your mouth to your stomach. The esophagus lacks the mucus lining of the stomach and is sensitive to acid. Eating very large meals can lead to heartburn because an overflowing stomach pushes acid up into the esophagus.

pH and your blood

Under normal conditions, the pH of your blood is within the range of 7.3–7.5, close to neutral but slightly basic. Blood is a watery solution that contains many solutes including the dissolved gases carbon dioxide (CO_2) and oxygen. Dissolved CO_2 in blood produces a weak acid. The higher the concentration of dissolved CO_2, the more acidic your blood becomes.

pH 6

pH 8

pH 7.4

Figure 16.16: *Under normal conditions, your blood pH ranges between 7.3 and 7.5. Holding your breath causes blood pH to drop. High blood pH can be caused by hyperventilating.*

Blood pH is controlled through breathing

Your body regulates the dissolved CO_2 level by breathing. For example, if you hold your breath, more carbon dioxide enters your blood and the pH falls as your blood becomes more acid. If you hyperventilate (breathe more quickly than usual), less carbon dioxide enters your blood and the opposite happens. Blood pH starts to rise, becoming more basic. Your breathing rate regulates blood pH through these chemical reactions (Figure 16.16).

Neutralization reactions

Neutralization When an acid and a base are combined, they neutralize each other. Neutralization occurs when the positive ions from the base combine with the negative ions from the acid. This process also goes on in your body. As food and digestive fluids leave the stomach, the pancreas and liver produce bicarbonate (a base) to neutralize the stomach acid. Antacids such as sodium bicarbonate have the same effect.

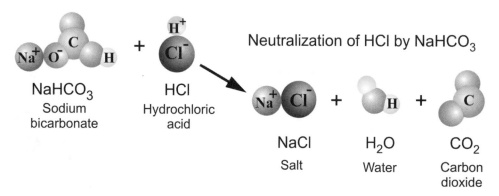

Neutralization of HCl by $NaHCO_3$

$NaHCO_3$
Sodium bicarbonate

HCl
Hydrochloric acid

NaCl
Salt

H_2O
Water

CO_2
Carbon dioxide

Adjusting soil pH Neutralization reactions are important in gardening and farming. For example about 25 percent of the yards in the United States have soil that is too acidic (pH less than 5.5) to grow grass very well. For this reason, many people add *lime* to their yard every spring. A common form of lime is ground-up calcium carbonate ($CaCO_3$) made from natural crushed limestone. Lime is a weak base and undergoes a neutralization reaction with acids in the soil to raise the pH.

Neutralization of acid in soil For example, sulfuric acid (H_2SO_4) in soil reacts with the calcium carbonate to form the salt calcium sulfate ($CaSO_4$) also known as gypsum. Sulfuric acid is in acid rain and is created in the atmosphere from pollutants in the air. Many of the walls of buildings and homes are made with "plaster board," which is a sheet of gypsum (plaster) covered with paper on both sides.

Test your soil

Almost any garden center carries soil test kits. These kits have pH test papers inside and are designed to help gardeners measure the pH of their soil.

Get a soil test kit and test samples of soil from around your home or school. Repeat the test taking new soil samples after a rainfall to see if the pH changes. See if you can answer the following questions.

1. What kinds of plants thrive in the pH of the soil samples you tested?
2. Is the soil the proper pH for the plants you found where you took your soil samples?
3. What kinds of treatments are available at your local garden center for correcting soil pH?

16.2 Section Review

1. List three ways that acids and bases are different.
2. Many foods are acidic. List four examples.
3. Answer these questions about water.
   a. Is water an acid, a base, neither, or both?
   b. What is the pH of pure water?
4. Nadine tests an unknown solution and discovers that it turns blue litmus paper red, and it has a pH of 3.0. Which of the following could be the unknown solution?
   a. sodium hydroxide
   b. vinegar
   c. ammonia
   d. soap
5. What makes a strong acid strong?
6. What makes a strong base strong?
7. Give two examples of a pH indicator.
8. Describe in your own words how the amount of carbon dioxide dissolved in your blood affects your blood pH.
9. Two years ago, you joined a project to study the water quality of a local pond. During the second spring, you noticed that there were not as many tadpoles (first stage in frog development) as there were the previous year (Figure 16.17). You want to know if the number of tadpoles in the pond is related to the pH of the pond. The records that document the water quality and wildlife started 10 years ago. Describe the steps you would take to determine whether a change in the pH of the pond water is affecting the population of frogs and their ability to reproduce.

Figure 16.17: *Question 9.*

Acid rain

Many environmental scientists are concerned about acid rain. Do research to answer the following questions.

1. What kinds of acids are in acid rain?
2. What is the typical pH of acid rain?
3. What is the cause of acid rain?
4. What are some environmental impacts of acid rain?
5. What can be done to reduce acid rain?

pH: A Balancing Act

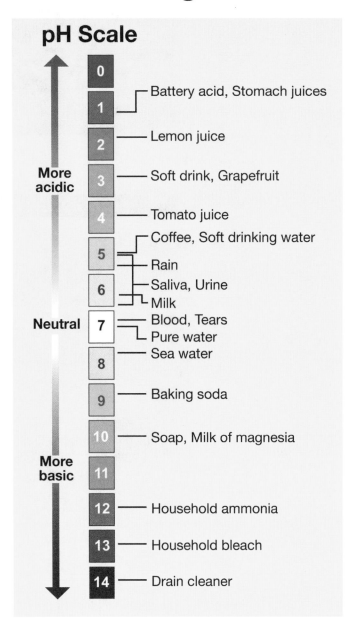

pH Scale

0	
1	Battery acid, Stomach juices
2	Lemon juice
More acidic 3	Soft drink, Grapefruit
4	Tomato juice
5	Coffee, Soft drinking water
	Rain
6	Saliva, Urine
	Milk
Neutral 7	Blood, Tears
	Pure water
8	Sea water
9	Baking soda
10	Soap, Milk of magnesia
More basic 11	
12	Household ammonia
13	Household bleach
14	Drain cleaner

Acids, bases, and *you*

As you can see from the chart on the left, solutions can be described as having a certain pH. A solution can be an acid (acidic), a base (alkaline), or neutral. Acids and bases are everywhere. Many of our favorite foods are acidic: Lemons and oranges, for instance, contain citric acid. We depend on gastric acid in our stomachs to digest our food, and if we suffer from discomfort caused by that same gastric acid, we can help neutralize it with a base like baking soda.

Your blood's normal pH range is between 7.35 and 7.45. You can compare this with many other ordinary solutions in the chart on the left. Our bodies are constantly adjusting to keep blood pH in a normal range.

Imbalances

The human body's many different processes produce a great deal of acid, which then must be removed. For example, our lungs can dispose of excess acid; carbon dioxide can form carbonic acid by causing us to breathe faster. Our kidneys remove excess acid from the blood and dispose of it in urine. Disease or extreme conditions can interfere with the body's self-adjusting system.

Renal artery

Kidney

There are two types of imbalance. We can have too much acid in our body fluids (acidosis), or those fluids can be too alkaline (alkalosis). These imbalances are either respiratory or metabolic. When the lungs are not functioning properly, the imbalance is respiratory. When the body's physical and chemical processing of substances is not functioning properly, the imbalance is metabolic.

Acidosis and its causes

Respiratory acidosis occurs when the lungs cannot remove all of the carbon dioxide produced by the body. As a result, body fluids become too acidic. This can be caused by almost any lung disease, such as asthma, or by a deadly habit like cigarette smoking.

Treatment may include drugs that expand the air passages in the lungs. Inhaled oxygen may be used to raise the oxygen level in the blood. Stopping smoking is a given among these attempts to restore the body's pH balance.

Metabolic acidosis is a pH imbalance in which the body has too much acid. The body does not have enough bicarbonate needed to neutralize the excess acid. This can be caused by a disease like diabetes, or by severe diarrhea, heart or liver failure, kidney disease, or even prolonged exercise.

A result of prolonged exercise is a buildup of lactic acid, which causes the blood to become acidic. Fluids can restore the body's pH balance, which is why various sports drinks are popular among athletes. Those drinks are formulated to help the body maintain its pH balance under stress.

Alkalosis and its causes

The opposite of acidosis, alkalosis is the result of too much base in the body's fluids. Respiratory alkalosis is caused by hyperventilation, that is, extremely rapid or deep breathing that makes the body lose too much carbon dioxide. It can be provoked by anxiety. In such a case, the person may breathe (or be helped to breathe) into a paper bag. Why? Because the bag retains the exhaled carbon dioxide and it can be taken back in. Altitude or any disease that causes the body to lose carbon dioxide may also cause hyperventilation. Metabolic alkalosis is a result of too much bicarbonate in the blood. Other types of alkalosis are caused by too little chloride or potassium. Alkalosis symptoms include confusion, muscle twitching or spasms, hand tremors, nausea, and lightheadedness.

Balancing act: food, drink, exercise, calm, acid, base ...

By nature our slightly alkaline pH needs to remain balanced there. Yet, what we eat and drink changes our pH. If you eat a lot of meat, such as hamburgers, steak, and chicken, your body produces more acid than someone who eats a lot of vegetables and fruits. If we don't balance what we eat, the body has to rely on reserves. For example, if you eat a lot of meat and no vegetables, your pH becomes acidic. Your kidneys can handle 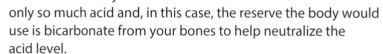 only so much acid and, in this case, the reserve the body would use is bicarbonate from your bones to help neutralize the acid level.

This is just one more instance in which the food we eat can affect our bodies in many ways. Maintaining a balanced diet is the first step toward good health—a little on the alkaline side (7.35–7.45).

QUESTIONS

1. What two organs regulate the acid-base balance?
2. What is a common cause of hyperventilation?
3. How is the alkalosis caused by hyperventilation treated?
4. Name a leading cause of respiratory acidosis.

Acid Rain and Stone Structures

Acid rain resulting from air pollution is a growing problem in the industrialized world. It can have devastating effects on the pH of our lakes. Interestingly, while the pH of some lakes has dropped dramatically in recent years, the pH of some nearby lakes during the same time period has changed very little. The type of rock that is found beneath and around the body of water is what makes the difference. Calcium carbonate, which is found in marble and limestone, has the ability to neutralize acid rain while other types of rocks and minerals have no effect. In this activity, we will make solutions of water and soak chips of different types of rock to see their effect on a dilute acid.

We will measure the pH of each solution using an indicator solution. The indicator solution appears red at a pH of 4, orange to yellow at a pH of 6.5, green to blue at a pH of 9, and violet to red-violet at pH of 10.

Materials:

chalk and/or marble chips; beakers; granite chips; white vinegar; Universal Indicator solution

What you will do

1. Place a small sample of marble chips in two 50 mL beakers.
2. Place a small sample of granite chips in one other beaker.
3. Be sure to keep some of the original indicator solution as a control.
4. Add 10 mL of vinegar-Universal Indicator solution to each.
5. Record the time and color of each solution according to the data table below.

Applying your knowledge

a. Compare the pH changes of the solutions containing granite and limestone.
b. Does the solution become more or less acidic as time passes?
c. What affect do you think acid rain has on marble statues?
d. Spelunking (cave exploration) is very popular in Ireland due to the large deposits of limestone. Explain how these caves could have formed.

Time	Color of solution (marble)	Approximate pH (marble)	Color of solution (granite)	Approximate pH (granite)
0 min				
5 min				
10 min				
20 min				
30 min				
40 min				
overnight				

Vocabulary

Select the correct term to complete the sentences.

solvent	acid	solute
equilibrium	pH	concentration
base	solubility	polar
alloy	solution	supersaturated

Section 16.1

1. The substance that dissolves particles in a solution is called the ____.

2. The substance that is dissolved in a solution is called the ____.

3. A mixture of two or more substances that is uniform at the molecular level is called a(n) ____.

4. A solution of two or more metals is known as a(n) ____.

5. A water molecule is an example of a(n) ____ molecule.

6. When the dissolving rate equals the rate at which molecules come out of solution, the solution is in ____.

7. The exact amount of solute dissolved in a given amount of solvent is the ____ of a solution.

8. A(n) ____ solution has a concentration greater than the maximum solubility.

Section 16.2

9. A substance that produces hydronium ions (H_3O^+) in solution is called a(n) ____.

10. A substance that produces hydroxide ions (OH^-) in solution is called a(n) ____.

11. ____ measures the acidity of a solution.

Concepts

Section 16.1

1. What would happen to the solubility of potassium chloride in water as the water temperature increased from 25°C to 75°C?

2. What are two ways to increase the dissolving rate of sugar in water?

3. Water is described as a polar molecule because it has
   a. a positive and a negative pole.
   b. two positive poles.
   c. two negative poles.
   d. no charge.

4. Water is a solvent in which of the following solutions?
   a. air
   b. liquid sterling silver
   c. saline (salt) solution

5. Very small concentrations are often reported in ppm. What does *ppm* stand for? Give three examples of concentrations that are described in ppm.

6. How would the fish in a lake be affected if large amounts of hot water from a power plant or factory were released into the lake?

7. When you open a can of room-temperature soda, why is it more likely to fizz and spill over than a can that has been refrigerated?

8. What happens to a supersaturated solution when more solute is added?

Section 16.2

9. What determines the strength of an acid?

10. What determines the strength of a base?

11. What is the pH of a neutral solution?

12. Indicate whether the following properties belong to an acid (A), a base (B), or both (AB).

    a. _____ creates a sour taste in food

    b. _____ creates a bitter taste in food

    c. _____ changes the color of red litmus paper to blue

    d. _____ changes the color of blue litmus paper to red

    e. _____ can be very corrosive

13. When hydroxide ions are added to a solution, does the pH increase or decrease?

14. Your stomach uses hydrochloric acid to break down the protein molecules in the food you eat. Give two reasons why this acid doesn't destroy your stomach and intestines during digestion.

15. Are hydronium ions contributed to a solution by an acid or a base?

16. If you add water to a strong acid, how will the pH of the diluted acid compare to the pH of the original acid?

    a. lower

    b. higher

    c. the same

17. How can ammonia (NH_3) be a base if it doesn't contain any hydroxide ions?

Problems

Section 16.1

1. What is the mass percent of table salt in a solution of 25 grams of salt dissolved in 75 grams of water?

2. You add 20 grams of baking soda ($NaHCO_3$) to 100 mL of water at 25°C.

    a. Approximately how much of the baking soda will dissolve in the water?

    b. What happens to the rest of the baking soda?

    c. How could you increase the amount of baking soda that will dissolve in 100 mL of water?

3. How much of the following materials will dissolve in 300 mL of water at 25°C?

    a. table salt

    b. sugar

    c. chalk

4. How many grams of sugar do you need to make a 20 percent solution by mass in 500 g of water?

Section 16.2

5. Solution A has a pH of 3 and solution B has a pH of 10.

    a. Which solution is a base?

    b. Which solution is an acid?

    c. What would happen if you combined both solutions?

6. Which of the following pH values is the most acidic?

    a. 1

    b. 3

    c. 7

    d. 8

7. Luke and Sian want to plant a vegetable garden in their yard. A soil testing kit measures the soil pH at 5.0, but the lettuce they want to plant in their garden does best at a pH of 6.5. Should they add an acid or a base to the soil to make it the optimum pH for growing lettuce?

8. Substance "X" has a pH of 6.5 and tastes sour. Is it an acid or a base?

Chapter 17

Chemical Reactions

When people think of chemistry, they often think of things that give off smelly odors or explode. The processes that make the "stink" in a "stink bomb" and cause explosions are examples of chemical reactions. Chemical reactions occur everywhere around you, every day. Chemical reactions occur in the engines of automobiles to make them run and they also happen in plants that release oxygen into the atmosphere.

In Chapter 16, you learned that a chemical strong enough to dissolve metal is in your stomach all the time. The chemical, hydrochloric acid, is a necessary part of the chemical reaction of breaking food down into nutrients that can be used by your body. In fact, chemical reactions are responsible for many processes that occur in your body every day. In this chapter you will learn what chemical reactions are and how they occur.

Key Questions:

1. Why are baking soda and vinegar such good ingredients for making a volcano model?

2. What does it mean to balance a chemical reaction equation?

3. When something burns, is there a chemical reaction taking place?

17.1 **Understanding Chemical Reactions**

If you leave a tarnished copper penny in acid for a few minutes, the penny becomes shiny again. The copper oxide that tarnished the penny was removed by a chemical reaction with the acid. Chemical reactions are the process through which chemical changes occur.

Chemical changes rearrange chemical bonds

Chemical change
Ice melting is an example of a *physical change*. During a physical change, a substance changes its form but remains the same substance. A *chemical change* turns one or more substances into different substances that usually have different properties. An example of chemical change is burning wood into ashes.

Using chemical changes
We use chemical changes to create useful materials. The rubber in car tires is an example of a material that has been modified by chemical changes. A chemical change called *vulcanization* inserts pairs of sulfur atoms into the long chain molecules of natural rubber. The sulfur ties adjacent molecules together like rungs on a ladder, and this makes vulcanized rubber much harder and more durable.

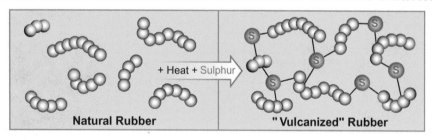

+ Heat + Sulphur

Natural Rubber   "Vulcanized" Rubber

Recognizing chemical change
A **chemical reaction** is a system of chemical changes that involves the breaking and reforming of chemical bonds to create new substances. A chemical reaction occurs when you mix baking soda with vinegar. The mixture bubbles violently as carbon dioxide gas, a new substance, is formed. The temperature of the mixture also gets noticeably colder. Bubbling, new substances, and temperature change can all be evidence of chemical change (Figure 17.1).

ã **VOCABULARY**

chemical reaction - a process that rearranges chemical bonds to create new substances.

Evidence of chemical change

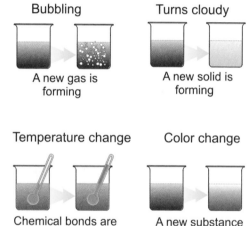

Bubbling   Turns cloudy

A new gas is   A new solid is
forming   forming

Temperature change   Color change

Chemical bonds are   A new substance
changing   is forming

Figure 17.1: *Four observations that may be evidence of chemical change.*

Products and reactants

Products and reactants How do we show the chemical reaction between baking soda and vinegar (Figure 17.2)? In cooking, you start with *ingredients* that are combined to make different *foods*. In chemical reactions, you start with **reactants** that are combined to make **products**. The reactants are substances that are combined and changed in the chemical reaction (baking soda and vinegar). The products are the new substances that result from the chemical reaction. The reactants and products may include atoms, compounds, and energy.

Products may change phase in a reaction The substances in a chemical reaction may be in different phases. In this reaction the reactants are a solid (baking soda) and a liquid solution (vinegar). What are the products? The bubbling that goes on is a clue that at least one of the products is a gas.

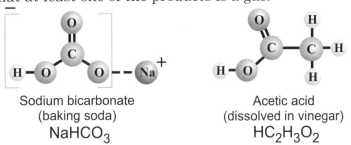

Sodium bicarbonate
(baking soda)
$NaHCO_3$

Acetic acid
(dissolved in vinegar)
$HC_2H_3O_2$

Start by counting the atoms in the products Chemically, the components that react are sodium bicarbonate ($NaHCO_3$) in the baking soda and acetic acid ($HC_2H_3O_2$) in the vinegar. The first step in understanding the reaction is to see what atoms are in the reactants. If you count them you see there are four elements: carbon, oxygen, sodium, and hydrogen. *The reaction must rearrange these same atoms into the products.*

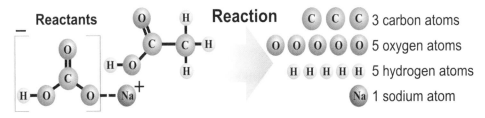

Reactants   Reaction

C C C 3 carbon atoms

O O O O O 5 oxygen atoms

H H H H H 5 hydrogen atoms

Na 1 sodium atom

Reactants

Reaction

Products

Figure 17.2: *The chemical reaction between baking soda and vinegar.*

The products of the reaction

Figuring out the products
A chemical reaction rearranges the existing atoms in the reactants to become new compounds in the products. In this case, the three carbon, five oxygen, five hydrogen, and one sodium atoms are rearranged to become sodium acetate ($NaC_2H_3O_2$), water (H_2O) and carbon dioxide (CO_2). Note that *the same exact atoms in the reactants are rearranged to make the products.* No new atoms are created!

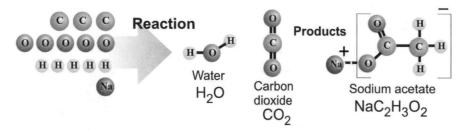

The whole reaction
We can now see the whole reaction clearly. Only three chemical bonds actually change. The sodium ion jumps to the acetic acid to make sodium acetate. The rest of the bicarbonate breaks up into water and carbon dioxide. Since carbon dioxide is a gas, that explains the bubbles observed during the reaction.

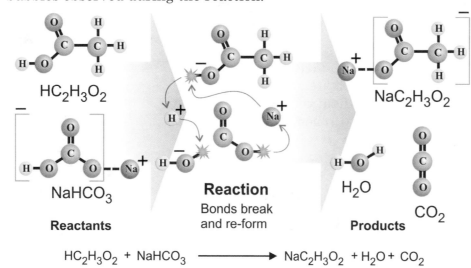

$$HC_2H_3O_2 + NaHCO_3 \longrightarrow NaC_2H_3O_2 + H_2O + CO_2$$

A chemical reaction rearranges the atoms of the reactants to form the new compounds of the products.

No new atoms are created!

A similar reaction occurs when an effervescent tablet is dropped into water. The tablet contains sodium bicarbonate and citric acid. The reactants are:

$NaHCO_3 + H^+$ (from citric acid) $+ H_2O$.

Can you figure out what the products are? (*Hint*: This reaction creates a bubbling gas, too.)

Chemical equations

Understanding a chemical equation

A **chemical equation** shows the exact numbers of atoms and compounds in a chemical reaction. Without drawing elaborate diagrams, we can write the baking soda and vinegar reaction as a chemical equation. The arrow shows the direction the reaction goes, from reactants to products.

ã **VOCABULARY**

chemical equation - an equation of chemical formulas that shows the exact numbers of atoms and compounds in a chemical reaction.

Chemical equation

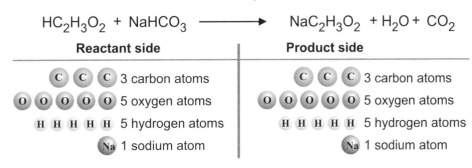

$$HC_2H_3O_2 + NaHCO_3 \longrightarrow NaC_2H_3O_2 + H_2O + CO_2$$

Reactant side	Product side
C C C 3 carbon atoms	C C C 3 carbon atoms
O O O O O 5 oxygen atoms	O O O O O 5 oxygen atoms
H H H H H 5 hydrogen atoms	H H H H H 5 hydrogen atoms
Na 1 sodium atom	Na 1 sodium atom

Conservation of mass

Notice that there are the exact same number of each type of atom on the reactant side of the equation as there are on the product side. For example, there are three carbon atoms in the reactants and three carbon atoms in the products. This demonstrates that *chemical reactions conserve mass*. The total mass of the reactants is equal to the total mass of the products because they are the same atoms! They have just been rearranged into new compounds.

Conservation of mass

The mass of the reactants equals the mass of the products.

Would doing the reaction this way demonstrate the conservation of mass?

Demonstrating conservation of mass

Once you understand atoms and reactions, conservation of mass is a perfectly obvious result. The mass is the same because *the atoms are the same atoms*. Of course, demonstrating the conservation of mass in this reaction is tricky because one of the products is a gas! It took a long time before people understood that mass is conserved because they were fooled by their own measurements. If you compared the mass of the reactants and products as shown in Figure 17.3, what do you think you would find? Can you think of a way to do the experiment so that no mass escapes being measured?

Figure 17.3: *If you tried to demonstrate conservation of mass this way, what would you find? Would the mass of the reactants equal the mass of the products?*

Balancing chemical equations

Multiple compound reactions The baking soda and vinegar reaction was a good one for learning about chemical equations because only one kind of each compound appeared. However, many reactions involve more than one compound of each type. A good example is the reaction that combines hydrogen and oxygen to produce water.

Start with the unbalanced reaction The reaction combines hydrogen and oxygen molecules as shown.

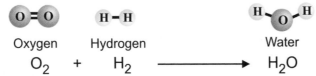

$$O_2 \ + \ H_2 \longrightarrow H_2O$$

Count the atoms on each side Count the atoms to see if there are the same number of each type of atom on the reactant and product sides of the equation.

Reactant side		Product side	
O O	2 oxygen atoms	O	1 oxygen atom
H H	2 hydrogen atoms	H H	2 hydrogen atoms

There is one more oxygen atom on the reactant side than there is on the product side. This means the reaction equation is not *balanced*. A balanced chemical equation has the same number of each type of atom on the product side and the reactant side.

The balanced chemical equation To balance the equation, we add another water molecule to the product side. Now there are equal numbers of oxygen atoms on both sides. However, there aren't equal numbers of hydrogen atoms, so another hydrogen molecule is added to the reactant side.

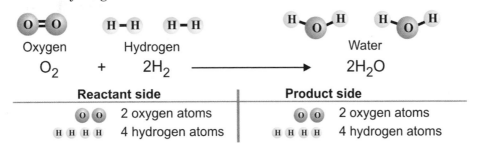

$$O_2 \ + \ 2H_2 \longrightarrow 2H_2O$$

Reactant side		Product side	
O O	2 oxygen atoms	O O	2 oxygen atoms
H H H H	4 hydrogen atoms	H H H H	4 hydrogen atoms

Understanding the numbers in a chemical equation

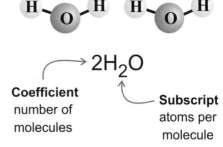

Coefficient number of molecules

Subscript atoms per molecule

The large number 2 in "2H$_2$O" tells you there are *two molecules* of H$_2$O in the reaction. The large number is called a *coefficient*. If a coefficient is not written it is understood to be "1."

The little numbers (subscripts) tell you how many atoms of each element there are in *one molecule*. For example, the subscript 2 in H$_2$O means there are two hydrogen atoms in a single water molecule.

The hydrogen–oxygen reaction releases a lot of energy and many people hope hydrogen will one day replace gasoline as a fuel for cars.

17.1 Section Review

1. What is the difference between a physical change in matter and a chemical change in matter?
2. In the following list, decide whether each item is a physical or a chemical change.
   a. liquid water freezes into solid ice
   b. wood burns to ashes
   c. a window shatters when hit with a rock
   d. an old car sits in a junkyard and rusts
   e. a cup of hot chocolate gives off steam
3. Answer the following questions about this chemical equation:

$$CH_4 + 2O_2 \rightarrow CO_2 + 2H_2O$$

   a. How many carbon atoms are on the reactant side of the equation? How many hydrogen? How many oxygen?
   b. How many carbon atoms are on the product side of the equation? How many hydrogen? How many oxygen?
   c. Is this equation balanced? How do you know?
   d. What does the coefficient "2" in front of the H_2O mean?
4. Which of the following reactions is balanced?
   a. $CS_2 + 3O_2 \rightarrow CO_2 + SO_2$
   b. $2N_2O_5 + NO \rightarrow 4NO_2$
   c. $P_4 + 5O_2 \rightarrow P_2O_5$
   d. $Cl_2 + 2Br \rightarrow 2Cl + Br_2$
5. What does "mass is conserved in a chemical reaction" mean?
6. It has been said that chemical equations are sentences in the language of chemistry. List three things that chemical equations can tell you about a chemical reaction.

Balancing chemical equations

1. Start with the correct chemical formula for each compound that appears as a reactant or product.
2. Write down the equation for the reaction (unbalanced).
3. Count the number of atoms of each element in the reactants and the products.
4. Adjust the coefficient of each reactant or product until the total number of each type of atom is the same on both sides of the equation. This is done by trial and error.

Important reminder: You can *not* change subscripts in order to balance an equation. For example, calcium chloride has the chemical formula, $CaCl_2$. You can *not* change the subscript on Cl from 2 to 3 and make $CaCl_3$ to get an extra chlorine atom. $CaCl_3$ is a totally different compound than $CaCl_2$. *You can only change coefficients to balance equations.*

17.2 Energy and Chemical Reactions

Have you ever felt the heat from a campfire or fireplace? If so, you have experienced the energy from a chemical reaction. *Burning* is a chemical reaction that *gives off* energy in the form of heat and light. In plants, photosynthesis is a chemical reaction that *uses* energy from sunlight (Figure 17.4). In fact, *all chemical reactions involve energy.*

The two types of reactions

Energy is involved in two ways
Energy is involved in chemical reactions in two ways: (1) At the start of a chemical reaction, energy is used to break some (or all) bonds between atoms in the reactants so that the atoms are available to form new bonds; and (2) energy is released when new bonds form as the atoms recombine into the new compounds of the products. We classify chemical reactions based on how the energy used in (1) compares to the energy released in (2).

Exothermic reactions
If forming new bonds releases *more* energy than it takes to break the old bonds, the reaction is **exothermic**. Once started, exothermic reactions tend to keep going because each reaction releases enough energy to start the reaction in neighboring molecules. A good example is the reaction of hydrogen with oxygen. If we include energy, the balanced reaction looks like this.

$$\underset{\text{Oxygen}}{O_2} \;+\; \underset{\text{Hydrogen}}{2H_2} \longrightarrow \underset{\text{Water}}{2H_2O} \;+\; \textbf{Energy}$$

Endothermic reactions
If forming new bonds in the products releases *less* energy than it took to break the original bonds in the reactants, the reaction is **endothermic**. *Endothermic reactions absorb energy.* These reactions need energy to keep going. An example of an important endothermic reaction is *photosynthesis*. In photosynthesis, plants use energy from sunlight to make glucose and oxygen from carbon dioxide and water.

$$\underset{\text{Carbon dioxide}}{6\,CO_2} \;+\; \underset{\text{Water}}{6\,H_2O} \;+\; \textbf{Energy} \longrightarrow \underset{\text{Glucose}}{C_6H_{12}O_6} \;+\; \underset{\text{Oxygen}}{6\,O_2}$$

VOCABULARY

exothermic - a reaction is exothermic if it releases more energy than it uses.

endothermic - A reaction is endothermic if it uses more energy than it releases.

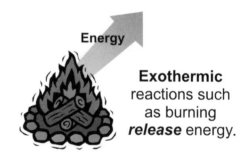

Exothermic reactions such as burning *release* energy.

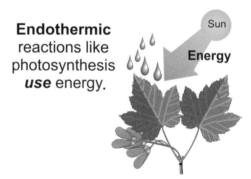

Endothermic reactions like photosynthesis *use* energy.

Figure 17.4: *Exothermic and endothermic reactions.*

Activation energy

An interesting question   Exothermic reactions occur because the atoms arranged as compounds of the products have lower energy then they had when arranged as compounds of the reactants. Since this is true, why don't all of the elements immediately combine into the molecules that have the lowest possible energy?

Activation energy   The answer has to do with **activation energy**. Activation energy is the energy needed to start a reaction and break chemical bonds in the reactants. Without enough activation energy, a reaction will not happen even if it releases energy when it does happen. That is why a flammable material like gasoline does not burn without a spark or flame. The spark supplies the activation energy to start the reaction.

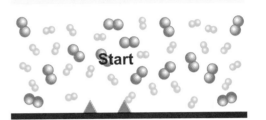

Reaction: $2H_2 + O_2 \rightarrow 2H_2O + energy$

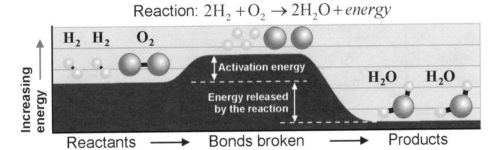

Energy from a spark splits a few nearby molecules.

An example of a reaction   The diagram above shows how the energy flows in the reaction of hydrogen and oxygen. The activation energy must be supplied to break the molecules of hydrogen and oxygen apart. Combining four free hydrogen and two free oxygen atoms into two water molecules releases energy. The reaction is exothermic because the energy released by forming water is greater than the activation energy. Once the reaction starts, it supplies its own activation energy and quickly grows (Figure 17.5).

Thermal energy   A reaction starts by itself when thermal energy is greater than the activation energy. Any reaction that could start by itself probably already has! The compounds and molecules that we see around us are ones that need more activation energy to change into anything else.

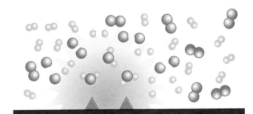
Released energy splits more molecules and the reaction becomes an explosion.

Figure 17.5: *Because energy released by one reaction supplies activation energy for new reactions, exothermic reactions can grow quickly once activation energy has been supplied.*

Addition reactions

Compounds are made in addition reactions

In an **addition reaction**, two or more substances combine to form a new compound. A good example of an addition reaction is the formation of rust (iron oxide, Fe_2O_3) from pure iron and dissolved oxygen in water. Iron oxide is an ionic crystal because the bonds between iron and oxygen are ionic bonds. Ionic crystals do not have structure diagrams like molecules, but they do have the specific ratio of atoms given by the chemical formula (2 Fe to every 3 O).

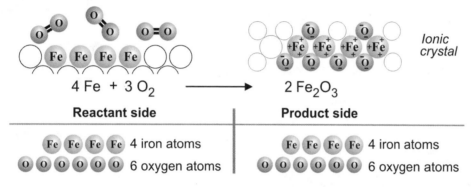

Polymerization is an addition reaction

Polymers are large molecules made up of repeating segments. Polymers are made by joining smaller molecules called monomers. The process of creating polymers is called **polymerization**. Polymerization is a series of addition reactions that join small molecules into very long chain molecules (Figure 17.6).

Acid rain

Some fossil fuels, like coal, contain sulfur. When these fuels are burned, the sulfur reacts with oxygen in the air to form sulfur dioxide in an addition reaction. In air polluted with sulfur dioxide, sulfur trioxide is create when sulfur dioxide reacts with oxygen. Finally, *sulfuric acid* is produced by a third addition reaction of sulfur trioxide with water.

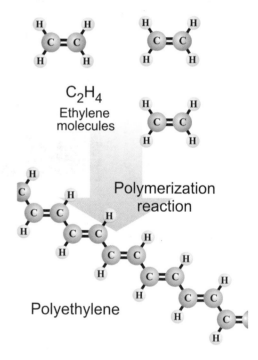

Figure 17.6: *Polymerization is a series of successive addition reactions that combine small molecules into large chain molecules.*

Decomposition reactions

Describing the phase of a product or reactant

In many cases, you want to know the form of the products and reactant in a reaction. Are they solid, liquid, or gas? Are they dissolved in water? The small symbols in the parentheses (*s, l, g, aq*) next to each chemical formula indicate the phase of each component in the reaction (Figure 17.7).

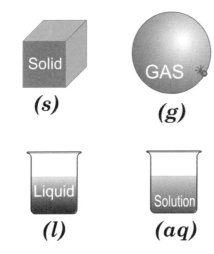

Decomposition reactions

A chemical reaction in which a single compound is broken down to produce two or more smaller compounds is called a decomposition reaction. The simplest kind of decomposition is the breakdown of a binary compound into its elements, as in the decomposition of water into hydrogen and oxygen with electricity.

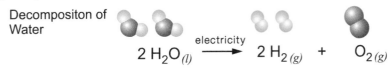

Decompositon of Water

$$2\ H_2O_{(l)} \xrightarrow{\text{electricity}} 2\ H_{2\ (g)} + O_{2\ (g)}$$

Larger compounds can also decompose to produce other compounds, as in the decomposition of baking soda with heat.

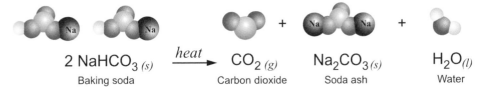

$$2\ NaHCO_{3\ (s)} \xrightarrow{heat} CO_{2\ (g)} + Na_2CO_{3\ (s)} + H_2O_{(l)}$$

Baking soda · Carbon dioxide · Soda ash · Water

symbol	meaning
(s)	substance is a solid
(l)	substance is a liquid
(g)	substance is a gas
(aq)	substance is dissolved in a solution (aqueous)

Figure 17.7: *What do the symbols shown in parentheses mean?*

Write a balanced decomposition reaction	Write a balanced chemical equation for the decomposition reaction of potassium chlorate ($KClO_3$) into potassium chloride (KCl) a salt substitute in food, and oxygen (O_2).
	1. Looking for: The balanced chemical equation
	2. Given: Products ($KClO_3$) and reactants (KCl, O_2)
	3. Relationships: The total number of each type of atom must be the same on both sides of the equation.
	4. Solution: The unbalanced equation is: $KClO_3 \rightarrow KCl + O_2$ The oxygen atoms are not balanced so we need to add molecules of $KClO_3$ and O_2 The balanced equation is: $2KClO_3 \rightarrow 2KCl + 3O_2$

Displacement and precipitation reactions

In single displacement, one element replaces another In single-displacement reactions, one element replaces a similar element in a compound. For example, if you place an iron nail into a beaker of copper (II) chloride solution, you will begin to see reddish copper forming on the iron nail. In this reaction, iron *replaces* copper in the solution and the copper *falls out* of the solution as a metal.

 **VOCABULARY**

precipitate - a solid product that comes out of solution in a chemical reaction.

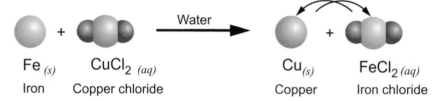

Fe $_{(s)}$	CuCl$_2$ $_{(aq)}$		Cu$_{(s)}$	FeCl$_2$ $_{(aq)}$
Iron	Copper chloride		Copper	Iron chloride

Precipitation occurs when one product is insoluble In many reactions, dissolved substances react to form substances that are no longer soluble. The insoluble product drops out of solution, forming a **precipitate**. A precipitate is a solid product that comes out of solution in a chemical reaction. Precipitates usually form many small particles that cause a cloudy appearance in a solution (Figure 17.8).

The limewater test for carbon dioxide is a precipitation reaction. In this test, a gas suspected of containing carbon dioxide is bubbled through a solution of CaO$_2$H$_2$ (limewater). Any carbon dioxide in the gas reacts to form a precipitate, turning the solution milky-white.

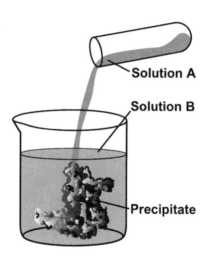

Figure 17.8: *The formation of a cloudy precipitate is evidence that a displacement reaction has occurred.*

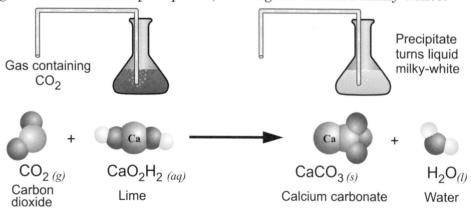

Gas containing CO$_2$

Precipitate turns liquid milky-white

CO$_2$ $_{(g)}$	CaO$_2$H$_2$ $_{(aq)}$		CaCO$_3$ $_{(s)}$	H$_2$O$_{(l)}$
Carbon dioxide	Lime		Calcium carbonate	Water

Combustion reactions

Petroleum is a mixture of hydrocarbons Almost 40 percent of all the energy we use comes from petroleum (oil) and two-thirds of that is gasoline and diesel fuel. Petroleum is not a single substance, but a complex mixture of many substances created over millions of years by the decay of plants and animals. The major elements in petroleum are hydrogen and carbon, with smaller amounts of oxygen, nitrogen, and sulfur.

Refining The *refining* process separates petroleum into molecules with different numbers of carbon atoms. The smaller molecules are used in gasoline. Heavier molecules become kerosene and heating oil. The heaviest molecules become tar and asphalt used for paving roads (Figure 17.9).

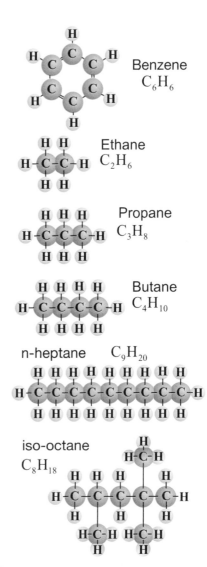

Range of molecule sizes	End use
C_1–C_{12}	Gasoline and light fuels, such as aviation fuel
C_{12}–C_{18}	Kerosene and heating oil
C_{19}–C_{30}	Grease, motor oil, wax
C_{31}–C_{36+}	Tar and asphalt

The reactions of burning gasoline In a perfect reaction, all the hydrocarbon molecules are completely burned to into carbon dioxide and water. Unfortunately, in an engine not all the fuel burns completely and pollutants such as carbon monoxide are also formed. Impurities such as sulfur in fuel and nitrogen in the air also have reactions that form pollutants including oxides of nitrogen and sulfuric acid.

Perfect combustion reaction

$$2\,C_8H_{18} + 25\,O_2 \xrightarrow{\text{spark}} 16\,CO_2 + 18\,H_2O$$

Iso-octane   Oxygen   Carbon dioxide   Water

Actual combustion reaction

$$2\,C_8H_{18} + 27\,O_2 + N_2 + S \rightarrow 15\,CO_2 + CO + 17\,H_2O + 2\,NO + H_2SO_4$$

Iso-octane   Oxygen   Nitrogen   Sulfur   Carbon dioxide   Carbon monoxide   Water   Nitrogen oxides   Sulfuric acid

Figure 17.9: *Some of the many molecules found in gasoline. These are examples of hydrocarbons, molecules made with only hydrogen and carbon.*

Nuclear reactions

What is a nuclear reaction?

Nuclear reactions change the nucleus of an atom. Up until 100 years ago, people were looking for a way to turn lead into gold. With today's understanding of nuclear reactions, it is now possible. However, we don't do it very often because the process is much more expensive than gold itself!

Nuclear versus chemical

Because they affect the nucleus itself, nuclear reactions can change one element into a different element. By comparison, chemical reactions do *not* change the types of atoms. Chemical reactions only rearrange atoms into different compounds. Nuclear reactions can also change an isotope into a different isotope of the same element. Remember, isotopes of the same element have the same number of protons but different numbers of neutrons in the nucleus.

Nuclear reactions involve more energy than chemical reactions

Nuclear reactions involve much more energy than chemical reactions. The energy in a nuclear reaction is much greater because nuclear reactions involve nuclear force, the strongest force in the universe. Chemical reactions involve electrical forces. The electrical force acting on an electron far from the nucleus is much smaller than the strong force acting on a proton or neutron *inside* the nucleus. The difference in strength between the forces involved is the reason nuclear reactions are so much more energetic than chemical reactions (Figure 17.10).

Mass and energy in nuclear reactions

Mass and energy are conserved together but *not* separately in nuclear reactions. This is because nuclear reactions can convert mass into energy. If you could take apart a nucleus and separate all of its protons and neutrons, the separated protons and neutrons would have more mass than the nucleus does all together. This bizarre fact is explained by Einstein's formula $E = mc^2$, which tells us that mass (m) can be converted to energy (E), when multiplied by the speed of light (c) squared. The mass of a nucleus is reduced by the energy that is released when the nucleus comes together.

nuclear reaction - a process that changes the nucleus of an atom and may turn one element into a completely different element.

Chemical reactions	Nuclear reactions
What part of the atom is involved?	
Outer electrons	Nucleus (protons and neutrons)
What changes?	
Atoms are rearranged into new molecules but the atoms stay the same.	Atoms may change into atoms of a different element.
How much energy is involved?	
A small amount	A huge amount

Figure 17.10: *Comparing nuclear and chemical reactions.*

17.2 **Section Review**

1. Name two ways energy is involved in chemical reactions.
2. Explain the difference between an exothermic and an endothermic reaction.
3. This is the chemical equation for the formation of rust:

$$4Fe_{(s)} + 3O_{2(g)} \rightarrow 2Fe_2O_{3(s)} + energy$$

   a. What do the symbols *(s)* and *(g)* mean?
   b. Is this reaction endothermic or exothermic?
   c. Is this a decomposition, addition, or displacement reaction?

4. Explain what *activation energy* is, and give an example.
5. What is a *polymer*, and what type of chemical reaction produces one?
6. What characteristic thing happens in a precipitation reaction?
7. Identify the following reactions as addition, decomposition, displacement, or combustion reactions.
   a. $2KCLO_3 \rightarrow 2KCl + 3O_2$
   b. $Mg + 2AgNO_3 \rightarrow Mg(NO_3)_2 + 2Ag$
   c. $6Li + N_2 \rightarrow 2Li_3N$
   d. $2C_3H_7OH + 9O_2 \rightarrow 6CO_2 + 8H_2O$

8. List three ways that nuclear reactions are different from chemical reactions.
9. What does it mean to *refine* petroleum, and why must this process be performed?
10. What do the symbols in $E = mc^2$ mean?

CHALLENGE

Propane—a common fuel

Propane, C_3H_8, is a fuel that is used by cooks and campers every day. It is burned in oxygen to make a flame that can cook food, provide heat and light, and even run refrigerators. Write the complete, balanced chemical equation for the combustion of propane.

There is a country that gets most of its fuel from plants, not from oil. Do you know what country that is? The answer is Brazil! Brazilians ferment sugar cane to make alcohol. They use alcohol instead of gasoline. Here in the United States, many companies are starting to do the same thing. Cars called "Flex-Fuel," or FF, can use E85 instead of regular gasoline. E85 is a mixture of 85 percent alcohol and 15 percent gasoline. The alcohol is made from corn. Since the process of making alcohol from corn uses almost as much energy as it produces, scientists are now developing ways to make alcohol from switch grass, a natural prairie grass.

STEM

How Do Hot and Cold Packs Work?

Some injuries, like a muscle pull, ankle sprain, bee sting, or burn require immediate application of a hot or cold compress. You can use a hot water bottle or an ice pack, but what if you are hiking or on a playing field, and you don't have access to these remedies?

Many stores sell chemical hot and cold packs, which can be used in an instant without refrigeration or a microwave. Chemical hot and cold packs are like mini chemistry labs hidden inside the plastic packaging.

Endothermic and exothermic reactions

Thermochemistry is the study of the energy given off or absorbed during a chemical reaction. During a chemical reaction, bonds between atoms and molecules are rearranged, and energy may be given off or taken up during the process.

Energy *absorbed*; pack feels cold

ENDOTHERMIC REACTION

Cold pack

Energy *released*; pack feels hot

EXOTHERMIC REACTION

Hot pack

With many chemical reactions, energy may be released in the form of heat. This is called an exothermic reaction. Exothermic reactions can produce hot temperatures or may even be explosive! Burning gasoline in a car's engine involves an exothermic reaction. Energy is released when iron rusts, so rusting is an exothermic reaction. Fireworks are exciting examples of exothermic reactions.

Some chemical reactions can only be completed if they absorb energy. When a chemical reaction absorbs heat from the environment, it is called an endothermic reaction. Endothermic reactions often result in cold temperatures. Refining aluminum ore involves endothermic reactions. The process of photosynthesis is an endothermic process also, since plants need to take in energy from the sun to make photosynthesis work.

What's inside hot and cold packs

Chemical hot and cold pack pouches are made of thick, strong plastic. The pouches contain a dry chemical in the form of a powder. Within the large pouch of hot and cold packs is an inner pouch made of thin, weak plastic. This inner pouch contains water. The packs are made active when the seal of the inner water pouch is broken and the contents are vigorously shaken. Water is released and mixes with the chemical in the outer pouch to create either an exothermic or endothermic reaction.

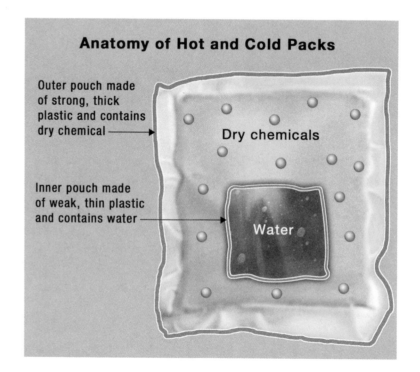

Anatomy of Hot and Cold Packs

Outer pouch made of strong, thick plastic and contains dry chemical →

Dry chemicals

Inner pouch made of weak, thin plastic and contains water →

Water

Many chemical hot packs contain calcium chloride or magnesium sulfate. These chemicals release heat energy when mixed with water and raise the temperature of the pack. Cold packs often contain ammonium nitrate. It absorbs heat energy and lowers the temperature of the pack. Commercial hot and cold packs typically last for about 20 minutes.

Hot and cold therapy

Physical therapists and sports trainers often use hot packs and cold packs to treat patients and athletes with injuries. However, the type of pack that should be used depends on the nature of injury.

Applying heat to your body can improve the flexibility of your tendons and ligaments. Tendons are bands of cordlike tissue that connect bone to muscle, while ligaments are cordlike tissues that connect bone to bone. Heat therapy can also reduce muscle spasms, reduce pain, and increase blood flow. The exact way in which heat relieves pain is not known. However, researchers think that heat inactivates nerves fibers that can force muscles to spasm. Heat may also induce the release of endorphins. Endorphins are chemicals in our body that block the transmission of pain by our nerves. Heat applied to body parts also relaxes the walls of blood vessels, resulting in increased blood flow. Health care professionals recommend using heat to untighten muscles and increase overall flexibility. However, it is best to avoid heating up already inflamed joints.

Like heat therapy, cold therapy may also be used to reduce muscle spasms. Muscle spasms are reduced with cold therapy because muscles fibers become less sensitive to being stretched. Cold is also useful for reducing pain and swelling. Cold therapy slows pain by reducing the speed of nerve impulses. Most tissue swelling is drastically decreased when cold and compression are applied to an injured area. The cold temperature constricts the walls of blood vessels, while the compression reduces the blood flow to the injured body part. Cold therapy is best used to reduce inflammation and swelling caused by sprains, strains, and bruises.

A variety of inexpensive, disposable hot and cold packs can be purchased at pharmacy stores. So next time you experience a minor injury, reach for an exothermic or endothermic reaction pack and take care!

QUESTIONS

1. Compare and contrast endothermic and exothermic reactions.

2. What are the structural components of hot packs and cold packs?

3. What are the differences between hot packs and cold packs?

4. How do physical therapists and sports trainers use hot packs and cold packs to treat patients and athletes with injuries?

Explore Hot and Cold Packs

All chemical reactions are either exothermic (release energy) or endothermic (absorb energy). In addition, some physical processes such as dissolution (dissolving) can also release or absorb energy. This is the basis for commercially available hot packs and cold packs. Most hot and cold packs work by breaking a membrane that separates a solid and water. Once the membrane is broken the solid dissolves in the water. Depending on the nature of the compound, heat is either released (hot pack) or removed from the environment (cold pack) during the process.

Materials:

thermometer; styrofoam cups; hot pack; cold pack; safety goggles; scissors; apron

What you will do

For the Hot Pack

1. Cut apart the outer pouch of hot pack and pour the solid into a styrofoam cup.
   Safety note: Do not touch the chemicals from the hot pack with your hands. Wear goggles and an apron!

2. Carefully cut the corner of the inner pouch and pour the water into another cup.

3. Measure and record the temperature of the water in the cup.

4. Pour the water into the cup containing the solid and quickly transfer the thermometer to the mixture.

5. Stir the mixture until it dissolves and record its final temperature.

For the Cold Pack

1. Repeat the above procedure with the cold pack.
   Safety note: Do not touch the chemicals from the cold pack with your hands. Wear goggles and an apron!

Experiment	Starting temperature (°C)	Final temperature (°C)
Part A: Hot Pack		
Part B: Cold Pack		

Applying your knowledge

a. What is the change in temperature for the hot pack? What is the change in temperature for the cold pack?

b. What compounds are used in commercial hot packs and cold packs?

c. Why does your skin feel cool when a cold pack is applied?

Chapter 17 Assessment

Vocabulary

Select the correct term to complete the sentences.

reactant	chemical equation	endothermic
exothermic	addition reaction	chemical reaction
products	polymerization	activation energy
nuclear reaction		decomposition reaction

Section 17.1

1. A(n) _____ occurs when you mix baking soda and vinegar.

2. The new substances that are created in chemical reactions are called _____.

3. A substance that changes during a chemical reaction is a(n) _____.

4. A(n) _____ is a short hand description of a chemical reaction using chemical formulas and symbols.

Section 17.2

5. A reaction is _____ if it releases more energy than it uses.

6. _____ is needed to start a reaction and break chemical bonds in the reactants.

7. In a(n) _____, the nucleus of an atom is changed, and one element may become a completely different element.

8. A series of addition reactions that join small molecules into large chain molecules is known as _____.

9. A reaction is _____ if it uses more energy than it releases.

10. Combining iron and oxygen to form rust is an example of a chemical reaction called a(n) _____.

11. The reaction that breaks down water into hydrogen and oxygen using electricity is known as a(n) _____.

Concepts

Section 17.1

1. Is tearing a piece of paper a physical change or a chemical change?

2. What happens to chemical bonds during chemical reactions?

3. The substance produced when iron is oxidized is
   a. water.
   b. oxygen.
   c. iron precipitate.
   d. rust.

4. The reactants in the equation $2H_2 + O_2 \rightarrow 2H_2O + energy$ are
   a. hydrogen and energy.
   b. hydrogen and oxygen.
   c. water and energy.
   d. oxygen and water.

5. The number of atoms of each element on both sides of a chemical equation must always be
   a. greater than one.
   b. less than two.
   c. different.
   d. equal.

6. The chemical formula $3H_2O$ means
   a. three atoms of hydrogen and three atoms of oxygen.
   b. six atoms of hydrogen and three atoms of oxygen.
   c. three atoms of water.
   d. three atoms of hydrogen and two atoms of oxygen.

7. How do balanced chemical equations illustrate the law of conservation of mass?

8. Which is an example of the use of activation energy?

 a. plugging in an iron
 b. playing basketball
 c. holding a match to paper
 d. eating

9. What physical and chemical changes occur when a wax candle burns?

Section 17.2

10. What conditions must be met in order for a reaction to be considered exothermic?

11. A "instant cold pack" is a plastic bag with a packet of water surrounded by crystals of ammonium nitrate. To activate the cold pack, you squeeze the plastic bag to release the water. When the water contacts the ammonium nitrate crystals, a reaction occurs and the pack becomes icy cold. Is the reaction inside the cold pack an endothermic or an exothermic reaction?

12. List two or more combustion reactions that are a part of your everyday life.

13. Calcium chloride and silver nitrate react to form a *precipitate* of silver chloride in a solution of calcium nitrate. This is an example of

 a. a combustion reaction.
 b. a displacement reaction.
 c. polymerization.

14. Explain why *mass* is not necessarily conserved in a nuclear reaction.

15. Write the balanced chemical equation for the decomposition of lithium carbonate (Li_2CO_3) into lithium oxide (Li_2O) and carbon dioxide (CO_2).

Problems

Section 17.1

1. Calculate the number of atoms of each element shown in each of the following.

 a. $CaSO_4$
 b. $4NaOCl$
 c. $Fe(NO_3)_2$
 d. $2Al_2(CO_3)_3$

2. Is this chemical equation balanced?
$2C_4H_{10}\ (g) + 13O_2\ (g) \rightarrow 8CO_2\ (g) + 10H_2O\ (l)$

3. The mass of an iron bolt was 5.4 grams when it was manufactured. After being bolted to an outdoor structure for several months, the mass of the bolt was found to have increased by 0.2 grams. Given the following balanced equation for the reaction, does this example support the law of conservation of mass? Why or why not?
$4Fe\ (s) + 3O_2\ (g) \rightarrow 2Fe_2O_3\ (s)$

Section 17.2

4. Many drain cleaners are a mixture of sodium hydroxide and aluminum filings. When these two substances mix in water, they react to produce enough heat to melt the fat in a clogged drain. The bubbles produced are hydrogen gas. The complete reaction occurs in two steps:
step 1: $Al(s) + NaOH(aq) \rightarrow Al(OH)_3(s) + Na^+(aq)$
step 2: $Na^+(aq) + H_2O \rightarrow Na_2O(s) + H_2(g)$

 a. Classify step 1 of the reaction as addition, displacement, or decomposition.
 b. Is this an endothermic or an exothermic reaction?
 c. Balance each equation for each step of the reaction.

The Chemistry of Living Systems

What is chemistry? If the image that comes to your mind is of a complicated array of tubes and smoking beakers, factories, and stinky fumes, this chapter will paint quite a different picture. Chemistry is you. Like all living organisms, your body is an incredibly complex chemical machine taking in chemicals from the food you eat and the air you breathe, causing countless chemical reactions to occur every second. In so many ways, the fundamental processes of life are chemistry.

If you take away the water, the rest of the human body is 53 percent carbon by weight. The chemistry of living things is the chemistry of carbon and its compounds. Carbon is the basic building block in the complex molecules that make up all living things. This chapter is your introduction to a branch of chemistry—organic chemistry—that is devoted solely to carbon and carbon compounds.

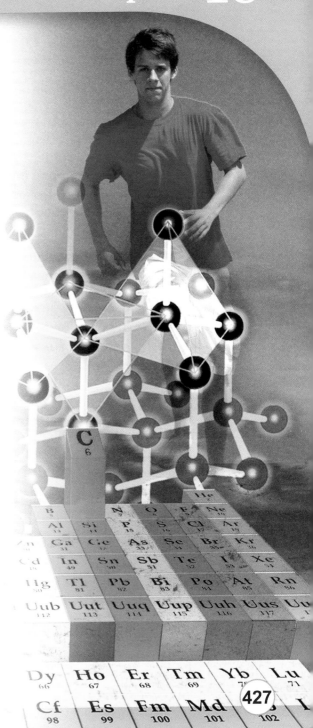

Key Questions:

1. Why is carbon so important to living things?

2. What are carbohydrates, fats, proteins, and DNA?

3. How does a living creature control its chemistry?

18.1 The Chemistry of Carbon

The chemistry of life is largely the chemistry of the element carbon. About 65 percent of the human body is water. Of the remainder, 91 percent is made up of only four elements: carbon, oxygen, nitrogen, and hydrogen (Figure 18.1). Of those four, carbon is the largest fraction at 53 percent. Carbon atoms often serve as the backbone to which oxygen, nitrogen, and hydrogen are connected. Carbon is so important because it is the lightest element that is able to make up to four bonds at the same time, including bonds with itself.

Carbon molecules

Carbon forms ring and chain molecules

Carbon has four electrons in its outer energy level, which means it has four valence electrons. Carbon can share one or more electrons to make covalent bonds with itself or as many as four other elements. Carbon molecules come in three basic forms: straight chains, branching chains, and rings. All three forms are found in important biological molecules. For example, glucose is a sugar made by plants and valine is an amino acid found in proteins—and both are built on carbon.

Rings

Benzene
C_6H_6

Straight chain

Glucose
$C_6H_{12}O_6$

Branched chain

Valine
$C_5H_{11}NO_2$

Organic chemistry is the chemistry of carbon

The three basic shapes are often combined (chains and rings) in the same molecule. **Organic chemistry** is the branch of chemistry that specializes in carbon and carbon compounds. Organic molecules are found in all living things and also in many nonliving substances such as candle wax and polyethylene plastic.

> **ã VOCABULARY**
>
> **organic chemistry** - the chemistry of carbon and carbon compounds.

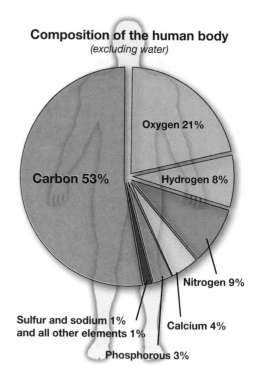

Composition of the human body
(excluding water)

- Oxygen 21%
- Carbon 53%
- Hydrogen 8%
- Nitrogen 9%
- Calcium 4%
- Phosphorous 3%
- Sulfur and sodium 1% and all other elements 1%

Figure 18.1: *After water, carbon is the most abundant element in the human body.*

Molecules in plants and animals

The four types of biological molecules
Living creatures are such complex organisms that even today we have much to learn about the chemical reactions that take place inside us. Scientists classify the organic molecules in living things into four basic groups: carbohydrates, proteins, fats, and nucleic acids. All living things contain *all four types* of molecules. And each type of molecule includes thousands of different chemicals, some specific to plants, some to animals. It is only in the past few decades that biotechnology has been able to reveal the rich chemistry of living things.

VOCABULARY

carbohydrates - energy-rich sugars and starches.

proteins - large molecules found in animal and plant tissue.

fats - energy-rich hydrocarbon chain molecules.

nucleic acids - biological molecules such as DNA that have the ability to store the genetic code.

Carbohydrates
Carbohydrates are mainly composed of carbon, hydrogen, and oxygen in a ratio of about 1:2:1. Carbohydrates exist as small molecules, like glucose, and long-chain molecules, like starches. Table sugar is a carbohydrate called *sucrose*. Sucrose is composed of two simple sugars, glucose and fructose, which are chained together (Figure 18.2).

Proteins
Proteins are large molecules composed of carbon, hydrogen, oxygen, nitrogen, and trace elements. Skin and muscle tissue are composed primarily of protein. A single protein may contain several thousand atoms in a complex structure.

Fats
Fats are medium-to-large nonpolar molecules that do not dissolve in water. Structurally, fats are long chains of carbon and hydrogen with different elements added every so often. Cholesterol is a fat that makes up part of the outer membrane of cells. Cholesterol is naturally essential to cells, but unnaturally high levels of cholesterol may lead to heart disease.

Nucleic acids
Nucleic acids such as DNA store the genetic code that allows organisms to reproduce. DNA is a huge molecule with millions of individual atoms. All the information that makes you a human is stored as a coded sequence of component molecules within DNA.

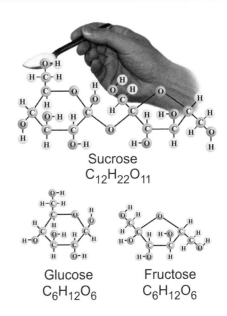

Sucrose
$C_{12}H_{22}O_{11}$

Glucose
$C_6H_{12}O_6$

Fructose
$C_6H_{12}O_6$

Figure 18.2: *Table sugar is sucrose, a carbohydrate made of two simple sugars: glucose and fructose.*

Carbohydrates

How carbohydrates are used   Carbohydrates are relatively small molecules used to store and transfer energy in living systems. Plant cells use energy from the Sun to build carbohydrates from carbon dioxide and water. Animal cells consume carbohydrates and extract the energy by breaking the carbohydrates down.

Starches and sugars   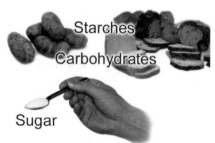 Carbohydrates are classified as either sugars or starches. Sugars are the smaller of the two types. Sugars break down relatively quickly in the body, releasing energy within a short time of being eaten. Glucose is the simplest sugar and is dissolved directly into the bloodstream.

Glucose is the simplest sugar   Glucose is the primary energy source for cells. When dissolved in water, the chain structure of a glucose molecule curls around on itself to become a ring (Figure 18.3). The glucose molecule can have several variations in the order of the OH-H-OH groups on either side of the carbon backbone. Some animals are so specialized that they can only digest one form of glucose and not the others.

Starches are chains of sugar   Starches are long chains of simple sugars joined together to make natural polymers. Because starches are larger molecules, they are slower to break down in the body and therefore can provide energy for a longer period than sugars. Corn, potatoes, and wheat contain substantial amounts of starches (Figure 18.4).

Cellulose   Cellulose is the primary molecule in plant fibers, including wood. The long-chain molecules of cellulose are what give wood its strength. Like starch, cellulose is made from chains of thousands of glucose molecules. However, in starch all the glucose units are the same orientation. In cellulose, alternate glucose units are inverted. This difference makes cellulose difficult for animals to digest. Trees grow so large partly because so few animals can digest wood.

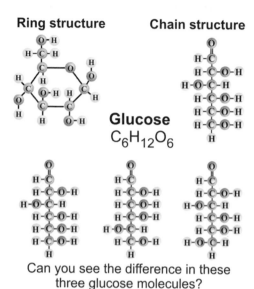

Can you see the difference in these three glucose molecules?

Figure 18.3: *Different structures of the glucose molecule.*

Starch
Starches are long chain molecules built from sugars.

Cellulose
Alternate sugars are inverted in cellulose.

Figure 18.4: *Starch and cellulose.*

Photosynthesis

The importance of photosynthesis

The energy that supports life on Earth starts with a reaction that takes energy from sunlight and stores it as chemical bonds in molecules of glucose and other simple sugars. This reaction is called photosynthesis. Photosynthesis occurs mostly in plants and in some types of bacteria.

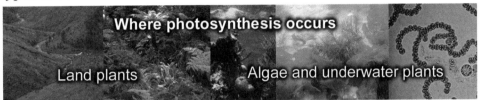

Where photosynthesis occurs

Land plants

Algae and underwater plants

The food chain

Photosynthesis is the foundation of the food chain on Earth (Figure 18.5). At the bottom of the food chain are producers, plants that take energy from the Sun and convert it to chemical energy in glucose and other organic molecules. Animals (including humans) ultimately get energy from photosynthesis because we eat plants or other animals that eat plants. Nearly all the energy in living things can be traced to this important reaction.

Photosynthesis releases oxygen

Photosynthesis also produces the oxygen in our atmosphere. Without photosynthetic organisms, Earth could not support life. Although oxygen is a common element on Earth, it is usually trapped by rocks and minerals in compounds like calcium carbonate ($CaCO_3$).

Photosynthesis removes CO_2

Photosynthesis removes carbon dioxide from the atmosphere. For every glucose molecule produced, six molecules of carbon dioxide are removed from the air, and six molecules of oxygen are produced. Carbon dioxide absorbs infrared radiation and therefore traps heat in the atmosphere. If too much carbon dioxide is present, the planet cannot cool itself by radiating energy into space. Increased levels of carbon dioxide are one factor in the warming of Earth by several degrees over the past 200 years. Can you think of ways to stabilize carbon dioxide levels?

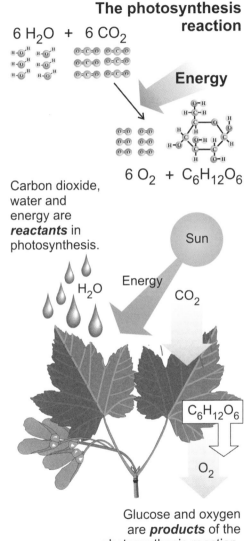

The photosynthesis reaction

$$6\ H_2O\ +\ 6\ CO_2$$

Energy

$$6\ O_2\ +\ C_6H_{12}O_6$$

Carbon dioxide, water and energy are **reactants** in photosynthesis.

Sun

H_2O Energy CO_2

$C_6H_{12}O_6$

O_2

Glucose and oxygen are **products** of the photosynthesis reaction.

Figure 18.5: *Photosynthesis is a chemical reaction that is the basis for the food chain on Earth.*

Respiration

Digestion Animals get energy and nutrients by breaking up glucose, starch, and other organic molecules. The digestive system breaks food down into molecules the body can use. Proteins are split into amino acids. Carbohydrates are reduced to simple sugars. Fats are split into glycerol and fatty acids. These nutrients are then absorbed into the blood and transported to all the cells of the body.

Cellular respiration On the molecular level, **cellular respiration** breaks down glucose into water and carbon dioxide again, extracting energy in the process. The reactions of respiration proceed in many steps, but the end result is that glucose and oxygen are used up and carbon dioxide and water are produced. Respiration is almost the reverse of photosynthesis, releasing energy that originally came from the Sun.

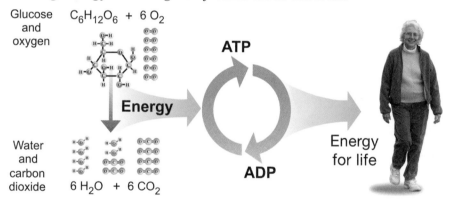

The ATP cycle Each cell converts the energy in glucose into chemical energy stored in molecules of ATP. A cycle between ADP and ATP is the energy source of cells. In a series of complex reactions that also require oxygen, one molecule of glucose is used to convert a maximum of 36 to 38 molecules of ADP to ATP. The ATP molecule is like a battery that distributes energy to where it is needed. Cells use the energy by converting the ATP back into ADP and the cycle starts over. Phosphorus is a critical part of the ADP–ATP cycle and one reason this element is an important nutrient.

cellular respiration - the reactions in cells that release energy from glucose.

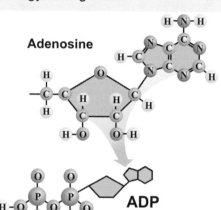

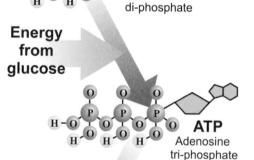

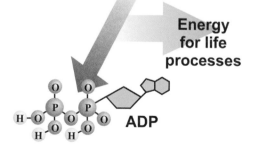

The importance of water

Why water is necessary

Liquid water is essential to life as we know it (Figure 18.6). The human body is typically between 60 and 65 percent water by weight. Most of the chemical reactions that sustain life *only work in solution*. Therefore, when scientists look for life on other planets, the first thing they look for is water. Evidence of water has been found on Mars, mostly as ice but also in small amounts in liquid and vapor form. That raises the tantalizing possibility that life may exist there. There are three important characteristics of water that make it essential for life.

Water is a good solvent

Water is a good solvent. In order to have a chemical reaction, molecules must be able to move around and contact each other. In a solid, this is just not possible. However, in a solution, molecules can move relatively large distances carrying energy and nutrients throughout a cell. Water also allows transport through the body on a larger scale. For example, oxygen is required by cells throughout the body, but it comes into the body in a centralized place: your lungs. Red blood cells absorb oxygen in the lungs and are carried throughout the body so they can distribute the oxygen.

Liquid over a wide temperature range

Water exists as a liquid over a large range of temperatures. In fact, virtually all living organisms on Earth are most active between the freezing and boiling point of water. The wide range over which water remains liquid allows most of Earth to be habitable most of the time. Very few biological processes can proceed when completely frozen because molecules: (a) cannot reach each other; and (b) have less thermal energy for activating reactions.

High specific heat

Water has a high specific heat—one of the highest of any substance known. Water's high specific heat means it takes a lot of energy to raise the temperature a small amount. This property of water helps living organisms maintain a stable body temperature even though outside temperatures may fluctuate a great deal.

2/3 of the Earth's surface is covered by water.

Your body is about 2/3 water by weight.

Figure 18.6: *Water is essential to our planet and to living things, including you.*

18.1 Section Review

1. About 80 percent of all chemical compounds on Earth contain carbon. Why is carbon found in so many compounds?

2. Complete the table by filling in the missing information.

Biological molecule	Composed of what atoms?	Example	Importance
carbohydrate		sugar	stores and transfers energy
fat			
protein	C, H, N, O and trace elements	found in skin and muscle tissue	
nucleic acid		makes up DNA	protein synthesis and heredity

3. Photosynthesis is a critically important process. Why?

4. Does photosynthesis involve a physical change or a chemical change?

5. List the reactants and products for
   a. photosynthesis
   b. cellular respiration

6. Why is water essential to life?

7. What are the characteristics of water that make it life-sustaining?

CHALLENGE

Photo by Scott Bauer, ARS/USDA

Termites are insects that eat wood. Wherever there is warmth, moisture, and wood, there will likely be termites too. Like ants, termites live in huge colonies of thousands of insects. In nature, termites help recycle dead trees into organic material. In houses however, termites can be a big problem. Do research on termites to answer the following:

1. What biological molecule can termites digest that most animals have great difficulty digesting?

2. What are some signs that a building may be infested with termites?

3. What parts of the world have the greatest problems with termites?

18.2 **Proteins, Fats, and Nucleic Acids**

Carbohydrates are the simplest of the important biological molecules. Proteins, fats, and nucleic acids are more complex molecules, containing thousands of individual atoms in a single molecule. Nucleic acids found in DNA are at the core of genetics, an active area of scientific research. The creation and functions of proteins are another area of active research. While we know a tremendous amount, we still have much to learn.

Fats

Fats provide long-term energy storage
Fats are high-energy molecules that plants and animals use to store energy in reserve for longer periods (Figure 18.7). Sugars break down too quickly to store energy reserves in a body. Fats are more complex molecules that take much longer to break down. Chemically, fats and oils are similar. Oils are fats that are liquid at room temperature.

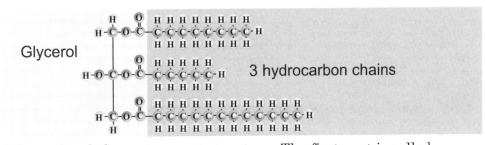

Glycerol

3 hydrocarbon chains

Saturated fats
A fat molecule has a two-part structure. The first part is called *glycerol*. Attached to the glycerol are three hydrocarbon chains. In a **saturated fat**, the carbon atoms are surrounded by as many hydrogens as possible (Figure 18.8, top).

Unsaturated fats
An **unsaturated fat** has fewer hydrogen atoms than it could have, meaning some of the carbon molecules have double bonds with each other instead of with hydrogen (Figure 18.8, bottom). Chemical processing of food adds some hydrogen to unsaturated fats in a process called *hydrogenation*. Because they are harder to digest, *partially hydrogenated* fats have a longer shelf life. However, research is showing that eating partially hydrogenated fats may be unhealthy.

saturated fat - a fat molecule in which each carbon is bonded with two hydrogen atoms.

unsaturated fat - a fat molecule that has fewer hydrogen atoms than a saturated fat.

Butter and oils are examples of fats

Figure 18.7: *Fats and oils are high-energy molecules that organisms use to store energy reserves.*

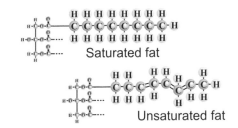

Saturated fat

Unsaturated fat

Figure 18.8: *The hydrocarbon chains in saturated and unsaturated fats.*

Proteins

Proteins are large molecules
Proteins are the basic molecular building blocks of cells and all parts of animals. Muscle, skin, blood, and internal organs contain proteins. Second only to DNA, proteins are among the largest organic molecules. A relatively small protein is shown in Figure 18.9.

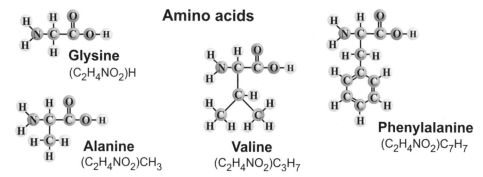

Amino acids

Glysine
$(C_2H_4NO_2)H$

Alanine
$(C_2H_4NO_2)CH_3$

Valine
$(C_2H_4NO_2)C_3H_7$

Phenylalanine
$(C_2H_4NO_2)C_7H_7$

Figure 18.9: *This small protein called erabutoxin B is the active ingredient in sea snake venon.*

Proteins are made of amino acids
Amino acids are the building blocks of proteins. Virtually all proteins found in animals are made from only 20 different **amino acids**. The amino acids in a protein form multiple chains that fold around each other in complex structures (Figure 18.10).

Shape and function
Only certain parts of a protein are chemically active. The shape of a protein determines which active sites are exposed. Many proteins work together by fitting into each other like a lock and key. This is one reason proteins that do the same function in one organism do not work in another organism. For example, a skin protein from an animal cannot replace a skin protein from a human.

Amino acids from food are used to build proteins
Food supplies new proteins that a body needs to live and grow. However, proteins from one organism cannot be directly used by another. Fortunately, the same 20 amino acids are found in proteins from almost all living things. In your body, digestion breaks down food protein into its component amino acids. Cells reassemble the amino acids into new proteins suitable for your body's needs.

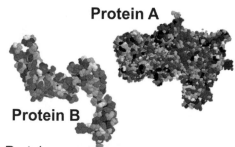

Protein A

Protein B

Proteins have complex shapes that fit other proteins or molecules in the body.

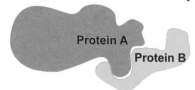

Protein A

Protein B

Figure 18.10: *The shape of a protein determines how it functions.*

Enzymes

The control problem Thousands of chemical reactions are going on in your body *every second* involving thousands of chemicals. The reactions proceed at just the right rate to produce energy as it is needed. When you exercise, the reaction rate increases because your body needs more energy. How does your body control its chemical reactions?

The temperature problem Sugar (glucose) does not turn into water and carbon dioxide by itself. Outside the body, this reaction needs the intense heat of a flame. Yet your body causes this reaction to occur at only 37°C. How does the body cause reactions like this to occur at such a low temperature?

The answer is that *enzymes* allow your body to initiate chemical reactions at a low temperature and to control the rate of reactions.

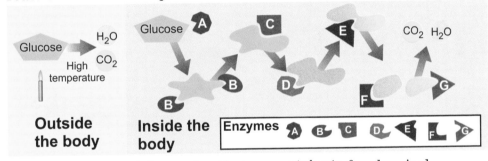

How enzymes solve the temperature problem **Enzymes** are special proteins that are **catalysts** for chemical reactions. A catalyst is a chemical that allows a reaction to have a much lower activation energy than it normally would. You can think of catalysts like *helper molecules* that allow a reaction to proceed in many small steps instead of all at once. Each step uses only the thermal energy provided by ordinary body temperature.

How enzymes solve the control problem The body controls the rate of reactions by regulating the amount of enzymes produced. For example, when a cell needs more energy, it produces more enzymes to break down glucose. Without those enzymes, glucose molecules stay together and store their energy for when it is needed.

enzymes - special proteins that are catalysts for chemical reactions in living things.

catalyst - a chemical that allows a reaction to have a much lower activation energy than it normally would have.

How do enzymes work?

Enzyme molecules have special shapes that allow them to bind to their target molecule. The body has thousands of different enzymes because each one is highly specific and only works on its target molecule.

Enzymes are quite sensitive to temperature and pH. Most will not work outside a narrow range of temperature and pH.

DNA and nucleic acids

Protein synthesis Cells must continually create the proteins they need from amino acids. This process is called **protein synthesis** and it occurs inside every cell of your body. How does protein synthesis work? How are the instructions for building proteins remembered and carried out?

DNA The answer involves DNA, a nucleic acid. A DNA molecule is put together like a twisted ladder, or *double helix* (Figure 18.11). Each side of the ladder is made of 5-carbon sugars called deoxyribose and phosphate groups. Nitrogen bases are paired in the center of the ladder. DNA is among the largest molecules known. A single DNA molecule contains more than one million atoms.

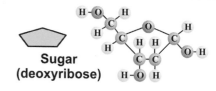

Sugar (deoxyribose)

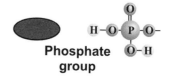

Phosphate group

The 4 nitrogen bases

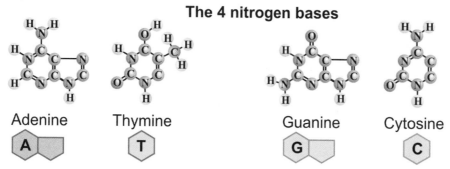

Adenine **A**   Thymine **T**   Guanine **G**   Cytosine **C**

The four nitrogen bases There are four nitrogen bases in two matched pairs, adenine (A) with thymine (T), and cytosine (C) with guanine (G). The assembly instructions for building a protein are coded in the sequence of nitrogen bases on one side of the ladder. For example, TAA-GCT-AGG-GCT-GGC-GGC-TAA tells the cell: start-alanine-arginine-alanine-glycine-glycine-stop. This code would result in a protein with that sequence of five amino acids.

TTT	Phenylalanine	GCT	Alanine	GGT	Glycine
TTA	Leucine	CCC	Proline	GGC	Glycine
ATG	Methionine	GTT	Valine	AGG	Arginine
TAA	start/stop	ACA	Threonine	AGT	Serine

DNA molecule

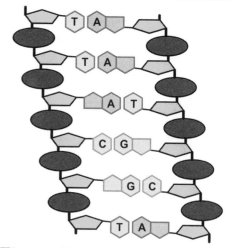

Figure 18.11: *The DNA molecule.*

DNA and reproduction

What reproduction does
When an organism reproduces, it must pass on the chemical information for how to create every single protein in the organism. This is an incredible amount of information considering how many proteins there are and how complex a protein is.

Splitting the DNA molecule
Fortunately, the DNA molecule is able to make exact replicas of itself. When a cell reproduces, enzymes split or "unzip" the DNA molecule down the center. Each half of the molecule contains a complementary code of nitrogen bases. Since guanine only pairs with cytosine and adenine only pairs with thymine, each half of the molecule contains the complete genetic information for how to make proteins.

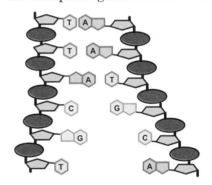

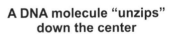

A DNA molecule "unzips" down the center

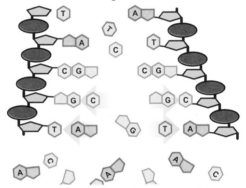

Each half is used as a template for making a new, identical DNA molecule

Rebuilding identical DNA molecules
Other enzymes called *polymerases* move along the unzipped DNA molecule rebuilding the nitrogen bases on each side. Still more enzymes rebuild the sugar and phosphate backbone on top of the completed nitrogen base pairs. At the end of the process, there are two identical DNA molecules.

Error checking
Another set of enzymes compares the old and new DNA strands for errors and corrects them by replacing nitrogen bases where necessary. We believe DNA replication occurs with less than one error out of every *billion* base pairs.

 VOCABULARY

mutation - change in the sequence of base pairs in DNA that may be passed on to successive generations.

Mutations and evolution

Even with odds of one in a billion, over time, the sequence of bases in a DNA molecule does change through random replication errors. Radiation from the environment and other processes also change DNA. Changes in DNA are called **mutations**. Changes in DNA lead to new proteins being built, which cause changes in living organisms that are passed on in successive generations. This is the chemical basis for evolution.

Vitamins

Vitamins   Most of the chemicals required for life, like proteins, can be synthesized by your own body. However, there are certain chemicals necessary for the chemistry of life that the human body does not make. Collectively, these are called *vitamins* and *minerals*. In addition to carbohydrates, fats, and proteins, your body must get vitamins and minerals from food.

Vitamin C   Ascorbic acid (Figure 18.12), also known as vitamin C, is required for the synthesis of several important chemicals in your brain and nervous system. Vitamin C is also needed to synthesize compounds used in the transfer of energy within cells (ADP/ATP). Vitamin C must be supplied daily through food.

Vitamin D   Vitamin D includes several fat-soluble compounds known chemically as *calciferols*. Vitamin D is not a true vitamin since it can be synthesized by your skin when cholesterol reacts with ultraviolet light. However, sunscreens and clothing partially block UV rays from reaching the skin and can result in vitamin D deficiency. To help prevent this possibility, foods such as milk are being fortified with vitamin D2 or vitamin D3. A severe deficiency of vitamin D leads to softening of the bones called *rickets* in children and *osteomalacia* in adults.

The B vitamins   The B vitamins include several compounds that must be obtained from food. The B vitamins often work together to bolster metabolism, maintain healthy skin and muscle tone, enhance immune and nervous system functions, and promote cell growth and division, including that of the red blood cells that help prevent anemia. All B vitamins are water soluble, and are dispersed throughout the body and must be replenished daily, with any excess excreted in the urine.

Folate   Folate is another vitamin especially important during periods of rapid cell division and growth such as infancy and pregnancy. Folate is needed to make DNA and RNA. Both adults and children need folate to make normal red blood cells and prevent anemia.

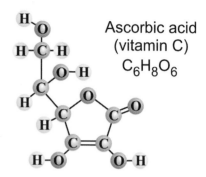

Ascorbic acid (vitamin C) $C_6H_8O_6$

Figure 18.12: Ascorbic acid, also known as vitamin C.

B vitamins

Vitamin B-1 (thiamine)

Vitamin B-2, also vitamin G (riboflavin)

Vitamin B-3, also vitamin P or vitamin PP (niacin)

Vitamin B-5 (pantothenic acid)

Vitamin B-6 (pyridoxine and pyridoxamine)

Vitamin B-7, also vitamin H (biotin)

Vitamin B-9, also vitamin M (folic acid)

Vitamin B-12 (cyanocobalamin)

18.2 Section Review

1. What is the difference between saturated and unsaturated fat? Why are *partially hydrogenated fats* useful for making potato chips but not particularly healthy for humans to eat?

2. Simple sugars are the building blocks of carbohydrates. What are the simple units that make up proteins?

3. Where does your body get the amino acids it needs for building proteins?

4. What type of biological molecule is an *enzyme*, and why are enzymes so important to living things?

5. Why is DNA important to the process of protein synthesis?

6. How does an organism pass on the chemical information for making proteins to the next generation?

7. Complete the table by filling in the missing information. You may have to do some research to fill in the last column.

Vitamin	Examples of why it is important	Foods that supply this vitamin
C		
D	strong bones	
B		
folate	needed to make RNA, DNA, and red blood cells	

8. One of the DNA sequences in Figure 18.13 is impossible. Which one is wrong? Why?

9. Which of the DNA sequences in Figure 18.14 contains a mutation?

10. A vitamin is a chemical
    a. in food that is needed but not produced in the body.
    b. that is produced in the body and not needed from food.
    c. that is found in food but not used by the body.
    d. that is found in the body but not found in food.

Which DNA molecule is correct?

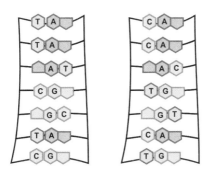

Figure 18.13: *Question 8.*

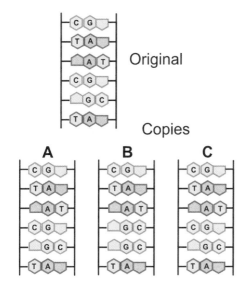

Figure 18.14: *Question 9.*

Good Fats vs. Bad Fats

What is your favorite food? French fries, ice cream, cookies, maybe, or candy? Does just reading that make your mouth water? Many of us eat these tasty treats every now and then, but eating too much of high-fat foods can be bad for our health. What does "high-fat" actually mean, and are all fats bad for us?

The lowdown on fats

We need a reasonable amount of fat in our diets. Fat helps support cell function and helps our bodies absorb vitamins. But a diet too high in certain fats can lead to many health problems, including obesity, diabetes, and heart disease.

High cholesterol is a leading risk factor for heart disease. It can cause the deposit of fatty buildups in our arteries called plaques. Plaques narrow the arteries and so reduce blood flow, a condition called atherosclerosis.

Cholesterol-carrying compounds called lipoproteins play a key role in the development of atherosclerosis and heart disease. Low-density lipoproteins (LDL) transport cholesterol from the liver to the rest of our body. When there is too much LDL cholesterol in the blood, it can begin to build up on the walls of the arteries. LDL cholesterol is called "bad cholesterol" because of this buildup. High-density lipoproteins (HDL) transport cholesterol from the blood back to the liver for removal. HDL cholesterol is less likely to be deposited in the arteries, and so is referred to as the "good cholesterol."

A low-fat diet will help to reduce the risk for heart disease. But what truly affects our health is the type of fat and the total amount we eat.

Unsaturated, saturated, and trans fats

Based on their chemical structure, fats are either unsaturated or saturated. An unsaturated fat has two or more carbon atoms that are not bonded to hydrogen. In a saturated fat, all the carbon atoms have the maximum number of hydrogen atoms attached.

Unsaturated fats, known as "good fats," lower LDL and reduce the risk for heart disease. Unsaturated fats are liquid at room temperature and are found in olive and canola oils, avocados, and some nuts. Fatty fishes, such as salmon and tuna, are good sources of unsaturated fat.

Saturated fats are referred to as "bad fats." Our livers easily convert them to LDL cholesterol, which increases the risk for heart disease. Saturated fats are solid at room temperature and are found in whole-milk dairy products like cheese, cream, and butter, and also in meat and poultry. Coconut and palm oils are among plant foods that are high in saturated fats.

Trans fatty acids, or trans fats, are included in the "bad fats" that raise LDL cholesterol levels. Food manufacturers produce trans fats by adding hydrogen to liquid vegetable oils, a process

known as hydrogenation. The more hydrogenated the oil, the harder it is at room temperature. For example, a tub of spreadable margarine is less hydrogenated than a stick of margarine. Trans fats are found in most fried foods and in many processed foods, such as cakes and cookies.

Food recommendations

For over 100 years, the U.S. Department of Agriculture (USDA) has made recommendations on the types and amounts of food we should eat. The USDA has developed "MyPlate," an interactive program incorporating recommendations from the USDA's 2015-2020 Dietary Guidelines for Americans. A tracker on the USDA website (www.choosemyplate.gov), can help you plan, analyze, and track your diet and physical activity.

The MyPlate symbol encourages people to pay attention to their food choices and create a healthier eating style. In terms of fat

intake, the USDA recommends low-fat or fat-free milk products, that less than 10 percent of calories from saturated fats, and that trans fats be kept to a minimum. Most fats we eat should come from unsaturated sources, such as fish, nuts, and vegetable oils.

Food labels

The FDA requires that food labels list not only overall fat but also saturated fat, trans fat, and cholesterol. Research shows that the type of fat we eat is more important than the amount. Food labels are designed to give consumers a complete picture of the foods they buy, and help them make healthier food choices and ultimately live better lives.

QUESTIONS

1. Why are low-density lipoproteins (LDL) called "bad cholesterol" and high-density lipoproteins (HDL) called "good cholesterol"?

2. How do unsaturated, saturated, and trans fats affect LDL and HDL levels?

3. Previous USDA recommendations have used a food pyramid instead of a divided plate. Why do you think they chose a plate for their symbol?

The Scoop on Nutrition Labels

All packaged foods are required to contain nutrition labels to help consumers choose healthy foods. A nutrition label shows the amount of calories, fat, cholesterol, carbohydrates, protein, and several vitamins and minerals in one serving of the food.

The exact amount of each nutrient a person needs depends on gender, age, activity level, and weight. An average female teenager should consume approximately 2,200 calories and not more than 73 grams of fat per day. A male should consume 2,800 calories and not more than 93 grams of fat. Protein requirements depend on body mass and amount of physical activity. Teenagers need between 1 and 1.5 grams of protein per kilogram of body mass.

Materials:

nutrition labels from food packages or from the internet; poster board

What you will do

1. Look at a variety of nutrition labels, including those for foods considered to be healthy and those that are unhealthy. You can use the Internet to find information on foods that don't come in packages, such as fruits and vegetables.

2. Suppose your doctor recommends a diet of 2,400–2,600 calories, fewer than 80 grams of fat, and at least 65 grams of protein. Use nutrition labels to select an assortment of food to eat in one day that meets these requirements and includes 100 percent of the daily requirement of vitamin A, vitamin C, vitamin D, calcium, and iron.

3. Make a poster describing your menu for the day. List the number of calories, grams of fat and protein, and percentage of each nutrient.

Applying your Knowledge

a. The term "empty calories" is used to describe foods that have a high number of calories but little nutritional value. List three foods that contain empty calories.

b. Which of the foods you selected for your menu contains the greatest amount of protein?

c. Which of the foods contains the greatest amount of fat?

d. Which three of your selected foods would you consider to be the most healthy? Explain why you chose these foods and what you think it means to say that a food is healthy.

Nutrition Facts

Serving Size 1 fruit 27/8 (140g)

Amount Per Serving	
Calories 69	Calories from Fat 2

	% Daily Value*
Total Fat 0g	0%
Saturated Fat 0g	0%
Trans Fat	
Cholesterol 0mg	0%
Sodium 1mg	0%
Total Carbohydrate 18g	6%
Dietary Fiber 3g	12%
Sugars 12g	
Protein 1g	

Vitamin A	7%	•	Vitamin C	138%
Calcium	6%	•	Iron	1%

*Percent Daily Values are based on a 2,000 calorie diet. Your daily values may be higher or lower depending on your calorie needs:

		Calories	2,000	2,500
Total Fat	Less than		65g	80g
Sat Fat	Less than		20g	25g
Cholesterol	Less than		300mg	300mg
Sodium	Less than		2,400mg	2,400mg
Total Carbohydrate			300g	375g
Fiber			25g	30g

Calories per gram:
Fat 9 • Carbohydrate 4 • Protein 4

NutritionData.com

Chapter 18 Assessment

Vocabulary

Select the correct term to complete the sentences.

nucleic acid	fat	carbohydrates
photosynthesis	unsaturated	proteins
cellular respiration	organic chemistry	saturated
catalyst	protein synthesis	nitrogen bases
amino acids	mutations	enzymes

Section 18.1

1. The branch of chemistry that specializes in carbon and carbon compounds is called ____.

2. The chemical energy that supports the food chain on Earth comes from a reaction called ____.

3. The reaction that breaks down glucose and releases its stored energy is called ____.

4. Sugars and starches are classified as ____.

5. DNA is an example of a(n) ____.

Section 18.2

6. High-energy ____ molecules are used to store energy in reserve.

7. ____ are made up of amino acids.

8. When a fat molecule has as many hydrogen atoms as possible bonded to each carbon atom, it is called a(n) ____ fat.

9. When a fat molecule has some carbon atoms double bonded to each other, along with hydrogen atoms, it is called a(n) ____ fat.

10. ____ are organic molecules that are the building blocks of proteins.

11. ____ allow your body to initiate chemical reactions and control the reaction rates.

12. Changes in DNA are called ____.

13. Enzymes are a type of ____ for chemical reactions.

14. The process the cells in your body use to build proteins from amino acids is called ____.

15. The molecular components within DNA that contain the code for building proteins from amino acids are ____.

Concepts

Section 18.1

1. What do all organic molecules have in common?

2. What makes carbon uniquely suited to being the basis for biological molecules?

3. Describe the four types of biological molecules. Give an example for each type.
   a. carbohydrate
   b. fat
   c. protein
   d. nucleic acid

4. What elements are carbohydrates made of?

5. Why do sugars break down so quickly in your body?

6. What is the difference between a starch molecule and a cellulose molecule?

7. How does the high specific heat of water make it beneficial to life?

8. Explain how photosynthesis and respiration are related carbon reactions.

9.   Which process adds oxygen (O_2) to Earth's atmosphere?

   a.   photosynthesis

   b.   cellular respiration

   c.   protein synthesis

10. What process removes carbon dioxide (CO_2) from the atmosphere?

   a.   photosynthesis

   b.   cellular respiration

   c.   protein synthesis

11. What process does the diagram illustrate?

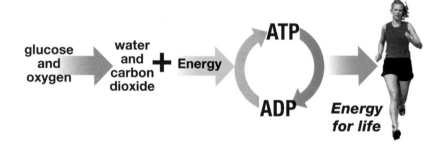

12. Digestion breaks down food into molecules the body can use. What type of molecules are each of the following broken down into?

   a.   proteins

   b.   carbohydrates

   c.   fats

Section 18.2

13. Describe how your body allows chemical reactions to occur at low temperature?

14. What is the function of fats in the human body?

15. What is the role of a catalyst in a chemical reaction? Describe how enzymes act as catalysts.

16. What is the structure of DNA called?

   a.   nitrogen bases

   b.   protein synthesis

   c.   double helix

17. How are mutations the chemical basis for evolution?

18. In the process of DNA reproduction, how are errors fixed?

19. Nitrogen bases

   a.   are amino acids.

   b.   hold the codes for building proteins.

   c.   initiate chemical reactions.

20. Which function does DNA perform?

   a.   It reproduces itself exactly.

   b.   It controls chemical reactions in the body.

   c.   It provides energy for cells.

Problems

Section 18.1

1.   Classify each of the following carbohydrates as containing mostly sugar, starch, or cellulose:

   a.   a stack of firewood

   b.   rice

   c.   jelly beans

   d.   a shirt made of cotton

   e.   an apple

2.   The human body is made mostly of

   a.   carbon, oxygen, nitrogen, and hydrogen.

   b.   oxygen, calcium, carbon, and hydrogen.

   c.   hydrogen, iron, nitrogen, and oxygen.

3. All plants use the process of photosynthesis. However, this process wasn't always understood. In one classic experiment, a small plant and its soil were weighed. The plant was given only water for a solid year. At the end of the year, the plant weighed much more than it did at the end of the first of the year. The soil weighed the same amount. Where did the extra weight of the plant come from?

4. A product of cellular respiration is energy. What is this energy used for?

5. Which of the following compounds are organic?

   a. nucleic acid
   b. CH_4
   c. H_2O
   d. hydrochloric acid
   e. table salt
   f. sugar

Section 18.2

6. Identify each of the following as a carbohydrate, fat, protein, or nucleic acid.

   a. glucose
   b. DNA
   c. cholesterol
   d. cellulose
   e. olive oil

7. An organic compound contains carbon, hydrogen, oxygen, and nitrogen. Could this compound be a fat? Could it be a nucleic acid? Explain.

8. What is the relationship between proteins and nucleic acids?

9. About how many different amino acids are found in animal proteins?

   a. 2
   b. 4
   c. 20

10. Which of the following is *not* part of the process for the body to get the essential proteins it needs?

    a. protein synthesis
    b. digestion of food protein into amino acids
    c. the manufacturing of amino acids from fats

11. Of the four nitrogen base pairs, adenine always pairs with

    a. adenine.
    b. guanine.
    c. thymine.
    d. cytosine.

12. Your body produces proteins it needs through the process of protein synthesis. How does your body obtain the vitamins it needs?

13. The diagram shows an enzyme and three different molecules. Which of the three molecules would this enzyme target for a reaction?

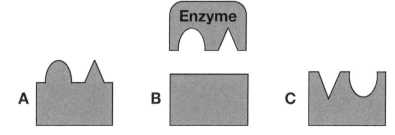

Glossary

A glossary is an alphabetical list of important words found in the sections in this book. Use this glossary just as you would use a dictionary: to find out the meaning of unfamiliar words. This glossary gives the meaning that applies to the words as they are used in the sections of this book. As with any subject, science has its own vocabulary. The study of science is more meaningful if you know the language of science.

A

absolute zero – lowest possible temperature, at which thermal energy is as close to zero as it can be, approximately –273 degrees Celsius.

absorption – when the energy of a wave is transferred to material as the wave passes through, resulting in a loss of amplitude.

acceleration – the rate of change of velocity.

acceleration due to gravity – the value of 9.8 m/s^2, which is the acceleration in free fall at the Earth's surface, usually represented by the small letter g.

accuracy – describes how close a measurement is to the true value.

acid – a substance that produces hydronium ions when dissolved in water. Acids have pH less than 7.

acoustics – the science and technology of how sound behaves.

activation energy – energy needed to break chemical bonds in the reactants to start a reaction.

addition reaction – two or more substances chemically combine to form a new compound.

additive color process – a process that creates color by adding proportions of red, green, and blue light together.

additive primary colors – red, green, and blue.

alkali metals – elements in the first group of the periodic table.

alloy – a solution of two or more solids.

amino acids – organic molecules that are the building blocks of proteins.

amorphous – solid with a random, jumbled arrangement of atoms.

ampere – the unit of electric current.

amplitude – the amount that a cycle moves away from equilibrium.

Archimedes' principle – states that the buoyant force is equal to the weight of the fluid displaced by an object.

asteroid – an object that orbits the Sun but is too small to be considered a planet.

astronomical unit – a distance equal to 150 million kilometers, or the distance from Earth to the Sun.

atomic mass – the average mass of all the known isotopes of an element, expressed in amu.

atomic mass unit – a unit of mass equal to 1.66×10^{-24} grams, which is one twelfth the mass of the isotope carbon-12.

atomic number – the number of protons in the nucleus. The atomic number determines what element the atom represents.

average – a mathematical process in which you add up all the values, then divide the result by the number of values.

average speed – the total distance divided by the total time for a trip.

axis – one of two (or more) number lines that form a graph.

B

balanced forces – result in a zero net force on an object.

base – a substance that produces hydroxide ions when dissolved in water. Bases have a pH greater than 7.

Bernoulli's principle – a relationship that describes energy conservation in a fluid.

boiling point – temperature at which boiling or condensation occurs.

brittleness – the tendency to crack or break; the opposite of elasticity.

buoyancy – the measure of the upward force a fluid exerts on an object that is submerged.

C

carbohydrates – energy-rich sugars and starches.

catalyst – a chemical that allows a reaction to have a much lower activation energy than it normally would have.

cellular respiration – the reactions in cells that release energy from glucose.

Celsius – a temperature scale in which water freezes at 0 degrees and boils at 100 degrees.

chemical bond – a bond formed between atoms through the sharing or transferring of electrons.

chemical equation – an equation of chemical formulas that shows the exact numbers of atoms and compounds in a chemical reaction.

chemical formula – identifies the number and element of each type of atom in a compound.

chemical properties – characteristics of matter that can only be observed when one substance changes into a different substance, such as iron into rust.

chemical reaction – a process that rearranges chemical bonds to create new substances.

color – the sensation created by the different energies of light falling on your eye.

comet – an object in space made mostly of ice and dust.

compound – a substance whose smallest particles include more than one element chemically bonded together.

compression –a squeezing force that can act on a spring.

concentration – the ratio of solute to solvent in a solution.

conductor – a material with a low electrical resistance. Metals such as copper and aluminum are good conductors.

constant speed – speed of an object that travels the same distance each second.

constructive interference – when waves add up to make a larger amplitude.

control variable – a variable that is kept constant in an experiment.

convection – the transfer of heat by the motion of matter, such as by moving air or water.

conversion factor – a ratio used to convert from one unit to another, such as from feet to meters.

coordinates – values that give the position relative to an origin.

covalent bond – a type of chemical bond formed by shared electrons.

crystalline – solid with a regular, orderly arrangement of atoms.

cycle – a unit of motion that repeats.

D

decibel – measure of the loudness (amplitude) of sound.

deduce – to figure something out from known facts using logical thinking.

density – the mass of matter per unit volume.

destructive interference – when waves add up to make a smaller, or zero, amplitude.

diffuse reflection – "dull" surface reflection, where each incident ray produces many scattered rays.

dissolve – to separate and disperse a solid into individual molecules or ions in the presence of a solvent.

Doppler effect – an increase or decrease in frequency caused by the motion of a source of sound.

ductility – the ability to bend without breaking.

E

efficiency – the ratio of output work divided by input work. Efficiency is often expressed as a percent with a perfect machine having 100 percent efficiency.

elasticity – the ability to be stretched or compressed and then return to original size.

electric charge – a fundamental property of matter that can be either positive or negative.

electric circuit – a complete path through which electric current can flow.

electric current – a flow of tiny particles that carries electrical energy in wires and machines. The particles (usually electrons) are typically much smaller than atoms and can flow around and between atoms even in solid matter.

electrical conductor – a material that allows electricity to flow through easily.

electromagnet – a magnet made with wires and electric current.

electromagnetic induction – using a moving magnet to create electric current or voltage.

electromagnetic spectrum – the entire range of electromagnetic waves including all possible frequencies such as radio waves, microwaves, X-rays, and gamma rays.

electromagnetic wave – a wave of electricity and magnetism that travels at the speed of light. Light is an electromagnetic wave.

electron – a particle with an electrical charge (-e) found inside of atoms but outside the nucleus.

element – a pure form of matter that cannot be broken down into other elements. There are about 90 elements that occur naturally.

elementary charge – the smallest unit of electric charge that is possible in ordinary matter; represented by the lowercase letter e.

endothermic – a reaction is endothermic if it uses more energy than it releases.

energy – the ability to change or to cause change.

energy level – one of the discrete allowed energies for electrons in an atom.

engineering – a career that uses science to design, create, and work with technology.

enzymes – special proteins that are catalysts for chemical reactions in living things.

equilibrium – occurs when a solution has the maximum concentration of dissolved solute.

equilibrium – state in which the net force on an object is zero.

error – the difference between a measurement and the true value.

exothermic – a reaction is exothermic if it releases more energy than it uses.

experiment – a situation specifically set up to investigate relationships between variables.

experimental variable – a variable that changes in an experiment.

F

Fahrenheit – a temperature scale in which water freezes at 32 degrees and boils at 212 degrees.

fats – energy-rich hydrocarbon chain molecules.

ferromagnetic metal – a material, like iron, which has strong magnetic properties.

fluid – a form of matter that flows when a force is applied.

fluorescence – a process that makes light directly from electricity.

force – a push or a pull.

free fall – accelerated motion that happens when an object falls with only the force of gravity acting on it.

free-body diagram – a diagram showing all the forces acting on an object.

frequency – how often something repeats, expressed in hertz.

friction – a force that resists the motion of objects or surfaces.

G

galaxy – a group of stars, dust, gas, and other objects held together by gravitational forces.

gas – a phase of matter that flows and also expands or contracts to fill any container.

gas planets – Jupiter, Saturn, Uranus, and Neptune.

gram (g) – a unit of mass equal to 1/1000 of a kilogram.

group – a column of the periodic table is called a group.

H

halogens – elements in the group containing fluorine, chlorine, and bromine, among others.

harmonic motion – motion that repeats in cycles.

heat – thermal energy that is moving or is capable of moving.

heat conduction – the transfer of heat by the direct contact of particles of matter.

hertz – the unit of frequency. One hertz is one cycle per second.

horsepower – a unit of power equal to 746 watts.

hypothesis – an unproven or preliminary explanation that can be tested by comparison with scientific evidence. Early hypotheses are rarely correct and are often modified as new evidence becomes available.

I

incandescence – a process that makes light with heat.

index of refraction – a number that measure how much a material is able to bend light.

inertia – the property of an object that resists changes in its motion.

input – forces, energy, or power supplied to make a machine work.

inquiry – a process of learning that starts with questions and proceeds by seeking the answers to the questions.

insoluble – a substance is insoluble in a particular solvent if it does not dissolve in that solvent.

insulator – a material with a high electrical resistance. Plastic and rubber are good insulators.

intermolecular forces – forces between atoms or molecules that determine the phase of matter.

ion – an atom that has an electric charge different from zero. Ions are created when atoms gain or lose electrons.

ionic bond – a bond that transfers an electron from one atom to another resulting in attraction between oppositely charged ions.

isotopes – atoms of the same element that have different numbers of neutrons in the nucleus.

J

joule – a unit of energy. One joule is enough energy to push with a force of 1 newton for a distance of 1 meter.

K

Kelvin scale – a temperature scale that starts at absolute zero and has units the same as Celsius degrees.

kilogram (kg) – the basic metric unit or SI unit of mass.

kinetic energy – energy of motion.

L

law of conservation of energy – energy can never be created or destroyed, only transformed into another form. The total amount of energy in the universe is constant.

lens – an optical device for bending light rays.

light – a form of energy that travels at 300,000 km/s and includes all the colors that can be seen by the human eye.

light ray – an imaginary line that represents a beam of light.

light year – the distance light travels through space in one year— 9.46×10^{12} km.

linear motion – motion that goes from one place to another without repeating.

liquid – a phase of matter that flows and easily changes shape.

longitudinal – a wave is longitudinal if its oscillations are in the direction it moves.

M

machine – a device with moving parts that work together to accomplish a task.

magnetic – the property of creating or responding to forces from magnets.

magnetic field – the influence created by a magnet that exerts forces on other magnets.

mass – the amount of "stuff" (matter) an object contains.

mass number – the number of protons plus the number of neutrons in the nucleus.

matter – everything that has mass and takes up space.

mechanical advantage – the ratio of output force divided by input force.

melting point – temperature at which melting or freezing occurs.

metal – elements that are typically shiny and good conductors of heat and electricity.

meteor – a chunk of burning rock traveling through Earth's atmosphere.

meteorite – a meteor that passes through Earth's atmosphere and strikes the ground.

Milky Way galaxy – the spiral galaxy to which our solar system belongs.

mirror – a surface that reflects light rays.

mixture – a substance that includes more than one type of element and/or compound.

molecule – a group of atoms held together by covalent bonds in a specific ratio and shape.

mutation – change in the sequence of base pairs in DNA that may be passed on to successive generations.

N

nanometer – a unit of length equal to one billionth of a meter (0.000000001 m).

natural frequency – the frequency at which a system oscillates when disturbed.

natural law – the set of rules that are obeyed by every detail of everything that occurs in the universe, including living creatures and human technology.

net force – the sum of two or more forces on an object.

neutron – a particle found in the nucleus with mass similar to the proton but with zero electric charge.

newton – the metric unit of force, equal to the force needed to make a 1-kg object accelerate at 1 m/s^2.

Newton's first law – an object at rest will stay at rest and an object in motion will stay in motion with the same velocity unless acted on by an unbalanced force.

Newton's law of universal gravitation – a mathematical rule that tells us how the strength of the force of gravity depends on mass and distance.

Newton's second law – acceleration is force ≥ mass.

Newton's third law – for every action force, there is a reaction force equal in strength and opposite in direction.

noble gases – elements in the group containing helium, neon, and argon, among others.

nonmetal – elements that are poor conductors of heat and electricity.

normal force – the force a surface exerts on an object that is pressing on it.

north, south – the two kinds of magnetic poles.

nuclear fusion – reactions which combine light elements such as hydrogen into heavier elements such as helium, releasing energy.

nuclear reaction – a process that changes the nucleus of an atom and may turn one element into a completely different element.

nucleic acids – biological molecules such as DNA that have the ability to store the genetic code.

nucleus – the tiny core at the center of an atom containing most of the atom's mass and all of its positive charge.

O

objective – describes evidence that documents only what actually happened as exactly as possible.

ohm – the unit of resistance. One ohm (Ω) allows 1 amp to flow when a voltage of 1 volt is applied.

orbit – the repeating circular (or elliptical) path an object takes around a gravity source, such as a planet or star.

organic chemistry – the chemistry of carbon and carbon compounds.

origin – the place where the position has a value of zero.

oscillator – a physical system that has repeating cycles.

output – the forces, energy, or power provided by the machine.

oxidation number – indicates the charge of an atom when an electron is lost, gained, or shared in a chemical bond. An oxidation number of 1+ means an electron is lost, 1- means an electron is gained.

P

pendulum – a device that swings back and forth due to the force of gravity.

period – (1) a row of the periodic table; (2) the time it takes for each complete cycle.

periodic force – a repetitive force.

periodic table – a chart that organizes the elements by their chemical properties and increasing atomic number.

periodicity – the repeating pattern of chemical and physical properties of the elements.

permanent magnet – a material that remains magnetic without outside energy being supplied.

pH – pH measures the acidity of a solution.

pH scale – the pH scale goes from 1 to 14 with 1 being very acidic and 14 being very basic. Pure water is neutral with a pH of 7.

photon – the smallest possible amount of light, like a wave-bundle.

physical properties – characteristics of matter that can be seen through direct observation such as density, melting point, and boiling point.

pitch – the perception of high or low that you hear at different frequencies of sound.

planet – a massive collection of matter that revolves around a star.

polar – describes a molecule that has charge separation, like water.

polymerization – a series of addition reactions that join small molecules into large chain molecules.

position – a variable that gives your location relative to an origin.

positive, negative – the two kinds of electric charge.

potential energy – energy of position.

pound – the English unit of force equal to 4.448 newtons.

power – the rate of doing work or moving energy. Power is equal to energy (or work) divided by time.

precipitate – a solid product that comes out of solution in a chemical reaction.

pressure – a distributed force per unit area that acts within a fluid.

prism – a glass shape with flat, polished surfaces that can both bend and reflect light.

products – the new substances which result from a chemical reaction.

projectile – any object moving through air and affected only by gravity.

protein synthesis – using the information in DNA to assemble proteins from amino acids.

proteins – large molecules found in animal and plant tissue.

proton – a particle found in the nucleus with a positive charge exactly equal and opposite to the electron.

Q

quantum theory – the theory that describes matter and energy at very small (atomic) sizes.

R

radioactive – a nucleus is radioactive if it spontaneously breaks up, emitting particles or energy in the process.

random – scattered equally in all directions.

reactants – the substances which are combined and changed in the chemical reaction.

reflection – the process of bouncing off a surface. Light reflects from a mirror.

refraction – the process of bending while crossing a surface. Light refracts passing from air into water or back

repeatable – describes evidence that can be seen independently by others if they repeat the same experiment or observation in the same way.

resistance – determines how much current flows for a given voltage. Higher resistance means less current flows.

resonance – an exceptionally large amplitude that develops when a periodic force is applied at the natural frequency.

restoring force – any force that always acts to pull a system back toward equilibrium.

S

saturated – a solution is saturated if it contains as much solute as the solvent can dissolve.

saturated fat – a fat molecule in which each carbon is bonded with two hydrogen atoms.

scientific method – a process of learning that begins with a hypothesis and proceeds to prove or change the hypothesis by comparing it with scientific evidence.

significant difference – two results are only significantly different if their difference is much larger than the estimated error.

simple machine – an unpowered mechanical device that accomplishes a task with only one movement.

sliding friction – the friction force that resists the motion of an object moving across a surface.

slope – the ratio of the rise (vertical change) to the run (horizontal change) of a line on a graph.

solar system – the sun, planets, and their moons, and other objects that are gravitationally bound to the sun.

solid – a phase of matter that holds its shape and does not flow.

solubility – the amount of solute that can be dissolved under certain conditions.

solute – any component of a solution other than the solvent.

solution – a mixture of two or more substances that is uniform at the molecular level.

solvent – the component of a solution that is present n the greatest amount.

specific heat – the amount of heat needed to raise the temperature of one kilogram of a material by one degree Celsius.

spectral line – a bright colored line in a spectroscope.

spectroscope – an instrument that separates light into a spectrum.

spectrum – the characteristic colors of light given off or absorbed by an element.

specular reflection – "shiny" surface reflection, where each incident ray produces only one reflected ray.

speed – the distance an object travels divided by the time it takes.

stable – a nucleus is stable if it stays together.

star – an enormous hot ball of gas held together by gravity which produces energy through nuclear fusion reactions in its core.

static electricity – a tiny imbalance between positive and negative charge on an object.

static friction – the friction force that resists the motion between two surfaces that are not moving.

steel – an alloy of iron and carbon.

strength – the ability to maintain shape under the application of forces.

subtractive color process – a process that uses absorption to create color by subtracting colors from white light.

subtractive primary colors – cyan, magenta, and yellow.

supersaturated – a concentration greater than the maximum solubility.

supersonic – faster than the speed of sound.

system – a group of objects, effects, and variables that are related.

T

technology – the application of science to solve problems or accomplish useful tasks.

tension – a pulling force that acts in a rope, string, or other object.

terrestrial planets – Mercury, Venus, Earth, and Mars.

the dissolving rate equals the rate at which molecules come out of solution (undissolve).

theory – a scientific explanation supported by much evidence collected over a long period of time.

thermal conductor – a material that allows heat to flow easily.

thermal energy – energy due to temperature.

thermal equilibrium – when things are at the same temperature and no heat flows.

thermal radiation – electromagnetic waves produced by objects because of their temperature.

thermometer – an instrument that measures temperature.

tide – a cycle of rising and falling sea levels that repeats every 12 hours.

transverse – a wave is transverse if its oscillations are not in the direction it moves.

U

unbalanced forces – result in a net force on an object that can cause changes in motion.

uncertainty principle – it is impossible to know variables exactly in the quantum world.

unsaturated fat – a fat molecule that has less hydrogen atoms than a saturated fat.

V

valence electrons – electrons in the highest unfilled energy level of an atom. These electrons participate in chemical bonds.

value – the particular number (with units) or choice that a variable may have.

variable – a quantity that can be precisely specified, often with a numerical value.

vector – a variable that gives direction information included in its value.

velocity – a variable that tells you both speed and direction.

volt – the unit of electric potential.

W

watt – a power of 1 joule per second.

wave – a traveling oscillation that has properties of frequency, wavelength, and amplitude.

wavelength – the distance from any point on a wave to the same point on the next cycle of the wave.

weight – a force that comes from gravity pulling down on any object with mass.

white light – light containing an equal mix of all colors.

work – a form of energy that comes from force applied over distance. A force of 1 newton does 1 joule of work when the force causes 1 meter of motion in the direction of the force.

Index

The index gives the page numbers where you can find a word, definition, information about a topic or a large category. You can use the index when you are studying and need to find information quickly. The index is a good place to look up a vocabulary word to get more information about the meaning of a word.

Index

457

Index

459

Index